STUDY GUID

TEACHER EDITION

MW00653582

MERRILL
BIOLOGY
AN EVERYDAY EXPERIENCE

Authors
Albert Kaskel
Paul Hummer, Jr.
Lucy Daniel

GLENCOE
Macmillan/McGraw-Hill

New York, New York
Columbus, Ohio
Mission Hills, California
Peoria, Illinois

A MERRILL BIOLOGY PROGRAM

Biology: An Everyday Experience, *Student Edition*
Biology: An Everyday Experience, *Teacher Edition*
Biology: An Everyday Experience, *Teacher Resource Package*
Biology: An Everyday Experience, *Study Guide*
Biology: An Everyday Experience, *Transparency Package*
Biology: An Everyday Experience, *Laboratory Manual, Student Edition*
Biology: An Everyday Experience, *Laboratory Manual, Teacher Edition*
Biology: An Everyday Experience, *Computer Test Bank*

Send all inquiries to:
Glencoe Publishing Company
936 Eastwind Drive
Westerville, OH 43081

Printed in the United States of America

ISBN: 0-02-827301-X

1 2 3 4 5 6 7 8 9 10 HESS 00 99 98 97 96 95 94

TABLE OF CONTENTS

TO THE TEACHER

Study Guide

Each chapter of **Biology: An Everyday Experience** is organized into two to four major teaching sections. The six-page *Study Guide* provides the average to below average student with an aid to learning and understanding vocabulary and major concepts in each of these major sections.

You may have students work on the *Study Guide* for each major section when you make the reading assignment. Students should complete the worksheets for independent practice as they read the text. The Study Guides use a variety of question methods, including: outlining, true or false, defining, fill in the blank, or matching.

Name _____ Date _____ Class _____

BIOLOGY IN USE

In your textbook, read about people who use biology in Section 1:1. Then, answer the questions below.

1. Many people use biology every day. What do the people shown below need to know about biology?

_____ _____ _____

_____ _____ _____

_____ _____ _____

_____ _____ _____

2. Many people use biology in their hobbies. The column on the right lists ways biology can be used in hobbies. In front of the hobbies on the left, write the letter or letters of the way people use biology in each hobby.

_____ **1.** growing houseplants   **a.** know about different kinds of plants

_____ **2.** jogging   **b.** know about the habits of birds

_____ **3.** bird watching   **c.** know how to make plants grow

_____ **4.** swimming   **d.** know about bones and muscles

_____ **5.** identifying wild flowers **e.** know about classifying things

Name _____ Date _____ Class _____

BIOLOGY IN USE

In your textbook, read about the tools of biology in Section 1:1.

3. Biologists use many tools when they study living things. You may use some of the same tools. Label the tools shown below. Fill in the blanks below each picture.

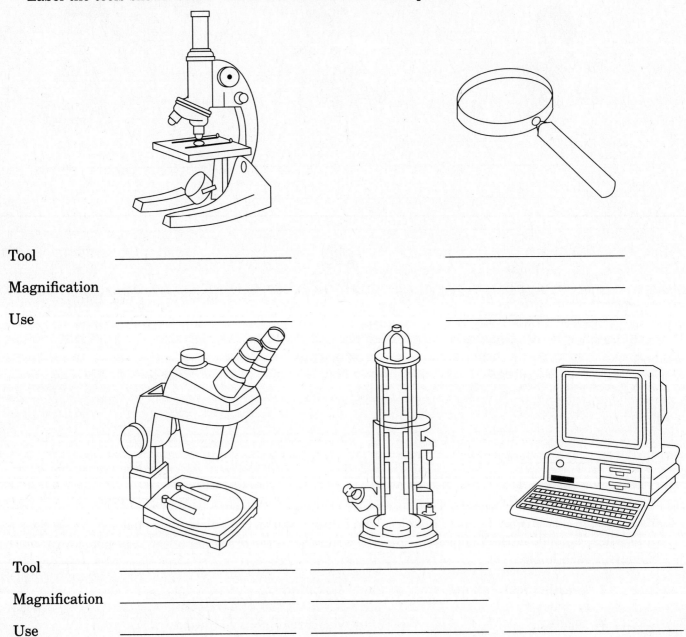

Tool _____   _____

Magnification _____   _____

Use _____   _____

Tool _____   _____   _____

Magnification _____   _____   _____

Use _____   _____   _____

_____   _____   _____

_____   _____   _____

Name _____ Date _____ Class _____

MEASUREMENTS USED IN BIOLOGY

In your textbook, read about measurements used in biology in Section 1:2.

1. Examine the recipe below and answer the questions. Circle all the measurements on the recipe card.

Whole Wheat Bread	14 g dry yeast	Dissolve yeast in warm water.
	826 mL warm water 40°C	Add other parts and mix.
	80 mL oil	Knead dough with hands for 10 min.
	158 mL honey	Let rise for 1 hour.
	7 g salt	Punch dough and work again for 10 min.
	120 g white flour	Divide dough into 3 parts.
	1135 g wheat flour	Form into loaves each 15 cm long.
		Let rise ½ hour.
	Makes 3 loaves	Bake in greased pans for 35 min at 200°C.

a. How many milliliters of liquid parts were added together in the recipe? _____

b. How many grams of dry parts were added together in the recipe? _____

c. Complete the following table using the recipe.

Measurement		What is being measured	
Number	**Unit**	**In general**	**In this recipe**
14	g	mass	yeast
826		volume	
			oil
			wheat flour
40	°C	temperature	water temperature
200			
35			baking time

Name _____ Date _____ Class _____

MEASUREMENTS USED IN BIOLOGY

In your textbook, read about measuring volume in Section 1:2.

2. Look at the graduated cylinder on the right. Note the lines and numbers printed on its sides. The graduated cylinder is filled to the 45 mL mark. Read the level of the liquid in each of the graduated cylinders below. Write the correct volume on the line below each graduated cylinder.

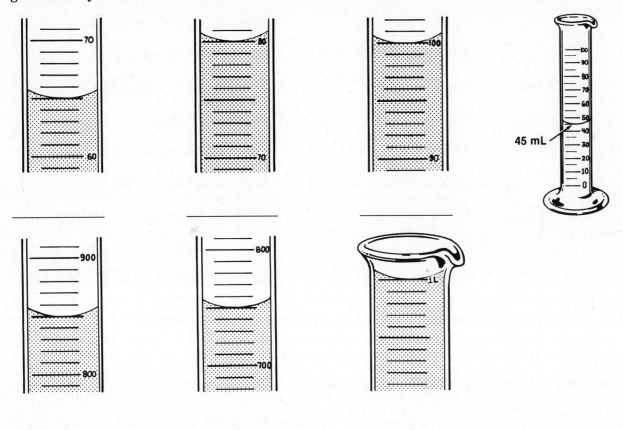

In your textbook, read about measuring temperature in Section 1:2.

3. In each space, write one of the following phrases that best matches the temperature shown. Use these phrases—water for bath, water freezes, water boils, a cool day, and human with fever.

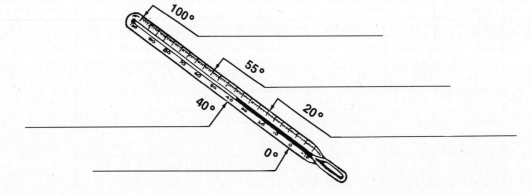

Name _____ Date _____ Class _____

SCIENTIFIC METHOD

In your textbook, read about scientific method in Section 1:3. Then, complete the exercises below.

Long ago, many people believed that living things could come from nonliving things. They thought that worms came from wood and that maggots came from decaying meat. This idea was called spontaneous generation. In 1668, an Italian biologist, Francesco Redi, did experiments to prove that maggots did not come from meat. One of his experiments is shown below.

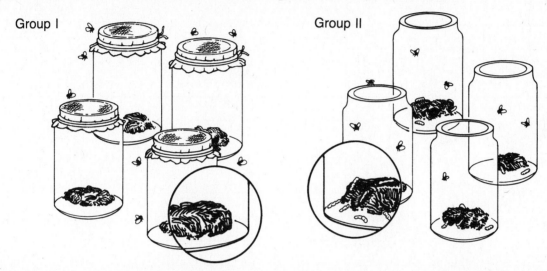

Redi placed pieces of meat in several jars. He divided the jars into two groups. He covered the first group of jars with fine cloth. He left the second group of jars uncovered. Redi observed the jars for several days. He saw flies on the cloth of the covered jars, and he saw flies laying eggs on the meat in the uncovered jars. Maggots appeared only on the meat in the group of jars left uncovered.

1. Scientists use a series of organized steps called scientific method to solve problems. List the steps

that are often used. _____

_____

2. What was the problem in Redi's experiment? _____

3. What do you think his hypothesis was? _____

_____

4. How did he test his hypothesis? _____

_____

5. What was the variable in his experiment? _____

6. What was the control in his experiment? _____

7. What do you think Redi's conclusion was? _____

VOCABULARY

Review the new words in Chapter 1 of your textbook. Then, complete this puzzle.

ACROSS

9. a statement that can be tested
10. SI unit of mass—1000 grams
11. a microscope that has an eyepiece lens and an objective lens for each eye
12. use of scientific discoveries to solve everyday problems
13. something that causes changes in an experiment
14. a hypothesis that has been tested over and over again
15. temperature scale used by scientists
16. recorded facts or measurements from an experiment

DOWN

1. study of living and once-living things
2. International System of Units (abbreviation)
3. method used to solve a problem
4. SI unit of length
5. the standard for comparing results in an experiment
6. the amount of space a substance occupies
7. to test a hypothesis
8. microscope used in class

Name _____ Date _____ Class _____

LIVING THINGS AND THEIR PARTS

In your textbook, read about the features of living things in Section 2:1.

1. Underline the feature of life that you think each of the following pictures shows best.

Living things grow.

Living things reproduce.

Living things need food.

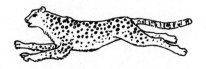

Living things need energy.

Living things grow.

Living things reproduce.

Living things develop.

Living things need food.

Living things reproduce.

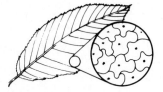

Living things reproduce.

Living things are made of cells.

Living things need energy.

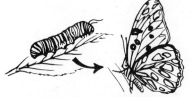

Living things need food.

Living things need energy.

Living things develop.

Living things grow.

Living things need energy.

Living things need food.

Living things are adapted.

Living things develop.

Living things need food.

Living things develop.

Living things respond.

Living things reproduce.

2. Explain how:

 a. developing is different from growing. _____

_____

 b. living things get energy from food. _____

_____

Name _____ Date _____ Class _____

LIVING THINGS AND THEIR PARTS

In your textbook, read about the chemistry of life in Section 2:1.

1. Fill in the boxes below with the correct words.
   What living things are made of:

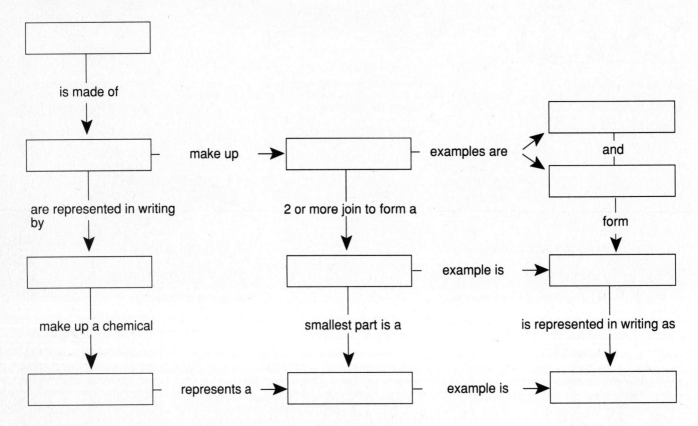

In your textbook, read about the cell theory in Section 2:1.

2. What contribution did each of the following people make to the cell theory?

   a. Robert Hooke _____.

   b. Robert Brown _____.

   c. Schleiden and Schwann _____

   _____.

3. The major ideas of the cell theory are:

   a. _____

   b. _____

   c. _____

Name _____ Date _____ Class _____

CELL PARTS AND THEIR JOBS

In your textbook, read about cell parts and their jobs in Section 2:2.

1. Label the parts of these two cells in the spaces provided.

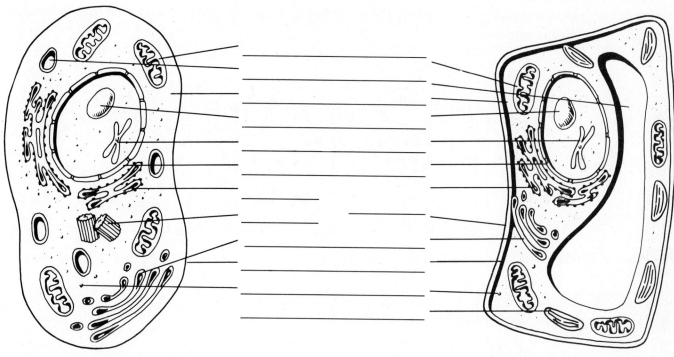

Cell A   Cell B

2. Read the descriptions of cell parts below and write in the name of the cell part. Use the color indicated to shade the pictures above.

  a. Use red for the part that gives the cell shape and holds the cytoplasm. _____

  b. Use green for parts that make food. _____

  c. Use brown for the thick outer covering that protects and supports the cell. _____

  d. Use blue for the part that stores substances. _____

  e. Use black for parts that release energy from food. _____

  f. Use purple for parts that carry hereditary information. _____

  g. Use pink for the cell part that helps with cell reproduction. _____

  h. Use orange for the parts that package and store chemicals. _____

3. List two cell parts found only in a plant cell. _____

4. Where in a cell do most chemical reactions take place? _____

Name _____ Date _____ Class _____

SPECIAL CELL PROCESSES

In your textbook, read about diffusion and osmosis in Section 2:3.

1. The first picture below, labeled *Before*, shows a cell surrounded by oxygen molecules before diffusion takes place. Each of the small black dots represents an oxygen molecule. Which of the three pictures labeled *After* shows where these oxygen molecules would be found after diffusion takes place? Circle your answer.

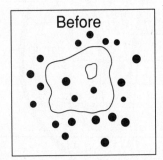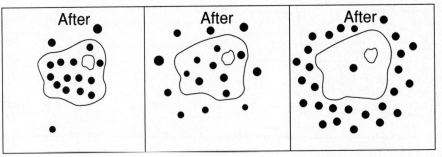

2. What is diffusion? _____

_____

3. How do molecules get through the cell membrane? _____

_____

4. What is osmosis? _____

5. Which way would the water molecules move in the following situations?

   a. cucumber slice is placed in salt water _____

   b. salt is poured on a snail _____

   c. vegetables are sprinkled with water _____

   d. potato slice is placed in pure water _____

6. Circle the letter in front of the sentence that best explains the process of osmosis.

   a. Osmosis is the movement of water into or out of a cell from where it is in large amounts to where it is in small amounts.

   b. Osmosis is the movement of water into or out of a cell from where it is in small amounts to where it is in large amounts.

   c. Osmosis is the movement of salt into or out of a cell from where it is in large amounts to where it is in small amounts.

Name _____ Date _____ Class _____

SPECIAL CELL PROCESSES

In your textbook, read about the organization of cells, tissues, and organs in Section 2:3.

7. Place a check mark in the correct column for each phrase or diagram on the left.

	Tissue	Organ	Organ system
Groups of cells all doing the same job			
Stomach, mouth, and intestines all working together			
Made up of a group of tissues			
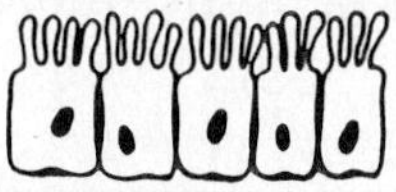			
Small intestine			
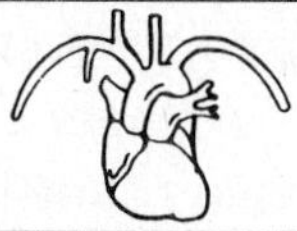			
Leaf			
Muscle			
Bark			
Outer surface of a leaf			

8. How is an organ different from a tissue? _____

_____

_____

_____

9. What is an organism? _____

10. Compare a one-celled organism with a many-celled organism. _____

_____

_____

_____

Name _____ Date _____ Class _____

VOCABULARY

Review the new words in Chapter 2 of your textbook. Then complete the puzzle. The letters in the dark boxes will summarize what you are studying in Chapter 2.

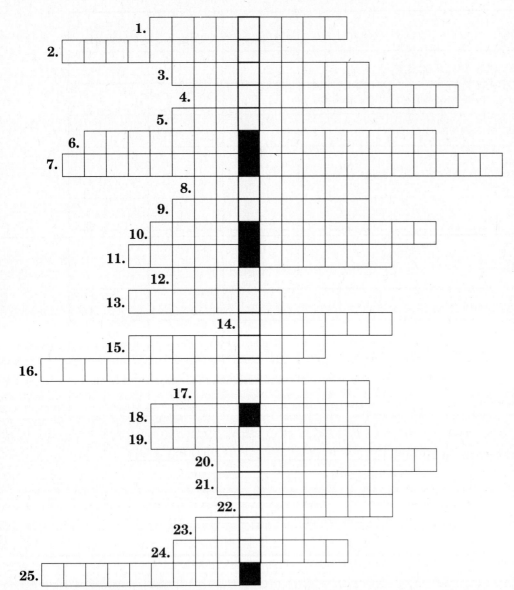

10. controls what moves into cells
11. group of organs working together
12. basic unit of all living things
13. movement of water across a membrane
14. stores water, food, and minerals
15. part near the nucleus that helps with reproduction
16. all the changes that occur as a living thing grows
17. living thing
18. thick outer covering of a plant cell
19. trait that helps a living thing survive
20. cell part with information that determines a living thing's traits
21. cell part where protein is made
22. controls the activities of the cell
23. group of tissues that work together
24. living thing that eats other living things
25. smaller body inside the nucleus that helps make ribosomes

1. clear jellylike material in cells
2. cell part that contains chlorophyll
3. form offspring similar to parents
4. cell parts that release energy
5. group of similar cells carrying out a job
6. structure that surrounds the nucleus
7. process by which food is broken down and energy is released
8. living thing that makes its own food
9. movement of a substance from where there is a large amount to where there is a small amount of it

Name _____ Date _____ Class _____

WHY THINGS ARE GROUPED

In your textbook, read about why things are grouped in Section 3:1.

1. Separate the items pictured into two groups. Put the letters of the items in the proper section of the chart below.

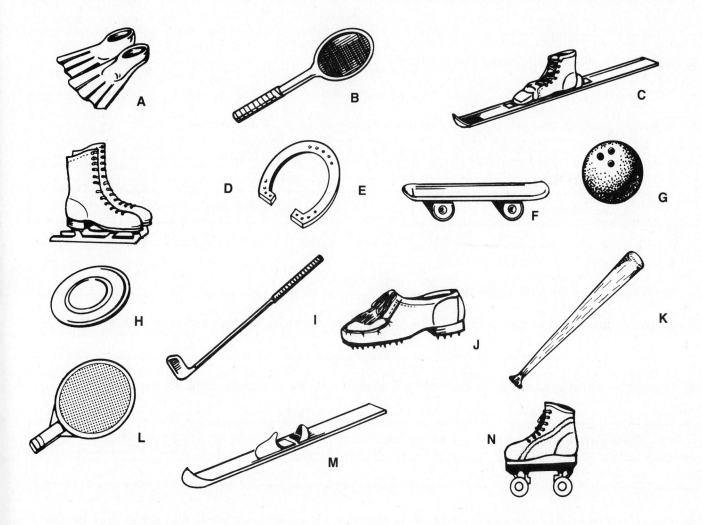

Items for feet	Items held in hand(s)

2. Regroup the items using the chart below.

Used only outdoors	Used only indoors	Used indoors or outdoors

Name _____ Date _____ Class _____

WHY THINGS ARE GROUPED

3. Which of the two ways of grouping these items might be used by a sporting goods store? _____

_____

4. Why do different people classify the same things in different ways? _____

_____

5. List two reasons why humans group things. _____

_____

6. A certain student grouped the items in the pictures on page 13 as follows:

Group 1	Group 2
D N	A B C E F G H I J K L M

   a. What trait was used for Group 1? _____

   b. What trait was used for Group 2? _____

7. Of the three ways to classify these items you have seen, which is the right way? the wrong way?

_____

8. Group the items again using a different set of traits. Write the traits used on the lines.

Trait **wheels**	Trait **spikes**	Trait **no wheels or spikes**

9. Group the items again using a set of traits that has not been used. Write the traits used on the lines.

Trait _____	Trait _____	Trait _____
A M	C D	B E F G H I J K L N

Name _____ Date _____ Class _____

METHODS OF CLASSIFICATION

In your textbook, read about early and modern methods of classification in Section 3:2.

1. Study Figure 3-2 of Aristotle's classification in your textbook and look at the pictures of living things shown below. Then, answer the questions that follow.

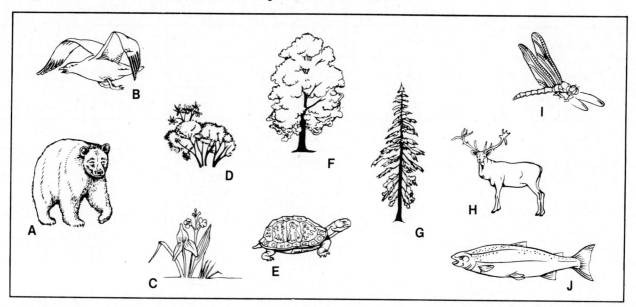

a. Why did Aristotle place E and J in the same group? _____

b. Why were B and I placed together? _____

c. Why were A and H placed in the same group? _____

d. What were Aristotle's two main groups? _____

e. What characteristic did Aristotle use to divide animals into groups? _____

f. What characteristic did Aristotle use to divide plants into groups? _____

_____

2. What were three important changes Linnaeus made in Aristotle's system of classification?

_____

_____

_____

3. Number these classification divisions in order from the smallest (1) to the largest (7).

_____ species   _____ phylum   _____ family

_____ kingdom   _____ order   _____ genus   _____ class

Name _____ Date _____ Class _____

HOW SCIENTISTS CLASSIFY

In your textbook, read about how scientists classify today in Section 3:3. Then, examine the classification of the three animals in the chart below.

	Animal A	Animal B	Animal C
Kingdom	Animal	Animal	Animal
Phylum	Chordate	Chordate	Chordate
Class	Mammal	Aves	Aves
Order	Primates	Passeriformes	Passeriformes
Family	Pongidae	Fringillidae	Fringillidae
Genus	*Pan*	*Spizella*	*Serinus*
Species	*troglodytes*	*passerina*	*canarius*

1. Comparing Animals A and B, how many groups are the same? _____

2. Comparing Animals A and C, how many groups are the same? _____

3. Comparing Animals B and C, how many groups are the same? _____

4. Which two animals (A and B, A and C, or B and C) are most alike in classification?

   _____

5. Which two animals have more of the same traits? _____

6. Which two animals have more of the same body parts? _____

7. Which two animals are most closely related? _____

8. What is the scientific name of Animal A? _____

9. What does the first word of the scientific name represent? _____

10. What does the second word of the scientific name represent? _____

11. What are three reasons for using scientific names? _____

    _____

    _____

Name _____ Date _____ Class _____

HOW SCIENTISTS CLASSIFY

In your textbook, read about the evidence used in classifying in Section 3:3.

1. The diagrams below compare the forelimbs of a human, a dog, a horse, a bird, a bat, and an organism that lived long ago. Use the numbers shown on the human arm to label similar parts on the forelimbs of the other animals. Then complete the statements that follow.

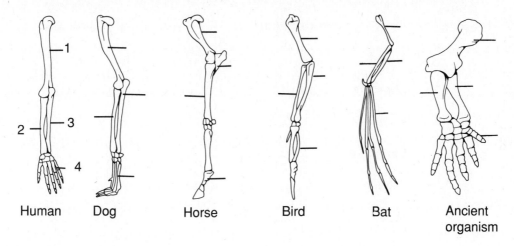

Human   Dog   Horse   Bird   Bat   Ancient organism

    a. Each limb is similar in _____ .

    b. This similarity is evidence of a _____ .

In your textbook, read about the five-kingdom system of classification in Section 3:3.

2. The names of each of the five kingdoms are found in the column on the left below. List the traits of each group in the space provided on the right.

    a. monerans _____

                  _____

    b. protists _____

                  _____

    c. fungi _____

                  _____

    d. plants _____

                  _____

    e. animals _____

                  _____

Name _____ Date _____ Class _____

VOCABULARY

Review the new words used in Chapter 3 of your textbook. Then, complete the puzzle and definitions below.

1. Use these words to fill in the blanks of the puzzle.

class	scientific name	species
genus	traits	phylum
order	kingdom	family

Animal — — — — — — —

Chordate — — — — — — —

Mammal — — — — — —

Carnivore — — — — —

Felidae — — — — — —

Felis — — — — —

domesticus — — — — — —

Felis domesticus is the — — — — — — — — — — — — — — of the

house cat. The name comes from the — — — — — — that the animal has.

2. Define each of the following words or phrases.

a. trait _____

b. order _____

c. classify _____

d. family _____

e. class _____

f. species _____

g. phylum _____

h. genus _____

3. A kingdom is the largest group of living things. List the five kingdoms into which scientists

classify living things today. _____

_____

Name _____ Date _____ Class _____

VIRUSES

In your textbook, read about viruses in Section 4:1.

1. Use the words *chromosome-like part* and *protein coat* to label the bacterial virus shown below.

2. List six traits of viruses.

   a.
   _____
   _____

   b. _____

   c. _____
   _____
   _____

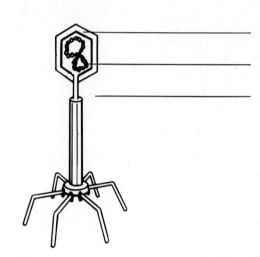

   d. _____
   _____

   e. _____
   _____

   f. _____

3. Study the incorrect statements about viruses below. Change the underlined word or words to make each sentence correct. Write the correct new word or words on the line to the right.

   a. Viruses cause disease *only in humans*.   _____

   _____

   b. Each kind of virus infects *many* hosts.   _____

   c. The rabies virus will infect only the *digestive* system of   _____
      mammals.

   d. Cold sores are caused by a virus that remains *active*.   _____

   e. Viruses are always *larger* than cells they infect.   _____

   f. Viruses reproduce *outside* of living cells.   _____

   g. Viruses *do not change* the hereditary material in the host cell. _____

Name _____ Date _____ Class _____

VIRUSES

4. The stages of a virus infecting a bacterial cell shown below are out of order. Label the diagrams 1 through 5 to show the correct order. Then, describe what is happening in each stage.

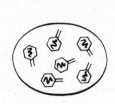 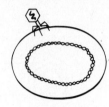   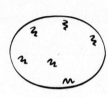

_____   _____   _____   _____   _____

Stage 1 _____

Stage 2 _____

Stage 3 _____

Stage 4 _____

Stage 5 _____

5. The following diseases are caused by viruses: Newcastle disease, curly top, AIDS, distemper, dwarfism, herpes, mosaic disease, cowpox, measles, cold, bushy stunt, rabies, foot-and-mouth disease, chickenpox, dwarf mosaic. Fill in the chart below by placing the diseases under the proper headings.

Plant	Animal	Human

6. Humans and other animals can be protected against some viruses in several ways. List four methods of protection.

   a. _____   b. _____

   c. _____   d. _____

7. How are viruses spread in humans? _____

_____

Name _____ Date _____ Class _____

MONERA KINGDOM

In your textbook, read about the traits of bacteria in Section 4:2.

1. In the space below, draw and label the three different groups of bacteria.

2. Answer the following questions about bacteria in complete sentences.

   a. Where are they found? _____

   _____

   b. What conditions do they need to survive? _____

   _____

   c. How do they reproduce? _____

   _____

   d. How can some bacteria withstand extreme conditions? _____

   _____

   e. What do they use as food? _____

   _____

In your textbook, read about bacteria and disease in Section 4:2.

3. What are Koch's postulates? _____

   _____

4. What are communicable diseases? _____

   _____

5. How are communicable diseases spread? _____

   _____

   _____

6. What are two sexually transmitted diseases? _____

Name _____ Date _____ Class _____

MONERA KINGDOM

In your textbook, read about helpful bacteria in Section 4:2.

7. In the blank below each drawing, tell how bacteria are helpful.

_____ _____ _____

 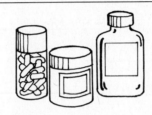 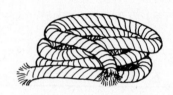

_____ _____ _____

_____ _____ _____

8. How are bacteria used in biotechnology? _____

_____

In your textbook, read in Section 4:2 about controlling bacteria.

9. Tell how each of the following controls bacteria.

  a. canning _____

_____

  b. pasteurization _____

  c. cooling _____

  d. freezing _____

  e. dehydration _____

  f. antiseptics _____

  g. disinfectants _____

  h. vaccines _____

  i. antibiotics _____

Name _____ Date _____ Class _____

MONERA KINGDOM

In your textbook, read about bacteria and blue-green bacteria in Section 4:2.

Below are pictures of monerans drawn by students.

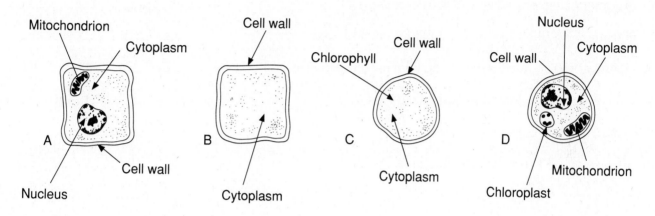

10. a. Which drawing of the bacterial cell is correct, A or B? _____

    b. List two things wrong with the other drawing. _____

_____

11. a. Which drawing of the blue-green bacteria is correct, C or D? _____

    b. List two things wrong with the other drawing. _____

_____

12. List two ways bacteria and blue-green bacteria differ. _____

_____

_____

13. How are bacteria and blue-green bacteria alike? _____

_____

14. How are blue-green bacteria helpful? _____

_____

_____

15. How are blue-green bacteria harmful? _____

_____

VOCABULARY

Review the new words used in Chapter 4 of your textbook. Then, complete the puzzle below.
Write the correct term in the space provided next to the definitions. Find the same word in the letter grid and circle it. Words may be written on horizontal, vertical, or diagonal lines.

1. organism that provides food for a parasite _____

2. chromosome-like part surrounded by protein coat _____

3. chemical that interferes with how viruses reproduce _____

4. one organism divides into two organisms _____

5. organism that uses dead material for food _____

6. disease passed from one organism to another _____

   _____

7. protective structure with a thick wall that some bacteria form _____

8. process of heating milk to kill bacteria _____

9. drug that kills or slows growth of bacteria _____

10. use of living things to solve practical problems _____

11. whiplike thread used for movement _____

12. substance made from weakened viruses or bacteria _____

```
B C D L E R T L A O P Q R O A L S I S P L N Y C
G A N T I B M W S T A M E N D O S P O R E R Z N
V X N Z O W S L V K N S T R X C Q Y L E S V A W
P D T T O S M P A V I R U S L E O S C W A W N O
A A O L I K B W T A D R L T M R S T O Q P C N J
R N N S S P N S U C C S R O I N A P L P R A I R
A N T I B I O T I C V N T I M A P M O L O P N K
O X D T Q T G A B I N T E R F E R O N S P T G L
I O F Z C O M Z O N H D R L T Y M V T Y H O S M
T S F L Y R U S T E O T Y O O P A H Y N Y A N V
E V L L E C P Q X C M X Z T A L S T N A T R T S
N P A S T E U R I Z A T I O N S C A P S E S E T
S C G N V O L F E T P R S D M L P A V S R E C R
W T E N H S N A B C W B I O T E C H N O L O G Y
X B L U O O G R E E T A C R T Y L C O C F M B P
Q S L R S Y C N S N R W F I S S I O N C E S R Q
J M U O T S I L S T M Z W X V T M R P L T R O S
C O M M U N I C A B L E D I S E A S E L V C J D
```

Name _____ Date _____ Class _____

PROTIST KINGDOM

In your textbook, read about animal-like protists in Section 5:1.

1. Label the following parts of an amoeba: nucleus, cytoplasm, food vacuole, cell membrane, false foot.

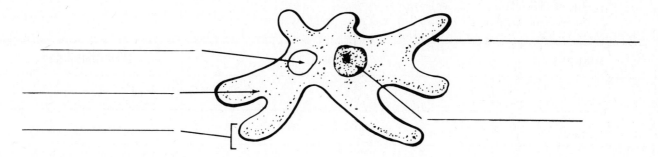

2. Label the following parts of a paramecium: large nucleus, small nucleus, cytoplasm, vacuole, cell membrane, cilia, mouth. Then, answer the question.

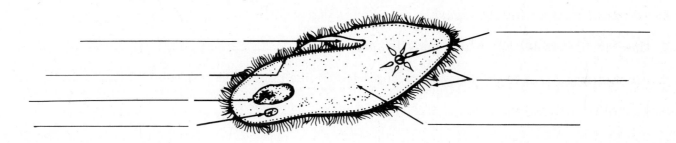

Explain how paramecia feed. _____

_____

In your textbook, read about plantlike protists in Section 5:1.

3. Write the phrase *like plants* or *like animals* after each of the following protist traits.

   a. can move about   _____

   b. have chlorophyll   _____

   c. have no cell wall   _____

   d. are producers   _____

   e. can make their own food _____

   f. give off oxygen   _____

Name _____ Date _____ Class _____

PROTIST KINGDOM

4. Write the following phrases under the correct headings in the table below.

have a flagellum	cell covering made of two parts	red or brown color
green color	form thick layers when they die	used in toothpaste
cause red tide	boat, rod, disk, or triangle shape	
have two flagella	found mostly in fresh water	

Euglena	Diatoms	Dinoflagellates

In your textbook, read about funguslike protists in Section 5:1.

5. How do slime molds differ from plantlike protists? _____

6. At what stage(s) in their life cycle are slime molds like animal-like protists? _____

_____

_____

7. At what stage(s) in their life cycle are they like fungi? _____

_____

FUNGUS KINGDOM

In your textbook, read about fungi in Section 5:2.

1. Complete the following sentences about fungi.

    a. Fungi cannot make their own _____ .

    b. Hyphae are usually divided by _____ .

    c. The bodies of most fungi are made up of a network of threadlike _____ .

    d. Fungi reproduce by forming _____ .

    e. Fungi can also reproduce from pieces of _____ .

FUNGUS KINGDOM

2. Review the following words from Chapter 4. Then, define them in the spaces below.

  a. saprophyte _____

  b. parasite _____

3. Next to each picture, on the first line write the word *parasite* or *saprophyte,* to describe the kind of fungus shown. On the lower line, explain how you know that the fungus is a saprophyte or a parasite.

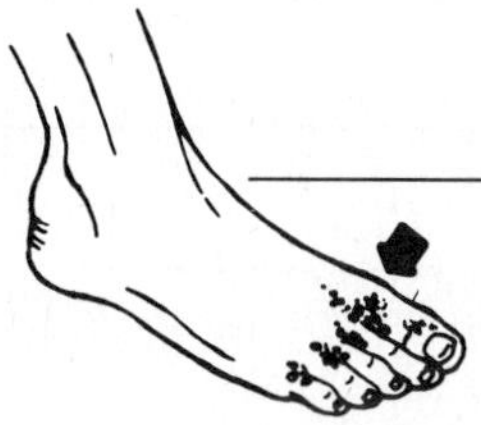

4. Put a check mark in the correct place on the table that indicates which traits are found in the different kinds of fungi.

Trait	Sporangium fungi	Club fungi	Sac fungi
reproduce by spores			
spores made in a saclike part			
cause Dutch elm disease			
spores made in a sporangium			
mushrooms belong here			
yeast belongs here			
spores made in club-shaped part			

Name _____ Date _____ Class _____

FUNGUS KINGDOM

5. Label the parts and identify the jobs of this bread mold by putting the correct letters in the circles provided.

Parts
A = hyphae
B = sporangium
C = spores
        Jobs
D = develops into new molds
E = produces spores
F = takes in food and water

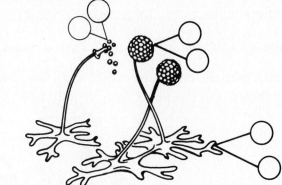

6. Label the parts of a mushroom shown below. Use the following table as a guide.

Part	Appearance
spores	at ends of club-shaped part, can be seen only with microscope
hyphae	threadlike, form networks underground
stipe	stemlike part
cap	top of mushroom, like an umbrella
gills	underside of cap, like ribs of umbrella
club-shaped part	found on underside of gills, very small in size

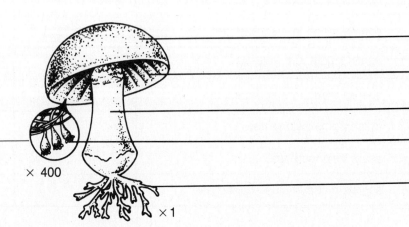

× 400

×1

Name _____ Date _____ Class _____

FUNGUS KINGDOM

7. Refer to Table 5-3 on page 107 of your textbook, and fill in the following blanks.

   a. List three ways in which fungi can be helpful. _____ _____

   _____

   _____

   b. List ways fungi can be harmful to things you own. _____

   _____

   c. List ways fungi can be harmful to people. _____

   _____

In your textbook, read about lichens in Section 5:2.

8. What is mutualism? _____

   _____

9. What is a lichen? _____

   _____

   a. List two examples of lichens. _____

   b. What is the role of the organism with chlorophyll? _____

   c. What is the role of the fungus? _____

   _____

10. Where do lichens live? _____

   a. How do they help form soil? _____

   _____

   b. How do lichens help some animals? _____

Name _____ Date _____ Class _____

VOCABULARY

Below is a list of pronunciations of words related to protists and fungi. Find the word in Chapter 5 and write it on the first blank to the right of the pronunciation. In the remaining space, write a definition of the word.

1. HI fee _____ _____

2. AL jee _____ _____

3. SPOR _____ _____
   _____

4. SIHL ee uh _____ _____

5. spuh RAN jee uh _____ _____
   _____

6. spor uh ZOH uhnz _____ _____
   _____

7. slime mohld _____ _____
   _____

8. LI kun _____ _____
   _____
   _____

9. proht uh ZOH uhnz _____ _____
   _____

10. BUHD ing _____ _____
    _____

11. MYOOCH uh wuh LIZ uhm _____ _____
    _____

12. MUHL tee SEL yuh luhr _____ _____
    _____

Name _____ Date _____ Class _____

PLANT CLASSIFICATION

In your textbook, read about plant features in Section 6:1.

1. Shade green those parts of the living things shown below that are usually green.
2. Draw an X through each living thing that does not contain chlorophyll.
3. Circle each living thing that can make its own food.

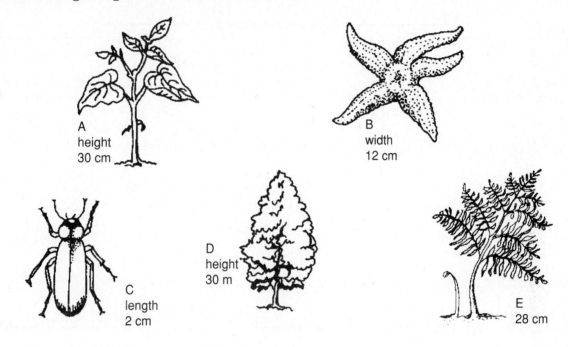

A
height
30 cm

B
width
12 cm

C
length
2 cm

D
height
30 m

E
28 cm

4. Which of the diagrams (A, B, C, D, or E) are plants? _____

5. List four features of plants that are different from the features of animals.

   a. _____

   b. _____

   c. _____

   d. _____

6. What is the main difference between plants and animals? _____

_____

7. What is photosynthesis? _____

_____

8. Where does photosynthesis occur in plants? _____

_____

Name _____ Date _____ Class _____

PLANT CLASSIFICATION

9. Fill in the blanks below with the following words or phrases.

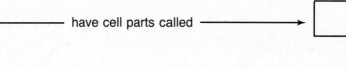

light energy   chloroplasts   photosynthesis
green color   chlorophyll   plants

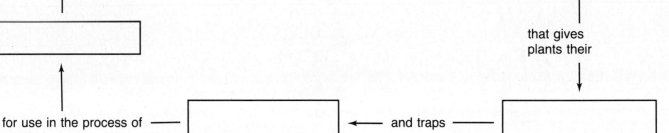

10. What are vascular plants? _____

_____

11. What are nonvascular plants? _____

_____

12. Why must nonvascular plants grow close to the ground? _____

_____

13. Define the following words.

    a. root _____

_____

    b. stem _____

_____

    c. leaf _____

Name _____ Date _____ Class _____

NONVASCULAR PLANTS

In your textbook, read about mosses and liverworts in Section 6:2. Then answer the following questions.

1. How are mosses and liverworts similar? _____

_____

2. How can mosses be classified? _____

3. Describe the leaves and stems of liverworts. _____

_____

4. List three ways that mosses and liverworts are helpful. _____

_____

_____

_____

5. Why do mosses and liverworts need water to survive? _____

_____

6. Where are moss spores produced? _____

_____

VASCULAR PLANTS

In your textbook, read about ferns in Section 6:3.

1. Circle the correct word in each sentence.

   a. Ferns are vascular plants that reproduce by _____ seeds / spores _____.

   b. Ferns have special tubelike cells called _____ xylem / phloem _____

   that carry water and dissolved minerals from the roots to the leaves.

   c. The leaves of a fern grow out of a stem that lies _____ underground / above ground _____.

   d. The spore cases of ferns are found on the _____ top / bottom _____ side of the leaves.

   e. If a spore lands in a _____ moist / dry _____ place, it grows into a small, heart-shaped plant.

   f. The heart-shaped plant produces _____ spores / sperm and eggs _____.

   g. Ferns _____ do / don't _____ have a vascular system.

Name _____ Date _____ Class _____

VASCULAR PLANTS

In your textbook, read about conifers in Section 6:3.

2. In the blanks provided, place a check mark next to the statements that are true for conifers.

   a. _____ Conifers produce seeds.

   b. _____ Their leaves are green all year.

   c. _____ Many have small, needle shaped leaves.

   d. _____ Conifers are nonvascular plants.

   e. _____ They have woody stems.

   f. _____ They have thin, broad leaves.

   g. _____ Conifers are the smallest group of cone-bearing plants.

   h. _____ They are often called evergreens.

3. Using Figure 6-10 in your textbook as a guide, write in the blank the part of a conifer described below.

   a. produces pollen _____

   b. grains in which sperm form _____

   c. produces eggs _____

   d. contains a young plant _____

   e. protects developing embryos _____

4. How does pollen reach the female cone? _____

5. How do seeds escape from within a cone? _____

_____

6. In what ways are conifers important to humans? _____

_____

_____

Name _____ Date _____ Class _____

VASCULAR PLANTS

7. Decide which of the following sentences are true and which are false. Write the word *true* in the blank next to the sentences that are true. For sentences that are false, replace the underlined word with a word that would make the sentence true. Write that word in the blank.

_____ a. Seeds of flowering plants are formed inside a flower.

_____ b. Flowering plants are nonvascular.

_____ c. The flower is involved in reproduction.

_____ d. Sperm cells are formed within female flower parts.

_____ e. In a flowering plant, a fertilized egg forms a flower.

_____ f. Male flower parts develop into an embryo.

_____ g. Flowering plants make up the smallest group of all types of plants.

_____ h. Seeds contain a supply of food for the developing embryo.

8. Complete the following table. Put a check mark in the column of each kind of plant that has the trait listed.

Trait	Moss and liverwort	Fern	Conifer	Flowering plant
Nonvascular				
Vascular				
Has no tubelike cells				
Has tubelike cells				
Has roots, stems, leaves				
Doesn't have roots				
Spores				
Seeds				
Cones				
Flowers				
Most common of plants				
Gives off oxygen				

Name _____ Date _____ Class _____

VOCABULARY

Review the new words used in Chapter 6 of your textbook. Then, complete the exercise.
Fill in the blank in each of the sentences below with the correct word from the following list.

chlorophyll	flowers	sexual reproduction	nonvascular plant
xylem	photosynthesis	egg	fertilization
embryo	conifer	vascular plants	moss
sperm	phloem	fern	flowering plant
seed	pollen		

1. The chemical that gives plants their green color is _____.

2. _____ plants don't have tubelike cells in their stems and leaves.

3. A small nonvascular plant that has both stems and leaves but no roots is a _____.

4. An _____ is a female reproductive cell.

5. _____ have tubelike cells in their roots, stems, and leaves.

6. A _____ produces seeds in cones.

7. A male reproductive cell is a _____.

8. A _____ produces seeds inside a flower.

9. A _____ is a vascular plant that reproduces with spores.

10. _____ cells carry food from the leaves to all parts of the plant.

11. _____ are the tiny grains of seed plants in which sperm develop.

12. _____ are the reproductive parts of flowering plants.

13. A _____ contains a new, young plant and stored food.

14. The young plant in a seed is the _____.

15. _____ cells carry water from the roots to the leaves.

16. In _____, a new organism forms from the union of two reproductive cells.

17. The joining of the egg and the sperm is _____.

18. _____ is the process in which plants use water, carbon dioxide, and energy

from the sun to make food.

Name _____ Date _____ Class _____

ANIMAL CLASSIFICATION

In your textbook, read about how animals are classified in Section 7:1.

1. What is the difference between vertebrates and invertebrates? _____

_____

2. What is symmetry? _____

_____

3. What is the difference between radial and bilateral symmetry? _____

_____

_____

_____

4. List four traits of animals.

    a. _____

    b. _____

    c. _____

    d. _____

5. The animal kingdom is one of five kingdoms into which scientists group living things. Scientists group animals into nine major groups.

    a. What are these groups called? _____

    b. Which group contains the largest number of different kinds of animals? _____

    _____

    c. Which group contains the smallest number of different kinds of animals? _____

    d. Which group contains the simplest animals? _____

    e. Which group contains the most complex animals? _____

6. What main group of animals makes up the chordate phylum? _____

7. What main group of animals makes up the rest of the animal kingdom? _____

Name _____ Date _____ Class _____

SPONGES AND STINGING-CELL ANIMALS

In your textbook, read about sponges and stinging-cell animals in Section 7:2.

1. How do sponges get their food? _____

   _____

   _____

2. How do the different types of cells help a sponge function? _____

   _____

   _____

3. Complete the following sentences about stinging-cell animals.

   a. The body of these animals is a hollow, _____ structure.

   b. Most of these animals live in _____ .

   c. Their armlike parts are called _____ .

   d. Each armlike part has many _____ .

   e. The body has an opening called a _____ .

   f. The bodies of these animals have _____ cell layers.

   g. These animals use _____ to move their armlike parts.

4. Explain how each of the following parts helps the animal function.

   a. disc _____

   b. stinging cells and triggers _____

   _____

   c. tentacles _____

5. Circle the letter of the animal shown below that is not a stinging-cell animal.

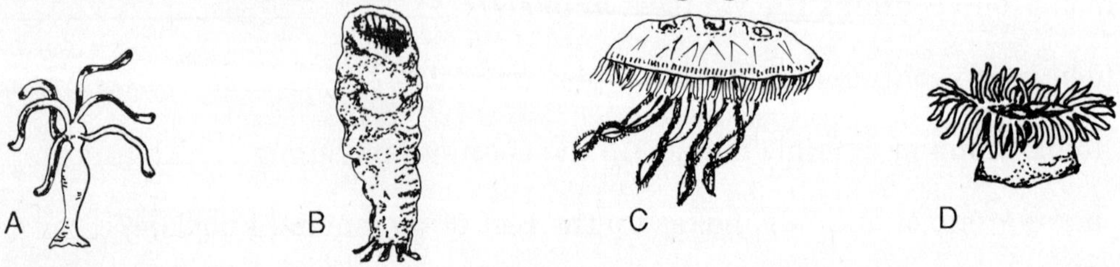

   A   B   C   D

6. What traits helped you choose your answer for question 5? _____

   _____

Name _____ **Date** _____ **Class** _____

WORMS

In your textbook, read about flatworms in Section 7:3.

1. Study the steps of the pig tapeworm life cycle in Figure 7-9 of your textbook. Then, answer the following questions.

   a. What two host animals are part of the tapeworm's life cycle? _____

   b. Which animal will contain cysts of the worm? _____

   c. In which animal will the worm reproduce? _____

   d. In which animal will the worm's body sections break off and leave the host's body in its solid

      waste? _____

   e. In which animal will young worms travel to the muscles and burrow into them? _____

   f. In which animal will worms attach to the inside of the intestines? _____

2. Why aren't tapeworms common in the United States? _____

   _____

   _____

3. On the blanks below, label the parts of this planarian and briefly describe the job each part does.

part _____   part _____

job _____   job _____

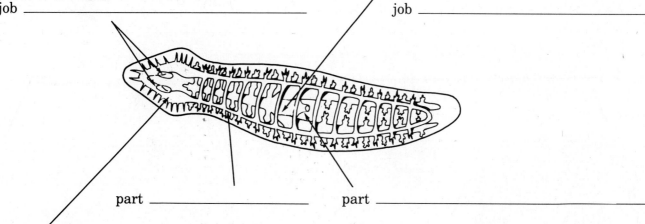

                    part _____   part _____

part _____   job _____

job _____

4. How do planarians differ from most other flatworms? _____

   _____

Name _____ Date _____ Class _____

WORMS

In your textbook read about roundworms in Section 7:3.

5. On the blanks provided, label the parts of this roundworm.

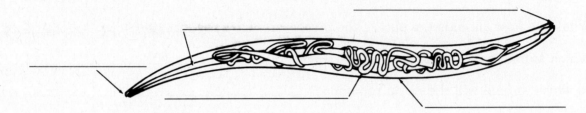

In your textbook, read about segmented worms in Section 7:3.

6. Name a segmented worm that is a parasite. _____

7. Name a segmented worm that is not a parasite. _____

8. On the blanks below, label the parts of this earthworm and briefly describe the job each part does.

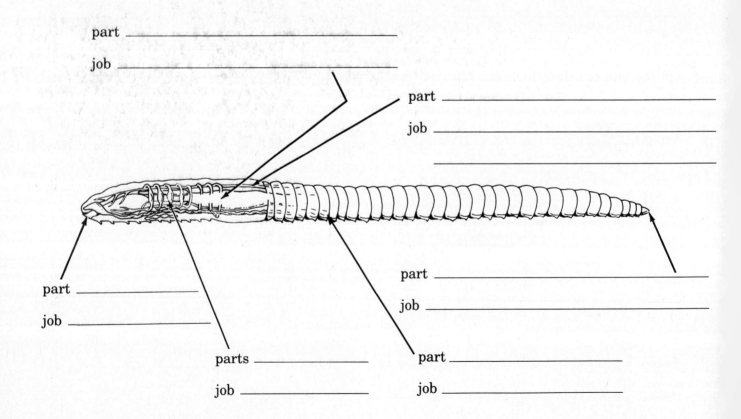

part _____

job _____

part _____

job _____

_____

part _____

job _____

part _____

job _____

part _____

job _____

parts _____

job _____

Name _____ Date _____ Class _____

SOFT-BODIED ANIMALS

In your textbook, read about soft-bodied animals in Section 7:4.

1. Match the groups of traits on the left with the pictures of soft-bodied animals on the right. Write the letter of the correct soft-bodied animal on the line following each group of traits.

no shell
large eyes and a water jet   ____
soft body

single shell
soft body   ____
glides on a muscular foot

two shells
soft body   ____
often buried in sand

soft body
small inside shell   ____
large eyes and a water jet

soft body
no shell   ____
looks like snail without shell

2. List four traits of all soft-bodied animals. _____

_____

_____

3. What kind of soft-bodied animal is diagramed below? _____

   a. Use one arrow to label where water moves into the body in the diagram below. Use another arrow to show where water moves out of the body.
   b. Use an arrow to show the direction the soft-bodied animal is moving.
   c. What other kind of soft-bodied animal moves like this one? _____

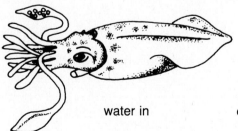

water in   direction of motion   water out

Name _____ Date _____ Class _____

VOCABULARY

Review the new words in Chapter 7 of your textbook. Then, complete the sentences on the right using the words listed below.

anus	invertebrates	roundworm	sponges	tentacles
cysts	mantle	segmented worm	stinging-cell animal	vertebrates
flatworm	planarian	soft-bodied animal	symmetry	tapeworm
hookworm	pores			

1.  This animal is a _____. It belongs

   to the _____ phylum.

   The young worms form _____ in muscles.

2. 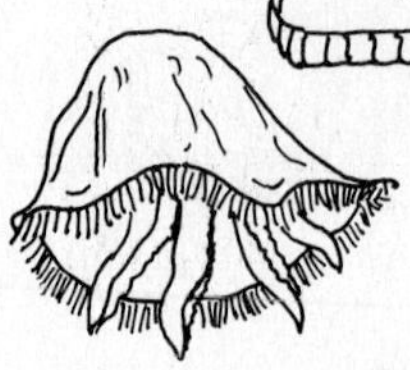 Jellyfish are in the _____ phylum.

   They have armlike parts called _____.

3. 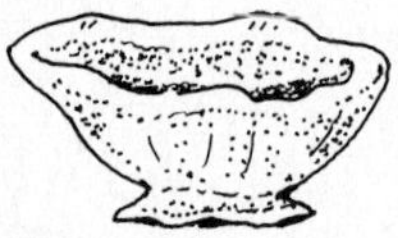 The simplest animals are the _____.

   The tiny holes in their bodies are called _____

4.  This animal belongs to the _____

   phylum. Its body is covered by thin, fleshy tissue called a

   _____.

5. 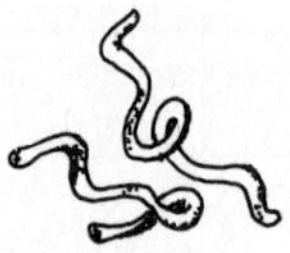 Animals that belong to the _____

   phylum have round, ropelike bodies. This worm has two openings in

   its body, a mouth and an _____.

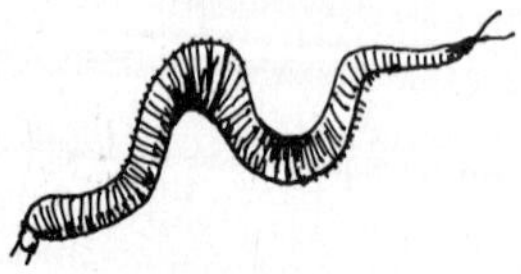

6. An animal in this phylum is the _____.

7. This worm belongs to the _____ phylum.

8. 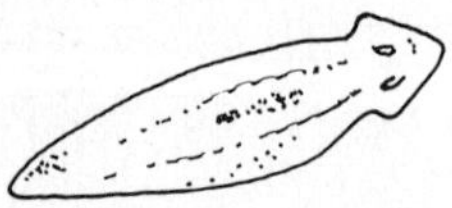 This animal is a _____. It belongs to the

   same phylum as the tapeworms.

9. A few simple animals, such as sponges, do not show _____.

10. Animals without backbones, like the animals shown above, are

    _____. _____

    are animals with backbones.

Name _____ Date _____ Class _____

INVERTEBRATES

In Section 8:1 of your textbook, read about jointed-leg animals.

1. List three traits of jointed-leg animals. _____

_____

2. Look at the pictures below. Use the letters A to E to answer the questions that follow.

A. 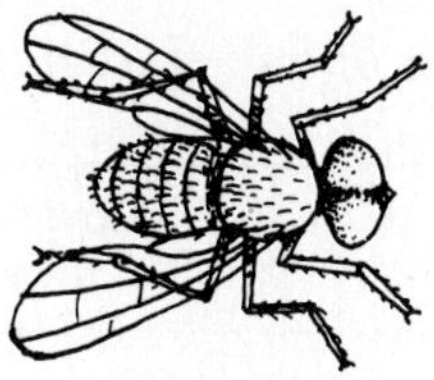   B. 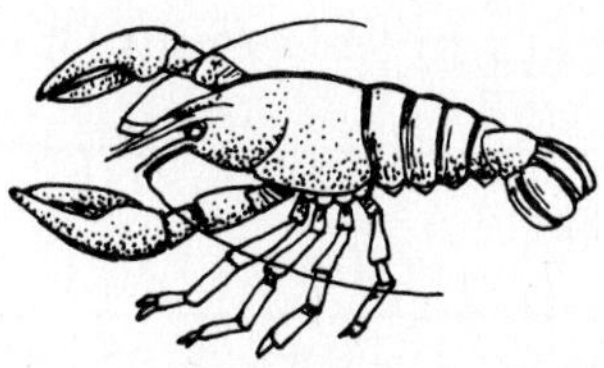   C.

D. all of the above   E. none of the above

   a. Which animal is an invertebrate? _____

   b. Which animal has two pairs of antennae? _____

   c. Which animal is in the insect class? _____

   d. Which animal has an endoskeleton? _____

   e. Which animal has a segmented body? _____

   f. Which animal has eight legs? _____

   g. Which animal has a head, thorax, and abdomen? _____

   h. Which animal has 10 legs? _____

   i. Which animal has two pairs of wings? _____

   j. Which animal has more than 30 legs? _____

In Section 8:1 of your textbook, read about spiny-skin animals.

3. List three traits of spiny-skin animals. _____

_____

4. Describe how asexual reproduction can occur in a starfish. _____

_____

_____

Name _____ Date _____ Class _____

VERTEBRATES

In Section 8:2 of your textbook, read about chordates.

1. What trait identifies a chordate? _____

_____

2. In most vertebrates, what replaces the rod along its back? _____

In Section 8:2 of your textbook, read about characteristics of fish.

3. Put a checkmark in the column of each kind of fish that has the trait listed.

Trait	Jawless fish	Cartilage fish	Bony fish
have skeletons mostly of bone			
have toothlike scales			
are parasites			
group includes perch and trout			
have skeletons of cartilage			
group includes lamprey			
have smooth, bony scales			
have uncovered gills			
group includes sharks and rays			
have paired fins			
most have a swim bladder			
have tubelike bodies			

4. Fill in the correct answers in the blanks provided below each picture.

a. Class _____ **b.** Class _____ **c.** Class _____

Phylum _____ Phylum _____ Phylum _____

Name _____ Date _____ Class _____

VERTEBRATES

5. Explain the function of slime and scales in fish. _____

_____

_____

6. Explain how a swim bladder works. _____

_____

_____

In Section 8:2 of your textbook, read about amphibians.

7. Name the class and phylum to which the animal below belongs. List the major traits of this class.

Class _____ Phylum _____

Major traits of the class _____

_____

8. List two reasons why amphibians must live near water. _____

_____

9. What is a tadpole? _____

10. Using information from Figure 8-17 on page 169 of your textbook, complete the following table.

Trait	Tadpole	Adult frog
How is the body shaped?		
Is a tail present?		
What part is used for moving?		
What part is used for breathing?		
Where does it live?		

Name _____ Date _____ Class _____

VERTEBRATES

11. How are cold-blooded animals affected by the temperature in their surroundings? _____

_____

_____

12. How does hibernation help amphibians survive? _____

_____

In Section 8:2 of your textbook, read about reptiles.

13. Name the class and phylum to which the animal below belongs. List the major traits of this class.

Class _____ Phylum _____

Major traits of the class _____

_____

_____

14. List five kinds of reptiles. _____

15. List three reasons why a reptile can live entirely on land. _____

_____

_____

In Section 8:2 of your textbook, read about birds.

16. Compare the following traits of birds with those of reptiles. Using the words *same* or *different*, fill in the blanks provided with the answer that applies.

a. warm-blooded	_____	**e.** feathers	_____
b. scaly legs	_____	**f.** lungs	_____
c. shelled eggs	_____	**g.** beaks	_____
d. toes with claws	_____	**h.** hollow bones	_____

Name _____ Date _____ Class _____

VERTEBRATES

17. Explain the meaning of *warm-blooded*. _____

_____

_____

18. What do birds have that helps them keep a constant body temperature? _____

19. How are birds well adapted for flying? _____

_____

_____

20. How are the beaks of birds adapted for getting food? _____

_____

_____

In Section 8:2 of your textbook, read about mammals.

21. Name the class and phylum to which the animal below belongs. List the major traits of this class.

Class _____ Phylum _____

Major traits of the class _____

_____

22. a. What is a mammal? _____

_____

b. Are you a mammal? _____

23. a. What are mammary glands? _____

b. How are male mammary glands different from female mammary glands? _____

_____

24. List two groups of mammals whose young do not develop inside the mother's body. _____

_____

Name _____ Date _____ Class _____

VOCABULARY

Review the new words used in Chapter 8 of your textbook. Then, fill in the blanks.

Crayfish, insects, and spiders belong to the phylum of _____ . These

animals have _____ with many lenses. They also have legs, wings, and

_____ which are used for sensing smell and touch. These body parts

are called _____ . Animals in this phylum have a skeleton, called an

_____ , that is outside their bodies. As the animals grow, they shed

their outer skeletons. This process is called _____ .

The phylum of _____ includes sea urchins, starfish, and sand dollars.

These animals use their _____ to move, attach to rocks, and get food.

The phylum of _____ includes animals that have a rod along their back

at some time in their lives. Their skeleton, called an _____ , is inside

their body.

Fish live in water and breathe with _____ . They are

_____ animals because their body temperature changes with

their surroundings. _____ have no jaws, scales, or bones.

Their skeleton is made of _____ . _____

have jaws, scales, and a cartilage skeleton. _____ have jaws, scales,

and a bony skeleton.

_____ live part of their life in water and part on land.

_____ helps animals survive cold weather.

_____ have dry, scaly skin, can live on land, and breathe with lungs.

Birds have a beak, wings, and feathers. Their body temperature does not change with the

temperature of their surroundings. Thus, they are _____ animals.

_____ also have a constant body temperature. They have

hair on their bodies. The females produce milk from their _____ .

Name _____ Date _____ Class _____

WHAT NUTRIENTS ARE IN FOOD?

In your textbook, read about the nutrients found in food in Section 9:1.

1. The following diagram shows the percentage of nutrients present in males and females. The nutrients, however, are not labelled. Mark the diagrams as follows:
   (a) Pencil shading—nutrient used to build and repair body parts,
   (b) Dots—nutrient that is body's main source of energy,
   (c) xxxx—nutrient that makes up largest percent of body, and
   (d) No marking—nutrient that is body's stored source of energy.

2. Label the nutrients on the blanks in the diagram.

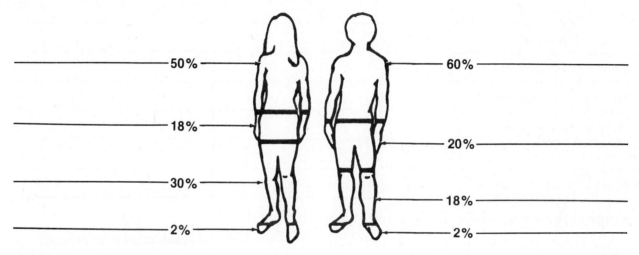

3. Using the above information from the diagram, label the bar graphs below as *male* or *female*.

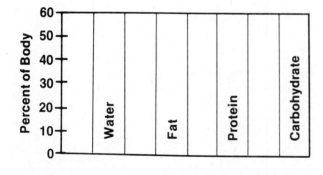 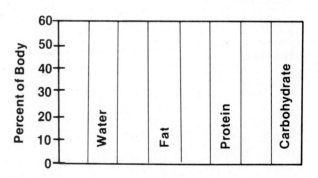

4. What nutrients were not included in the above diagram? _____

5. Do males or females usually have more fat in their bodies? _____

6. List three reasons why water is important for good health. _____

_____

Name _____ Date _____ Class _____

WHAT NUTRIENTS ARE IN FOOD?

8. Complete the following table by putting check marks in the correct columns.

	Fat	Protein	Carbohydrate
Present in butter, oils			
Body's main energy source			
Present in bread and fruit			
Makes up bone and muscle			
Need the most of daily			
Present in meat, fish			
Used most quickly in body			
10% of your diet each day			
Found as cell membranes			
Stored under skin			
Stored in blood and liver			

9. Examine these food labels. Then, answer the questions below.

Cereal (1 serving)

Nutrient	RDA
Vitamin A	20
Vitamin C	10
Riboflavin	30
Thiamine	10
Niacin	25
Calcium	40
Iron	60
Potassium	1

Breakfast drink (1 serving)

Nutrient	RDA
Vitamin A	30
Vitamin C	5
Niacin	2
Riboflavin	40
Thiamine	5
Calcium	50
Iron	4
Zinc	1
Phosphorus	1

a. Circle the vitamins on each label.

b. Underline the minerals on each label.

c. Which of the two foods supplies more Vitamin C in one serving? _____

Name _____ Date _____ Class _____

WHAT NUTRIENTS ARE IN FOOD?

10. **a.** In general, how much does the body need of each vitamin each day? _____

    _____

    b. Give an example of the amount needed in one day for any vitamin listed in your textbook in

    Table 9-1. Then, list the vitamin. _____

11. *Use Table 9-1 in your textbook to complete these questions.* Which vitamin is being described?

    a. is found in ham, eggs, and raisins   _____

    b. is also called niacin   _____

    c. you need 60 mg each day   _____

    d. keeps your membranes healthy   _____

    e. may cause night blindness if missing in diet _____

    f. may cause bowed legs if missing in diet   _____

    g. is found in yeast, milk, eggs   _____

    h. allows cells to carry out respiration   _____

12. **a.** In general, how much does the body need of each
    mineral each day?   _____

    b. Give an example of the amount needed in one day for any mineral listed in your textbook in

    Table 9-2. Then, list the mineral. _____

13. *Use Table 9-2 in your textbook to complete these questions. Which mineral is being described?*

    a. you need 0.325 g each day   _____

    b. may cause anemia if missing in diet   _____

    c. found in seafoods, iodized table salt   _____

    d. found in bacon, butter   _____

    e. needed to make muscles contract   _____

    f. found in nuts, sardines, milk, cheese   _____

    g. 1000 mg needed each day   _____

    h. helps form blood cells   _____

Name _____ Date _____ Class _____

CALORIES

In your textbook, read about the energy in food in Section 9:2.

1. Define *Calorie*. _____

2. What does it mean if someone says that a food contains 50 Calories? _____

_____

_____

3. What is the energy in food used for in your body? _____

_____

4. Complete the table below by determining the number of Calories in each food sample and writing the number in the column at the right.

Food sample	Amount of water in beaker	Starting temperature of water before burning food	Final temperature of water after burning food	Number of Calories in food
A	1000 g	18°C	19°C	1
B	1000 g	10°C	15°C	
C	1000 g	0°C	100°C	
D	1000 g	55°C	72°C	

5. A student ate the foods in the table below in one day. Complete the table by determining the total Calories taken in. Then, answer the questions on the following page.

Food	Calories	×	Amount eaten	=	Total
Egg	80		2		160
Milk	80		2 glasses		
Bread	70		4 slices		
Bologna	60		4 slices		
Cola	145		4 glasses		
Hamburger	250		2		
French fries	100		1 serving		

Name _____ Date _____ Class _____

CALORIES

6. Which food gave the student the most Calories? _____

7. Were the servings and mass of each food equal? _____

8. When comparing equal masses of food, which nutrient type will provide the most Calories?

_____

In your textbook, read about using Calories in Section 9:2.

9. Look at Table 9-4 in your textbook. Use the information in the table and in your textbook to help you answer the following questions.

  a. How many Calories do you need each day? _____

  _____

  b. What two things listed on the graph are important in determining how many Calories a

  person needs? _____

  c. How do Calorie needs differ as a person ages from 7 to 18? _____

  _____

  d. How do Calorie needs differ between males and females above the age of 10? _____

  _____

  e. If a typical female age 18 takes in 1500 Calories each day for one month, will she gain or lose

  weight? Why? _____

  _____

  _____

  f. If a typical male age 15 takes in 3500 Calories each day for one month, will he gain or lose

  weight? Why? _____

  _____

  _____

  g. How do Calorie needs vary with different kinds of activities a person does? _____

  _____

  _____

Name _____ Date _____ Class _____

VOCABULARY

Review the new words used in Chapter 9 of your textbook. Then, complete this crossword puzzle.

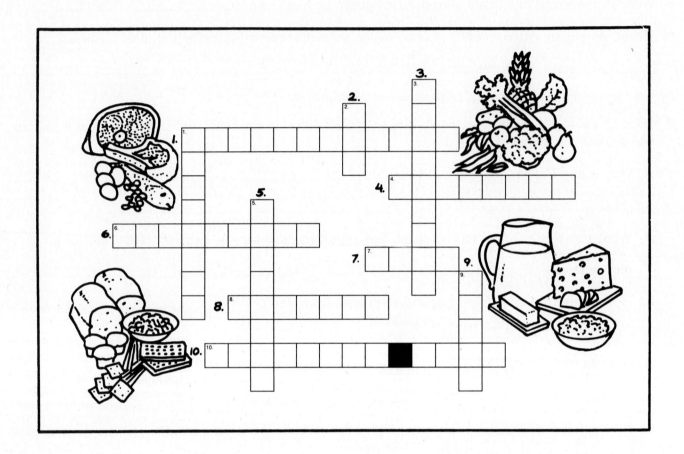

Across

1. nutrient that supplies energy
4. nutrients that help cells carry on daily chemical work
6. study of how body uses food
7. nutrient that supplies energy if body's first energy source is used up
8. main nutrient in meat
10. the right amount of each nutrient (two words)

Down

1. measure of energy in food
2. abbreviation for Recommended Daily Allowance
3. chemicals in food needed by body
5. iron and calcium are examples
9. makes up 50 to 60% of your body

Name _____ Date _____ Class _____

THE PROCESS OF DIGESTION

In your textbook, read about the breakdown of food in Section 10:1.

1. What is the meaning of the word *digestion*? _____

_____

2. How can the digestive system be compared to a factory? _____

_____

3. What is food used for once it is broken down? _____

_____

4. Decide whether the following phrases describe a physical or chemical change. Then, write the word *physical* or *chemical* in the blanks provided.

_____ **a.** Food is changed into a form cells can use.

_____ **b.** Food is ground up in the mouth.

_____ **c.** Starch is changed to glucose.

_____ **d.** Large pieces of food are broken down into small pieces.

_____ **e.** Food is chewed.

_____ **f.** Enzymes speed up chemical changes.

THE HUMAN DIGESTIVE SYSTEM

In your textbook, read about how the digestive system works in Section 10:2.

1. Write the following nutrients under the correct headings in the chart below.

fats   proteins   water   vitamins   minerals   carbohydrates

Nutrients that have to be digested	Nutrients that do not have to be digested

THE HUMAN DIGESTIVE SYSTEM

In your textbook, read about a tour through the digestive system in Section 10:2.

2. Label the following parts of the digestive system on the diagram below: stomach, liver, large intestine, small intestine, gallbladder, mouth, esophagus, salivary gland, pancreas, anus, and appendix.

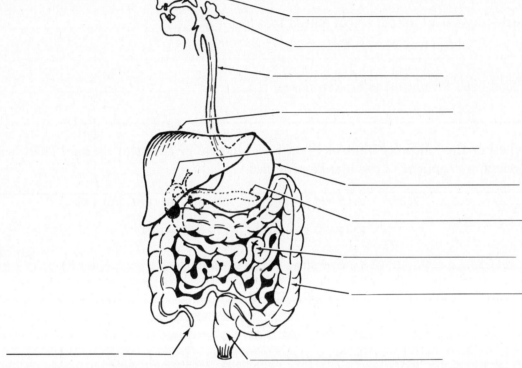

3. In the drawing above, shade in with a pencil those organs through which food actually passes.

4. The graph below shows how long food stays in different parts of the digestive system.

Use this graph to answer the questions that follow.

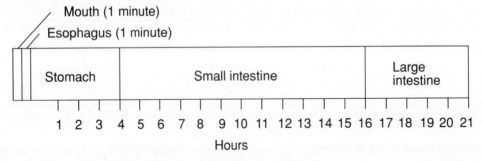

a. In which two organs does food stay for the shortest time? _____

b. About how long does food stay in the stomach? _____ in the small intestine?

_____ in the large intestine? _____

c. In which organ does food stay for the longest time? _____

THE HUMAN DIGESTIVE SYSTEM

5. Label the diagrams below. Then, color the organs according to this plan:
   green—organ that make bile
   red—organ that removes water
   blue—organ that stores bile
   yellow—organ that makes enzymes for digestion

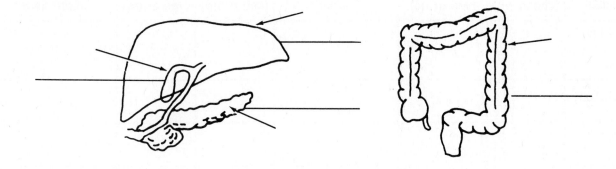

In your textbook, read about moving digested food into body cells in Section 10:2.

6. Label the following parts in the diagrams below: blood vessel, villus, small intestine, food molecules.

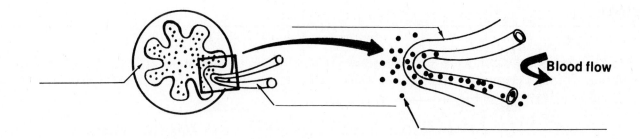

Blood flow

7. What organ contains the villi? _____

8. **a.** By what process does food pass into the blood? _____

   b. What happens to the food once it enters the blood? _____

   _____

   c. Explain the importance of villi. _____

   _____

Name _____ Date _____ Class _____

THE HUMAN DIGESTIVE SYSTEM

9. Complete the table below.

Organ	Enzyme formed here? (yes or no)	Food passes through this organ? (yes or no)	Name of nutrient acted upon or digested (fat, protein, carbohydrate, none)	Food absorbed here? (yes or no)	Water absorbed here? (yes or no)	Name of chemical made here
Mouth and salivary glands						
Esophagus						
Stomach						
Liver and gallbladder						
Pancreas						
Small intestine						
Large intestine						

10. Decide whether the following statements are true or false. If true, write *true* in the left-hand column. If false, change the underlined word to one that will make the statement true and write the correct word in the blank.

_____ **a.** Plant-eating animals usually have <u>short</u> digestive systems.

_____ **b.** An earthworm has <u>one</u> opening in its digestive system.

_____ **c.** A tapeworm has <u>no</u> digestive system.

_____ **d.** Meat-eating animals usually have <u>long</u> digestive systems.

_____ **e.** Humans are among the animals that have a <u>complex</u> digestive system.

Name _____ Date _____ Class _____

PROBLEMS OF THE DIGESTIVE SYSTEM

In your textbook, read about ulcers and heartburn in Section 10:2.

1. Examine the pictures below. Then, write in the blank the letter of the picture that illustrates the phrase.

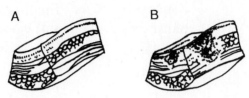

A   B

   a. ulcer in stomach lining _____   **c.** results of acid and enzymes working on cells _____

   b. normal stomach lining _____

2. **a.** What causes heartburn? _____

   b. Why is it called by the name "heartburn"? _____

_____

3. Label these parts in Diagram A:
   small intestine, esophagus, stomach, proper food amount in stomach
4. Label these parts in Diagram B:
   too much food in stomach, bulging stomach
5. Draw in and label where food can be found if the person in Diagram B has heartburn. Use an arrow to show where the food has come from.

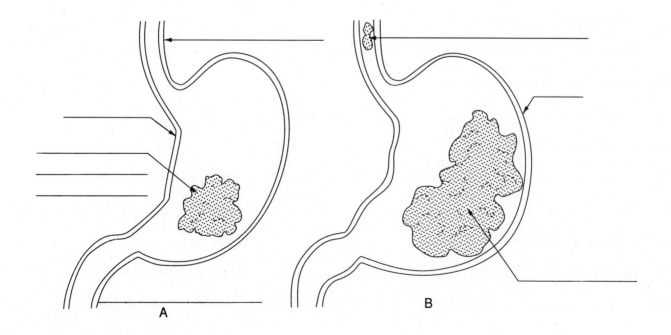

A   B

Name _____ Date _____ Class _____

VOCABULARY

Review the new words used in Chapter 10. Use the terms below to fill in the blanks in the sentences that follow.

mucus	digestive system	digestion	stomach	saliva
villi	physical change	esophagus	small intestine	enzymes
bile	chemical change	pancreas	gall bladder	hydrochloric
liver	salivary glands	appendix	large intestine	acid

1. Changing of food into a usable form is called _____.

2. _____ speed up the rate of chemical change.

3. _____ helps digest carbohydrates in the mouth.

4. _____ helps break down fats.

5. The tube that connects the mouth to the stomach is the _____.

6. _____ are located under the tongue and behind the jaw.

7. The _____ is an organ that makes three different enzymes.

8. The _____ stores bile.

9. Most digestion and absorption of food takes place in the _____.

10. The _____ removes water from undigested food.

11. The _____ is a small fingerlike part located where the small

    and large intestines meet.

12. The breaking of food into small pieces is _____.

13. Protein digestion begins in the _____.

14. Bile is made in the _____.

15. Fingerlike parts on the lining of the small intestine are called _____.

16. _____ turns food into a form that cells can use.

17. The _____ is a group of organs that take in food and change

    it into a form the body can use.

18. The chemical _____ is made by the stomach.

19. _____ protects the stomach and intestinal linings.

Name _____ Date _____ Class _____

THE PROCESS OF CIRCULATION

In your textbook, read about your body's pickup and delivery system in Section 11:1.

Joe Garcia owns a laundry service. Each day his trucks move out onto the streets to pick up dirty laundry from his customers' homes. The trucks also deliver the cleaned clothes that were collected before. The dirty laundry is taken to the store where the washing and cleaning takes place. The cleaned clothes are returned in the trucks to the customers and more dirty clothes are picked up.

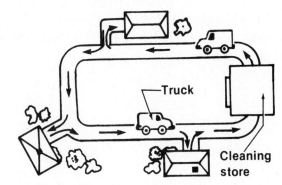

1. Parts of the circulatory system are similar in jobs to objects in the above story. Write the letter of the object in Section I in the space to the left of the part of the circulatory system in Section II that most nearly matches it in function.

Section I		Section II	
A. Roads	**D.** Homes	____ Body cells	____ Blood vessels
B. Trucks	**E.** Clean laundry	____ Oxygen	____ Wastes
C. Cleaning store	**F.** Dirty laundry	____ Blood	____ Heart and lungs

In your textbook, read about circulation in animals in Section 11:1.

2. Complete this chart using Yes or No answers.

Animal	Circulatory system present?	Blood present?	Heart present?	Blood vessels present?
Hydra				
Earthworm				
Insect				
Human				

3. **a.** Define open circulatory system. _____

_____

b. Define closed circulatory system. _____

_____

Name _____ Date _____ Class _____

THE HUMAN HEART

In your textbook, read about the structure of the human heart in Section 11:2.

1. Label the diagram below using these words: right atrium, right ventricle, left atrium, left ventricle, tricuspid valve, semilunar valve (used twice), bicuspid valve, right side of heart, left side of heart

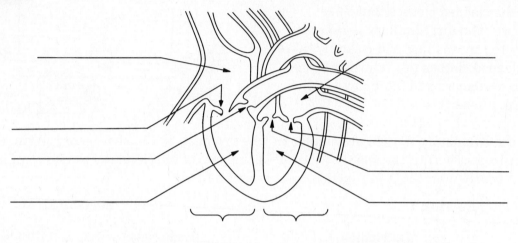

In your textbook, read about how the heart works as a pump in Section 11:2.

2. Complete the following chart by putting checkmarks in the correct columns.

	A	B
Atria are relaxed		
Ventricles are relaxed		
Atria are pumping		
Ventricles are pumping		
Ventricles are receiving blood from atria		
Atria are receiving blood returning to heart		
Blood is pumped to body		

Name _____ Date _____ Class _____

THE HUMAN HEART

In your textbook, read about the jobs of the heart in Section 11:2.

3. Identify the parts lettered *A-H* in the following diagram. Then, name the parts in the blanks provided.

A _____   E _____

B _____   F _____

C _____   G _____

D _____   H _____

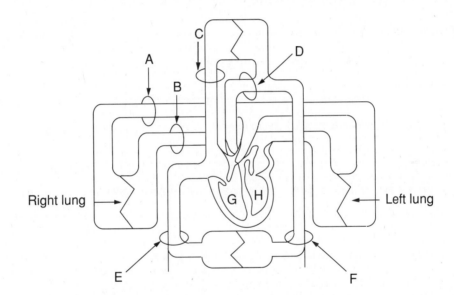

Right lung →   ← Left lung

4. Use the diagram to complete the table. Write the letters A-H under the correct headings.

Contains blood with much oxygen, little carbon dioxide	Contains blood with much carbon dioxide, little oxygen

5. Describe the main job of the right side of your heart. _____

_____

6. Describe the main job of the left side of your heart. _____

_____

Name _____ Date _____ Class _____

BLOOD VESSELS

In your textbook, read about arteries, veins, and capillaries in Section 11:3.

1. Circle the word or words that make the statement true.

   a. Arteries carry blood toward / away from the heart.

   b. Arteries carry blood under high / low pressure.

   c. Arteries have thin / thick muscular walls.

   d. An example of an artery is the vena cava / aorta.

   e. When your feel your pulse, you are feeling blood moving through your veins / arteries.

2. What is the main job of veins? _____

3. Compare the amount of muscle in veins and arteries. _____

   _____

4. Compare the pressure within veins and arteries. _____

   _____

5. Explain how the one-way valves in veins help maintain circulation. _____

   _____

   _____

6. Place a checkmark next to those statements below that are true.

   _____ **a.** Blood pressure is higher in capillaries than in arteries.

   _____ **b.** Capillary walls are only one cell thick.

   _____ **c.** The human body has more veins than capillaries.

   _____ **d.** Capillaries bring blood close to all body cells.

   _____ **e.** All the pickups of carbon dioxide and other cell wastes, and all the deliveries of oxygen, food, and other materials, occur in the capillaries.

Name _____ Date _____ Class _____

PROBLEMS OF THE CIRCULATORY SYSTEM

In your textbook, read about high blood pressure and heart attacks in Section 11:4.

1. The following diagrams show cross sections of three arteries. Choices A, B, and C may be used more than once and in combinations when answering these questions.

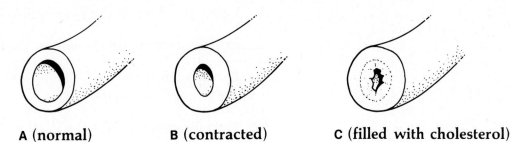

A (normal)   B (contracted)   C (filled with cholesterol)

   a. Which diagram or diagrams *might* have an upper blood pressure value of 160? _____

   Explain why. _____

   b. Which diagram or diagrams *might* have an upper blood pressure value of 110? _____

   Explain why. _____

   _____

2. What are coronary blood vessels? _____

   _____

3. What can happen if these vessels become clogged? _____

   _____ _____ _____ _____

   _____

In your textbook, read about preventing heart problems in Section 11:4.

4. How can diet help prevent heart problems? _____

   _____

5. Why is a smoker more likely to have heart problems than a nonsmoker? _____

   _____

   _____

Name _____ Date _____ Class _____

VOCABULARY

Review the new words used in Chapter 11 of your textbook. Then, read the statements below.

For each statement, write TRUE or FALSE on the first blank. Make a false statement true by changing the underlined term. Write the correct term on the second blank.

1. _____ _____ <u>Valves</u> are flaps in the heart and veins.

2. _____ _____ <u>Arteries</u> carry blood away from the heart.

3. _____ _____ The <u>circulatory system</u> is made up of blood, blood vessels, and the heart.

4. _____ _____ The <u>pulmonary vein</u> is the largest vein.

5. _____ _____ Blood pressure is the force of blood pushing against the walls of the <u>heart</u>.

6. _____ _____ <u>Atria</u> are the top chambers of the heart.

7. _____ _____ The <u>tricuspid</u> valves are located between the ventricles and their arteries.

8. _____ _____ Hypertension is caused by <u>low</u> blood pressure.

9. _____ _____ A <u>vena cava</u> is the smallest kind of blood vessel.

10. _____ _____ <u>Coronary vessels</u> carry blood to the heart.

11. _____ _____ <u>Capillaries</u> carry blood from the lungs to the left side of the heart.

12. _____ _____ The <u>semilunar</u> valve is located between the right atrium and right ventricle.

13. _____ _____ A <u>heart attack</u> is the death of a heart muscle.

14. _____ _____ The <u>aorta</u> carries blood from the heart to the lungs.

15. _____ _____ <u>Veins</u> carry blood back to the heart.

16. _____ _____ The <u>bicuspid</u> valve is located between the left atrium and the left ventricle.

17. _____ _____ <u>Cholesterol</u> can narrow arteries.

18. _____ _____ The <u>pulmonary artery</u> is the largest artery.

19. _____ _____ <u>Ventricles</u> are the bottom chambers of the heart.

Name _____ Date _____ Class _____

THE ROLE OF BLOOD

In your textbook, read about the functions of blood in Section 12:1.

Complete this outline of blood functions.

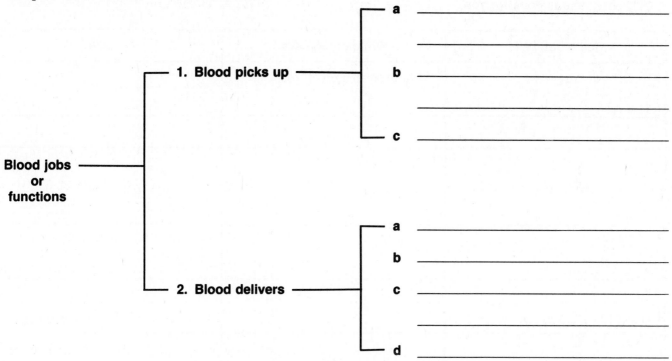

Blood jobs or functions

1. Blood picks up
   a _____
   b _____
   c _____

2. Blood delivers
   a _____
   b _____
   c _____
   d _____

PARTS OF HUMAN BLOOD

In your textbook, read about the living and nonliving parts of blood in Section 12:2.

1. Examine the diagram at the right of blood that has been sitting for an hour. Write the letter of the blood part being described in each of the words or phrases below. Write the correct letter next to each word or phrase.

   a. plasma _____

   b. liquid part _____

   c. blood cell part _____

   d. nonliving part _____

   e. living part _____

   f. mostly water _____

   g. includes cells that carry oxygen _____

   h. includes parts that aid in blood clotting _____

   i. includes proteins, nutrients, salts, and wastes _____

   j. red _____

   k. yellow _____

   l. includes cells that destroy harmful microbes _____

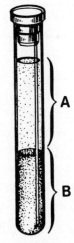

A

B

Name _____ Date _____ Class _____

PARTS OF HUMAN BLOOD

In your textbook, read about blood cells and platelets in Section 12:2.

2. Complete the table below by writing the phrases that follow in the correct column in the table. The first one is done for you.

Red blood cells	White blood cells	Platelets
	8000 in small drop of blood	

8000 in a small drop of blood
250 000 in a small drop of blood
5 million in a small drop of blood
not whole cells
destroy microbes
aid in blood clotting
can move between capillaries
   and among body cells
increase during infections
contain hemoglobin
remove dead cells

transport oxygen
made in spleen
if number is low, person feels tired
life span of 5 days
life span of 10 days
life span of 120 days
increase abnormally during leukemia
cell with a nucleus
cell with no nucleus
results in hemophilia if not working
look like doughnuts without holes
move like amoebas

Name _____ Date _____ Class _____

BLOOD TYPES

In your textbook, read about different types of blood in Section 12:3.

Examine the following chart carefully. Then, look at the four tubes of blood shown below. Fill in the spaces with the correct information from the chart and the following labels: red cells, plasma protein shape, red cell protein shape, plasma, red cell. Part of the first one is done for you.

Blood type	Red blood cell protein	Plasma protein	Cell protein plasma protein fit or no fit
O	none	⬭ ✚	no fit
A	⊏	⬭	no fit
B	⊏	✚	no fit
AB	⊏ ⊏	none	no fit

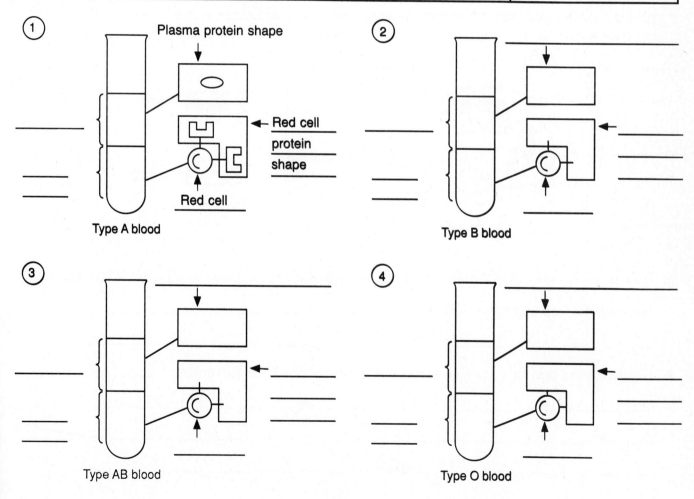

Name _____ Date _____ Class _____

IMMUNITY

In your textbook, read about immunity in Section 12:4.

1. Define immune system. _____

   _____

2. **a.** Define antigen. _____

   _____

   b. Are antigens helpful? Explain. _____

3. **a.** Define antibody. _____

   b. Are antibodies helpful? Explain. _____

   _____

4. Figures A, B, C, and D are labeled for you. You are to:
   a. draw the antigen onto the correct cell that normally has antigens on it.
   b. draw the antibody onto the correct cell that normally has antibodies on it.

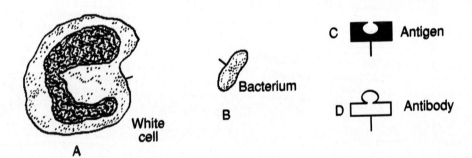

5. How is the meeting of the white blood cell and the bacterium shown in question 4 like the

   meeting of a lock and a key? _____

   _____

6. List two ways that this meeting can result in the death of the bacterium. _____

   _____

   _____

   _____

Name _____ Date _____ Class _____

IMMUNITY

7. What does the immune system do for months or years after the invasion of a certain antigen? __

_____

_____

8. If the same type of bacteria enter the body several years later, what will happen? _____

_____

9. a. What do the initials *DPT* stand for? _____

   b. What is in a DPT shot? _____

_____

   c. What happens when you receive this shot? _____

_____

_____

   d. What happens later on if the actual bacteria causing these diseases were to enter your body?

_____

_____

10. What is immunity? _____

_____

11. What do the initials *AIDS* stand for? _____

12. Is AIDS caused by a bacterium or a virus? _____

13. What type of cells does it attack? _____

14. How does AIDS harm the body? _____

_____

15. List four ways that AIDS can be spread from one person to another. _____

_____

_____

_____

VOCABULARY

Review the new words used in Chapter 12 of your textbook. Then, use the terms below to fill in the blanks in the sentences that follow.

immunity	bone marrow	plasma	hemoglobin
antigens	immune system	anemia	platelets
hemophilia	red blood cells	leukemia	antibodies
AIDS	white blood cells		

1. _____ is the yellow, nonliving part of blood.

2. _____ are the cells in the blood that carry oxygen to the tissues.

3. _____ is a protein in red blood cells that joins with oxygen.

4. When a person has _____ there are too few red blood cells or too little hemoglobin or both.

5. The cells in the blood that remove microbes and dead cells are _____.

6. When a person has _____, the number of white blood cells increases abnormally.

7. _____ are bloodlike parts important in blood clotting.

8. The blood of a person with _____ will not clot.

9. The _____ helps keep a person free of disease.

10. _____ are chemicals that destroy bacteria or viruses.

11. _____ are foreign substances that invade the body and cause disease.

12. _____ is the ability of a person who once had a disease to be protected from getting it again.

13. _____ is a disease of the immune system.

14. Red blood cells are made in _____, the soft center part of the bone.

Name _____ Date _____ Class _____

THE ROLE OF RESPIRATION

In your textbook, read about respiration in Section 13:1.

1. What is the function of the respiratory system? _____

_____

2. Explain why a large surface area is needed in a respiratory system. _____

_____

_____

3. Match the main methods of getting oxygen with the animals below. Write the letter of the method below each animal.
   A = skin   B = skin and lungs   C = lungs   D = gills   E = small tubes

____   ____   ____   ____   ____

HUMAN RESPIRATORY SYSTEM

In your textbook, read about respiratory system organs in Section 13:2.

1. Label the parts on the diagram below using these words: bronchus, nose, nasal chamber, lung, trachea, epiglottis, alveoli.

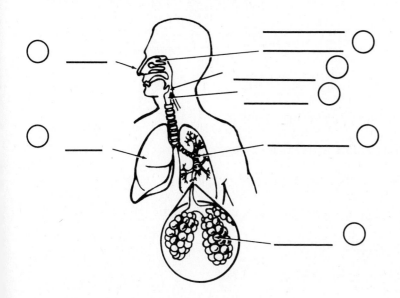

2. Place the letter of the description below in the correct circle next to the labeled part of the diagram.
   A = place where air is warmed or cooled
   B = clusters of air sacs where gas exchange occurs
   C = place where air first enters respiratory system
   D = the windpipe
   E = one of two major organs of respiration
   F = carries air from trachea into lung
   G = flap that prevents food from entering trachea

Name _____ Date _____ Class _____

HUMAN RESPIRATORY SYSTEM

In your textbook, read about gas exchange in Section 13:2.

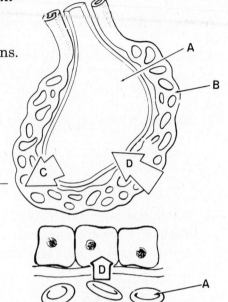

3. Examine the first diagram at the right. Then, answer the questions.

   a. What is part A? _____

   part B? _____

   b. What gas moves in the direction shown by arrow C?

   _____ arrow D? _____

4. Examine the second diagram at the right. Then, answer the questions.

   a. What is part A? _____

   part B? _____

   b. What gas moves in the direction shown by arrow C?

   _____ arrow D? _____

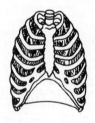

5. Below are two diagrams of the chest cavity during breathing. Circle the words that correctly complete the statements below each diagram.

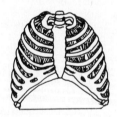

Rib cage moves out / in.   Rib cage moves out / in.

Rib cage moves up / down.   Rib cage moves up / down.

Diaphragm is relaxed / working.   Diaphragm is relaxed / working.

Air is pulled in / pushed out.   Air is pulled in / pushed out.

Diaphragm pushes up / moves down.   Diaphragm pushes up / moves down.

Lungs get squeezed / expand.   Lungs get squeezed / expand.

Person is breathing in / out.   Person is breathing in / out.

Name _____ Date _____ Class _____

PROBLEMS OF THE RESPIRATORY SYSTEM

In your textbook, read about respiratory problems in Section 13:3.

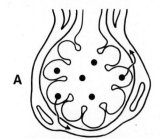 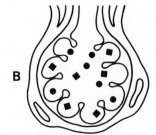 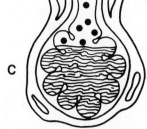 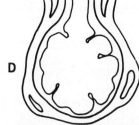

1. Drawing A shows the normal pathway of 2 oxygen molecules (black dots) going from the alveoli into a lung capillary. Finish the drawing by showing the path that the other 4 oxygen molecules will take in a normal person.
2. Drawing B shows alveoli filled with oxygen and carbon monoxide (squares). Finish the drawing by showing the path that the gas molecules will take when in the lungs of a person with carbon monoxide poisoning.

3. Explain why a person with the problem in diagram B could die. _____

_____

_____

4. Drawing C shows alveoli filled with pus, liquid, and mucus.

   a. What disease may cause this to occur? _____

   b. Can oxygen (black dots) reach the capillaries surrounding these alveoli? ____ Explain. _____

   _____

   _____

   c. Is this disease communicable or noncommunicable? _____

   Explain. _____

   _____

5. Drawing D shows the alveoli of a person with emphysema.
   a. How do these alveoli compare with those of a normal person?

   _____

   _____

   b. How is emphysema harmful? _____

   _____

Name _____ Date _____ Class _____

THE ROLE OF EXCRETION

In your textbook, read about waste removal in Section 13:4.

1. Explain what would happen if wastes were not removed from the body. _____

_____

_____

2. In the space provided, place a checkmark next to those statements that are true. For each statement that is false, change the underlined word to one that will make the statement true, and write it in the space.

   a. _____   Getting rid of wastes is called <u>digestion</u>.

   b. _____   <u>Urea</u> is a waste that results from the breakdown of body protein.

   c. _____   <u>Solid</u> wastes are removed by the excretory system.

   d. _____   Wastes are either made by body cells or are the remains of <u>undigested</u> food.

3. Label the parts on the diagram using these labels: ureter, urethra, kidney, urinary bladder, blood vessel from kidney, blood vessel to kidney.

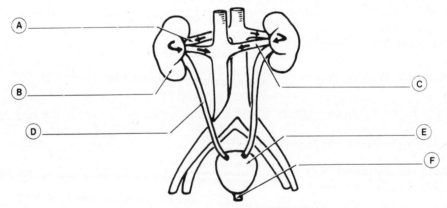

4. Beside each phrase, write the letter from the diagram above that shows the correct location.

   a. where urea is filtered from the blood ____

   b. where wastes are stored for a short time ____

   c. transports wastes from kidney to bladder ____

   d. brings wastes to kidneys ____

   e. where urine leaves body ____

   f. carries filtered blood away from kidney ____

Name _____ Date _____ Class _____

THE ROLE OF EXCRETION

5. Complete the chart below by writing the following phrases under the correct organ pictured.

body filter   contains alveoli
has sweat glands   removes urea
helps cool body   protective cover
removes CO_2 controls water and salt loss
removes water in breath

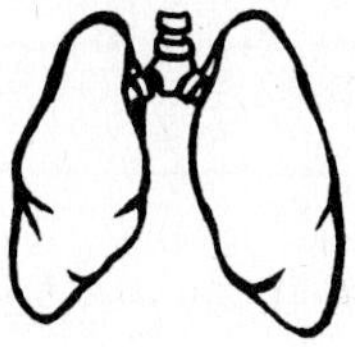

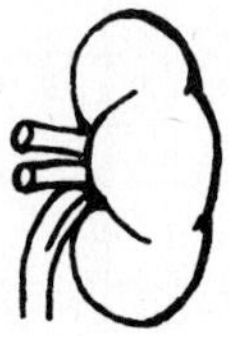

6. In the space provided, place a checkmark next to the statements that are true. For each statement that is false, change the underlined word to one that will make the statement true and write it in the space.

a. _____ Each kidney has about one million tiny filter units called <u>ureters</u>.

b. _____ <u>Blood</u> with blood cells, salts, sugar, urea, and water enters each filter unit.

c. _____ All materials except <u>urea</u> and excess water and salts diffuse back into the blood after filtering.

d. _____ Filtered waste carried out of the kidney to the bladder is known as <u>urine</u>.

e. _____ Each of the body's two to five million sweat glands gives off water and <u>sugar</u>.

f. _____ The skin <u>can</u> control water loss.

Name _____ **Date** _____ **Class** _____

VOCABULARY

Review the new words used in Chapter 13 of your textbook. Then, complete this puzzle.

1. Put the following words into two groups by adding them to this table under the proper heading: urethra, diaphragm, bronchi, ureter, trachea, nephron, alveoli, epiglottis, urinary bladder, respiratory system, excretory system.

Parts of the	Parts of the
lungs	kidney
rib cage	sweat glands

2. Put the following words into two groups by writing them in this table under the proper heading: urea, diaphragm, urine, emphysema, excess salt, pneumonia.

Respiration	Excretion

Name _____ Date _____ Class _____

THE ROLE OF THE SKELETON

In your textbook, read about functions of the skeleton in Section 14:1.

1. Below are five pictures. Under each, write what the item does or is used for. Then, write what job of the skeletal system is similar.

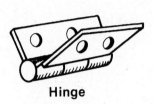

Hinge

Catcher's mask

Trunk

How used? _____

Skeleton job: _____

How used? _____

Skeleton job: _____

How used? _____

Skeleton job: _____

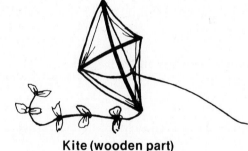

Kite (wooden part)

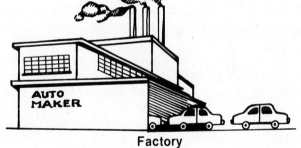

Factory

How used? _____

Skeleton job: _____

Does what? _____

Skeleton job: _____

In your textbook, read about bone growth in Section 14:1.

2. A child has 5 wrist bones. An adult has 8 wrist bones.

   a. How can these differences be used as evidence that bone tissue is alive? _____

   _____

   b. How has bone length in your legs changed since you were an infant? _____

   _____

   c. How can this change be used as evidence that bone tissue is alive? _____

   _____

THE ROLE OF THE SKELETON

In your textbook, read about bone structure in Section 14:1.

3. Label the following parts on the diagram below: cartilage, ligament, solid bone, spongy bone, marrow, outer membrane.
   Put the letters of the jobs or traits below in the correct circles on the blanks in the diagram.
   A = compact, and stores calcium   D = cushion between bones
   B = blood cells are made here   E = lightweight but adds strength
   C = fibers that hold bones together F = contains many nerves and blood vessels

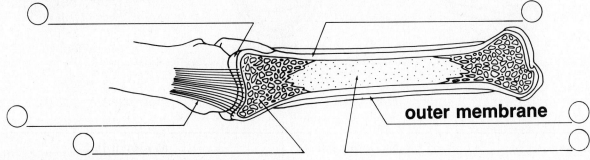

outer membrane

In your textbook, read about joints in Section 14:1.

4. Examine the diagram below. Then, answer the questions by putting the letter of the correct joint on the blanks beside each phrase.

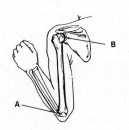

    a. allows twisting and turning of bones where they meet _____

    b. allows bones to move back and forth only _____

    c. allows movement of arm in a circle _____

    d. is a ball-and-socket joint _____

    e. is a hinge joint _____

5. **a.** Below each of the following diagrams, label the type of joint shown. Use these labels: ball-and-socket, hinge, fixed.
   b. Then, in the space provided, tell what type of movement each joint allows.

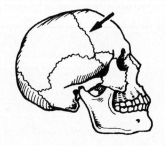 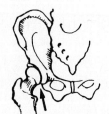 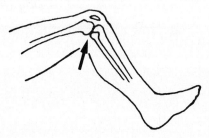

Type _____   _____   _____

Movement _____   _____   _____

Name _____ Date _____ Class _____

THE ROLE OF MUSCLES

In your textbook, read about human muscle types in Section 14:2.

1. Identify these three drawings as smooth, skeletal, or cardiac muscle. Label them correctly. They are about 1500 times natural size.

      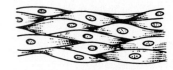

_____   _____   _____

2. Complete the table by checking the correct column for each trait listed.

Trait or location	Skeletal muscle	Cardiac muscle	Smooth muscle
Makes up your small and large intestines			
Makes up your heart			
Makes up your body muscles			
Has stripelike appearance			
Is voluntary			
Can be controlled			
Moves your bones			
Has no stripes			
Muscles form a tight weave			
Involuntary			
Is not connected to bone			
Can't be controlled			
Can contract			
Can shorten			
Most often eaten as meat			

Name _____ Date _____ Class _____

THE ROLE OF MUSCLES

In your textbook, read about how muscles work in Section 14:2.

3. Examine the drawing below and answer the questions.

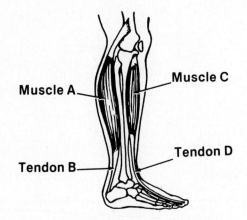

a. As muscle A contracts, which tendon is pulled? _____

b. Name the bone to which muscle A is attached. _____

c. Will the heel move up or down as muscle A contracts? _____

d. Name the bone to which tendon B is connected. _____

e. As muscle C contracts, which tendon is pulled? _____

f. Name the bone to which muscle C is attached. _____

g. Will the foot move up or down as muscle C contracts? _____

h. Name the bone to which tendon D is connected. _____

4. Examine the two diagrams below and answer the questions.

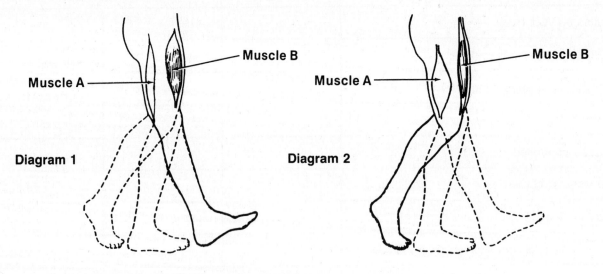

a. In which diagram is muscle A contracted? _____

b. In which diagram is muscle B contracted? _____

c. How can you tell which muscle is contracted? _____

_____

d. When one muscle of a pair is contracted, the other is _____.

5. In each diagram, draw a solid line over the dotted line that shows the correct position of the leg.

Name _____ Date _____ Class _____

BONE AND MUSCLE PROBLEMS

In your textbook, read about bone and muscle problems in Section 14:3.

1. What is arthritis? _____

2. One type of arthritis results in breakdown of the cartilage at the joints. How would this affect a

   person's life? _____

   _____

   _____

3. What can be done to help people whose joints are severely affected by arthritis? _____

   _____

4. What can happen to bones if a person doesn't get enough calcium in their diet? _____

   _____

5. What are ligaments? _____

   _____

6. What happens to ligaments that are sprained? _____

   _____

7. a. What is a muscle cramp? _____

   _____

   b. When does it occur? _____

   _____

8. a. What is muscular dystrophy? _____

   _____

   b. What effect does it have on muscles? _____

Name _____ Date _____ Class _____

VOCABULARY

Review the new words used in Chapter 14 of your textbook. Then, complete the puzzle. Use the words or phrases to fill in the blanks in the sentences. Do not use any term more than once.

skeletal system	solid bone	fixed joints	ligaments
spongy bone	hinge joints	muscular system	ball-and-socket joint
skeletal muscles	sprain	voluntary muscles	muscular dystrophy
cardiac muscle	tendons	involuntary muscle	smooth muscle
arthritis			

1. _____ is found only in the heart.

2. Muscle you have no control over is _____.

3. Bones are held together by _____. A _____ results when they are torn.

4. _____ is usually found toward the ends of bones. The outer part of bones is usually

   _____.

5. The _____ is a framework for the body.

6. All the muscles in your body make up the _____.

7. Muscles are connected to bones by _____.

8. Muscles you can control are _____.

9. Many body organs, such as arteries, are made up of _____.

10. _____ is a disease of the joints.

11. _____ is a disease that causes the wasting away of muscle tissue.

12. Muscles that move the bones of the skeleton are _____.

13. Your knees and elbows are _____.

14. Bones can turn in a circle at a _____.

15. Joints that don't move are called _____.

Name _____ **Date** _____ **Class** _____

THE ROLE OF THE NERVOUS SYSTEM

In your textbook, read about how animals keep in touch with their surroundings in Section 15:1.

1. What is a response? _____

_____

2. Complete the following chart by placing a check mark in the correct columns.

Animal	Nervous system	Nerve net	Nerve cord	Brainlike part	Brain	Eyespots	Eyes
Hydra							
Flatworm							
Spider							

HUMAN NERVOUS SYSTEM

In your textbook, read about the complex nervous system of humans in Section 15:2.

1. Complete these facts about nerve cells.

    a. Number in your body _____   **d.** Main job _____

    b. Special name   _____   _____

    c. Length of some   _____   **e.** Many bunched together _____

2. Match the parts of this diagram with the phrases below. Fill in the blanks with the correct letter.

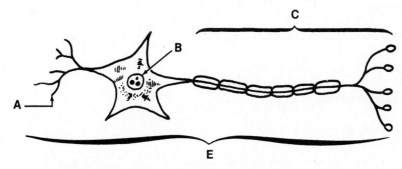

_____ **a.** Nucleus   _____ **d.** Part that receives messages

_____ **b.** Axon   _____ **e.** Part that sends messages

_____ **c.** Dendrite   _____ **f.** Neuron

Name _____ Date _____ Class _____

HUMAN NERVOUS SYSTEM

3. The diagrams below show the path that a message takes from the hand to the spinal cord and back again. One is incorrect. It has two major errors.

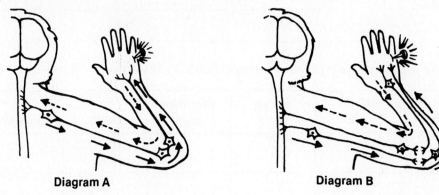

Diagram A   Diagram B

   a. Which diagram is incorrect? _____

   b. Describe the two major errors? _____

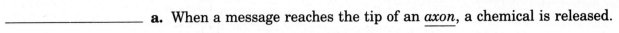

   _____

4. If the statement is true, place a check mark in the space provided. If it is false, change the underlined word to one that will make the statement true and write it down.

   _____ a. When a message reaches the tip of an *axon*, a chemical is released.

   _____ b. The *nucleus* is a small space between the axon of one neuron and the dendrite of another neuron nearby.

   _____ c. A message moves along a neuron from the *dendrite* to the *axon*.

5. Examine this diagram. It shows a simple sketch of the human nervous system. Put the correct letter in the blank to identify the part being described.

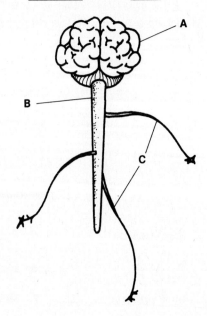

   a. Part that sends and receives messages to and

      from all body parts ____

   b. Protected by your vertebrae ____

   c. Protected by your skull ____

   d. Carries messages from skin to spinal cord ____

   e. Spinal cord ____

   f. Body nerves ____

Name _____ Date _____ Class _____

HUMAN NERVOUS SYSTEM

6. Complete this chart of the human brain.

a. Brain part b. Voluntary or involuntary	Job
a. _____ b. _____	_____ _____ _____
a. _____ b. _____	_____ _____
a. _____ b. _____	_____ _____

7. a. Label the drawing of a reflex below using the letters of the statements listed here.
   A. Message moves from spinal cord to arm muscle.
   B. Message moves from finger to spinal cord.
   C. Message reaches and enters spinal cord.
   D. Muscle contracting pulls hand away.
   E. Finger picks up message of sticking pin.

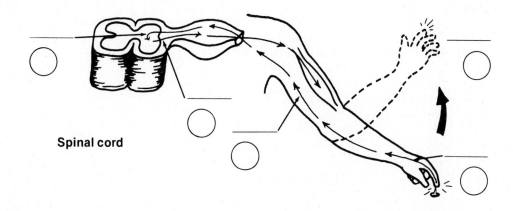

Spinal cord

b. Put the numbers 1 to 5 in the circles near the blanks to put the steps of the reflex in the correct order.

THE ROLE OF THE ENDOCRINE SYSTEM

In your textbook, read about the endocrine system in Section 15:3.

1. On the blanks below, write the name and job of the glands being shown.

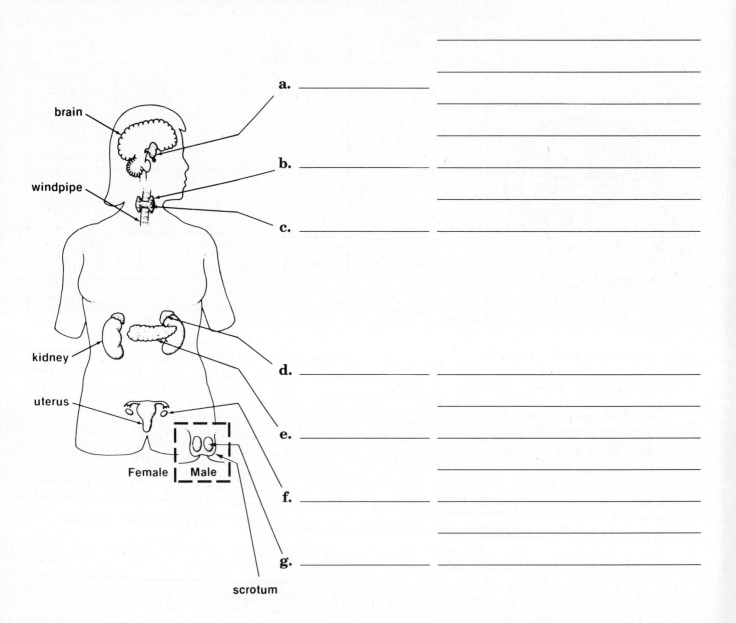

a. _____   _____
                               _____
                               _____
                               _____
b. _____   _____
                               _____
                               _____
c. _____   _____

d. _____   _____
                               _____
e. _____   _____
                               _____
                               _____
f. _____   _____
                               _____
g. _____   _____

Name _____ Date _____ Class _____

THE ROLE OF THE ENDOCRINE SYSTEM

2. What does thyroxine do? _____

_____

3. What happens if a person makes too little thyroxine? _____

_____

4. What happens if a person makes too much thyroxine? _____

_____

NERVOUS AND ENDOCRINE SYSTEM PROBLEMS

In your textbook, read about strokes and diabetes in Section 15:4.

1. How does a stroke affect the body? _____

_____

_____

_____

_____

2. What does insulin do? _____

3. a. What disease results if insulin is not present or cannot be used by the cells? _____

_____

b. People with this disease may begin to lose weight and have a high amount of sugar in their

blood. Explain how these two problems may be the result of this disease. _____

_____

_____

c. How may some people with this disease be helped? _____

_____

Name _____ Date _____ Class _____

VOCABULARY

Review the new words in Chapter 15 of your textbook. Then, circle the letter of the phrase or phrases that best define or explain each word below. Each word may have more than one correct answer.

1. Axon

    a. Releases a chemical into synapse

    b. Part of a neuron

    c. Carries message to next neuron

2. Brain

    a. Made up of two regions

    b. Parts can be voluntary or involuntary

    c. Receives messages from spinal cord

3. Diabetes mellitus

    a. Caused by too much thyroxine

    b. Involves pancreas and insulin levels

    c. Too much glucose in blood

4. Endocrine system

    a. Made up of small glands

    b. Sends messages in form of hormones

    c. Composed of neurons

5. Hormone

    a. Made by pituitary

    b. Has a dendrite end

    c. Carried by the blood

6. Insulin

    a. Made by the parathyroid gland

    b. Lets cells take in glucose

    c. Can be obtained from other animals for injection in humans

7. Medulla

    a. A region of the brain

    b. Jobs it controls are involuntary

    c. Controls blood pressure

8. Neuron

    a. Many form a nerve

    b. Carries messages

    c. Usually very short and thick

9. Pituitary gland

    a. Called master gland

    b. Found on windpipe

    c. Controls growth

10. Reflex

    a. Allows quick reaction

    b. May or may not involve the brain

    c. Usually protective

11. Synapse

    a. Space between neurons

    b. Closes when chemical reaches it

    c. Between axon of one neuron and dendrite of another

12. Thyroid gland

    a. Located in front of windpipe

    b. Makes thyroxine

    c. Controls oxygen use by cells

Name _____ Date _____ Class _____

OBSERVING THE ENVIRONMENT

In your textbook, read about the sense organs of four different animals in Section 16:1.

1. Use the diagrams below to answer the questions that follow. (Hint: Answers may be used once, more than once, or not at all.) Which animal:

Planarian   Cricket   Snake   Earthworm

   a. uses its tongue to detect smell? _____

   b. detects touch and chemicals with its antennae? _____

   c. has eyes similar to human eyes? _____

   d. uses knobs on its front end to detect food? _____

   e. has grooves on the roof of its mouth for detecting odor molecules? _____

   f. detects sound on its legs? _____

2. Use the following list of sense organs to fill in the blanks below: nerve cells, eyespots, compound eyes, eyes.

   a. Detects light and dark for a cricket   _____

   b. Detects light and dark for a snake   _____

   c. Detects light and dark for an earthworm   _____

   d. Detects light and dark for a planarian   _____

HUMAN SENSE ORGANS

In your textbook, read about the eye (Section 16:2).

1. Label the eye parts shown in the diagram and complete the chart.

Eye part	Function

HUMAN SENSE ORGANS

2. On the blanks below, write the name of the eye parts being shown.

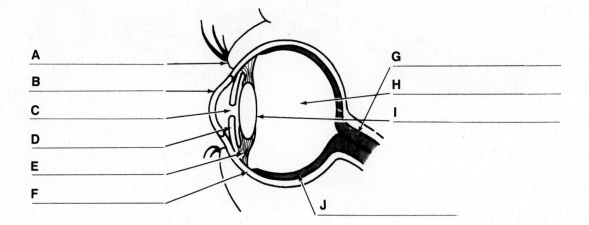

A _____

B _____

C _____

D _____

E _____

F _____

G _____

H _____

I _____

J _____

3. Match the eye parts shown in the diagram with the phrases listed below. Write the letters of the eye parts in the correct blanks.

a. Changes the shape of the lens ____

b. Protects and moistens outside of eye ____

c. Changes its shape for viewing at different distances ____

d. Adjusts the amount of light entering eye ____

e. Clear, outer covering at front of eye ____

f. Made of rods and cones ____

g. Opening in the center of the iris ____

h. Gives the eye its color ____

i. Carries messages from retina to brain ____

j. Liquid that keeps the eye round in shape ____

k. White outer covering of eye ____

Name _____ Date _____ Class _____

HUMAN SENSE ORGANS

In your textbook, read about the tongue and the nose in Section 16:2.

4. Complete the chart below by writing the following phrases in the correct columns: detects molecules of gas, has taste buds, four different tastes are detected, seven different odors are detected, olfactory nerve carries message to brain, detects molecules dissolved in water

Tongue	Nose

5. On the diagram below, label where the four different tastes are detected.

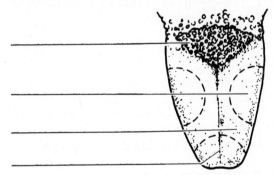

6. About how many taste buds does a person have? _____

7. Label the parts of the nose shown below.

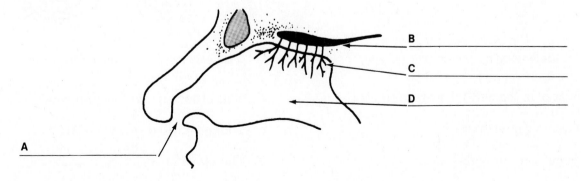

Name _____ Date _____ Class _____

HUMAN SENSE ORGANS

In your textbook, read about the ear and the skin in Section 16:2.

8. Label the diagram of the ear. In each circle, place the letter that best matches the part shown.

   a. Auditory nerve
   b. Ear flap
   c. Ear bones
   d. Eardrum
   e. Ear canal
   f. Nerve cells
   g. Cochlea
   h. Semicircular canals

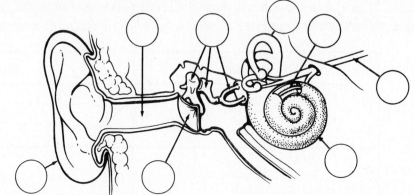

9. Match the ear part in Column I with its job or description in Column II. Write the letter of the job or description to the left of Column I.

   _____ eardrum

   _____ cochlea

   _____ nerve cells

   _____ ear canal

   _____ ear bones

   _____ semicircular canals

   _____ auditory nerve

   a. carries messages from ear flap to eardrum

   b. carries messages from cochlea to brain

   c. pick up eardrum vibrations and pass them to membrane in middle ear

   d. membrane that vibrates at end of ear canal

   e. inner ear parts that help keep balance

   f. liquid-filled, coiled chamber that contains nerve cells

   g. pick up motion of liquid in cochlea

10. Each kind of skin neuron below detects something different. On the blank after each statement, write the letter of the skin neuron that would detect that kind of condition.

| A | B | C | D | E |
| Detects pain | Detects pressure | Detects cold | Detects touch | Detects heat |

   a. Water is too chilly for swimming. _____   d. You brush up against someone. _____

   b. Cut on finger hurts. _____   e. You get kicked in the shins. _____

   c. Shoes are too tight. _____   f. The stove is on. _____

Name _____ Date _____ Class _____

PROBLEMS WITH SENSE ORGANS

In your textbook, read about problems with sense organs in Section 16:3.

1. Examine the diagrams below. Determine what vision problem is shown. In the space provided, name and describe the problem.

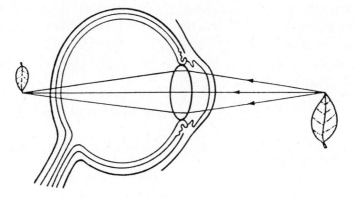

_____

_____

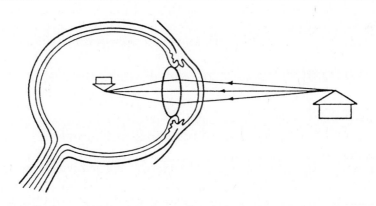

_____

_____

2. How are these problems corrected? _____

_____

3. What are two causes of deafness or hearing loss and how is each one treated?

   a. _____

   b. _____

   _____

Name _____ Date _____ Class _____

VOCABULARY

Review the new words used in Chapter 16 of your textbook. Then, use the terms below to fill in the blanks in the sentences that follow.

auditory nerve	cochlea	eardrum	rods
olfactory nerve	cones	epidermis	sclera
lens muscles	cornea	nearsighted	pupils
vitreous humor	irises	farsighted	retina
optic nerve	lenses	taste buds	dermis
semicircular canals			

1. The _____ is a tough, white covering that protects the eye.

2. Your _____ allow you to taste sweet, salty, bitter, and sour.

3. The _____ carries messages from neurons in the nose to the brain.

4. When you focus on distant objects, your _____ change the shape of

   the _____ in your eyes.

5. When sound waves enter your ear, they cause the _____ to vibrate.

6. The _____ keeps your eyes round in shape.

7. The skin is made of two layers: the _____ and the

   _____ .

8. The _____ is made of two kinds of neurons: _____

   that detect motion and _____ which detect color.

9. The _____ is a clear covering over the pupil.

10. The _____ in your inner ear help you keep your balance.

11. Your _____ determine the color of your eyes.

12. A _____ person might need to wear glasses to read a book.

    A _____ person might need to wear glasses to drive a car.

13. The nerve cells in the _____ send messages to the

    _____ , which carries messages of sound to the brain.

14. When you enter a dark room, your _____ become larger.

15. The _____ carries messages from the retina to the brain.

Name _____ Date _____ Class _____

BEHAVIOR

In Section 17:1 of your textbook, read about behavior.

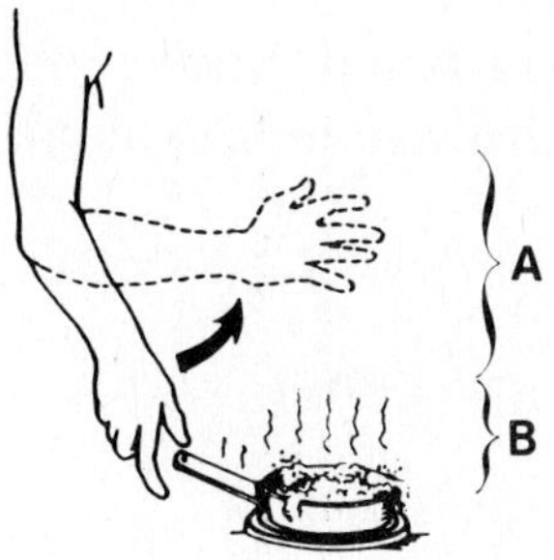

1. **a.** Define the word *stimulus*. _____

   _____

   b. In the diagram, which part (A or B) shows a stimulus? _____

   c. What is the stimulus being shown? _____

   d. How is the stimulus in the diagram being detected? _____

   _____

2. **a.** Define the word *response*. _____

   _____

   b. Which part of the diagram (A or B) shows the response? _____

   c. What is the response shown? _____

   d. Are muscles being used in the response? _____

3. Use the choices given below to fill in the table that follows.

Definitions	Traits	Examples
something you are born with	can be changed	sneezing
something you are not born with	cannot be changed	roller skating
you must be taught to do it	aided with a reward	reading
you do not have to be taught		blinking

	Innate behavior	Learned behavior
Definitions		
Traits		
Examples		

Name _____ Date _____ Class _____

BEHAVIOR

4. Determine if each of the following human behaviors is innate or learned. Write the word *innate* or *learned* on the blank beside each.

    a. speaking a foreign language _____   **f.** biting fingernails _____

    b. coughing _____   **g.** having a fever _____

    c. feeling pain _____   **h.** shivering _____

    d. sweating _____   **i.** riding a bicycle _____

    e. tying shoes _____

5. Determine if each of the following behaviors is innate or learned behavior for a dog. Write the word *innate* or *learned* on the blank beside each.

    a. fetching a newspaper _____   **d.** panting _____

    b. nursing as a puppy _____   **e.** wagging tail _____

    c. scratching _____   **f.** "speaking" for supper _____

6. Place a checkmark next to the human behaviors that would get better with practice.

    a. speaking a foreign language _____   **e.** eating with a fork _____

    b. feeling pain _____   **f.** riding a bicycle _____

    c. tying shoelaces _____   **g.** dreaming _____

    d. sweating _____   **h.** having a fever _____

7. Place a check next to the dog behaviors below that would get better with practice.

    a. sleeping _____   **d.** panting _____

    b. rolling over for a biscuit _____   **e.** sitting up _____

    c. fetching a newspaper _____

8. Using your answers from questions 6 and 7, explain if it is possible to:

    a. improve innate behaviors _____

    _____

    b. improve learned behaviors _____

    _____

SPECIAL BEHAVIORS

In Section 17:2 of your textbook, read about special behaviors that help reproduction.

 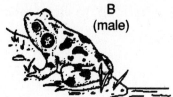 

A
(male)

B
(male)

C
(female)

1. a. Is frog A making a sound? _____

   b. Is frog B making a sound? _____

   c. Is frog C able to make croaking sounds? _____

   d. Which frog (A or B) will be able to "mate" with frog C? _____

   e. Explain. _____

2. What is a pheromone? _____

_____

3. A scientist experiments with silk moths. You predict the results and provide a reason why.
   a. Antennae of male moths are removed. The moths are released. Females are 100 meters away.

   Results _____

   Why? _____

   b. Eyes of female moths are covered. They are then placed in a cage that allows air to enter and leave. Males are released 100 meters away.

   Results _____

   Why? _____

   c. Antennae of female moths are removed. They are then placed in a cage that allows air to enter and leave. Males are released 100 meters away.

   Results _____

   Why? _____

   d. Female moths are placed in an airtight cage. Males are released 100 meters away.

   Results? _____

   Why? _____

Name _____ Date _____ Class _____

SPECIAL BEHAVIORS

In Section 17:2 of your textbook, read about special behaviors that help get food and protection.

1. The following two diagrams show bees "talking" to other members while inside their hives.

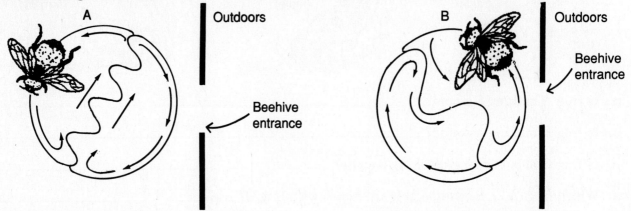

   a. Use arrows to indicate the direction that other bees will have to follow to find food.

   b. Which hive members will have to fly a shorter distance? (A or B)? _____

   Why? _____

   _____

   c. Explain how this behavior is helpful to the bee hive.

   _____

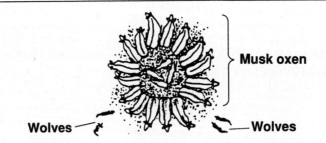

2. This picture is a bird's-eye view of a musk oxen herd about to be attacked by four wolves.

   a. Describe where you would expect to find the young oxen. _____

   b. How does this behavior help the young? _____

   c. Describe where you would expect to find the older oxen. _____

   d. How does this behavior help the older oxen? _____

   e. Why is this pattern of protection a useful behavior for the oxen? _____

   _____

Name _____ Date _____ Class _____

SPECIAL BEHAVIORS

In Section 17:2 of your textbook, read about migration and parental care.

1. Define migration. _____

_____

2. Give two examples of animals that migrate. _____

3. Give two reasons why animals migrate. _____

_____

4. Using your answer to question 3, explain why the:

   a. plover migrates. _____

   b. fur seal migrates. _____

_____

5. Using Figure 17-11 in your text, describe the path of migration for:

   a. plover _____

   b. fur seal _____

6. What seems to be the main way in which adult Adelie penguins can find their way back to their

   nests? _____

7. **a.** Does migration seem to be innate or learned? _____

   b. What experimental proof can be given using Adelie penguins as an example? _____

_____

_____

8. What is meant by parental care? _____

_____

9. Is parental care as important to most fish as it is to most mammals? Explain. _____

_____

_____

_____

Name _____ Date _____ Class _____

VOCABULARY

Review the new words used in Chapter 17 of your textbook.

Write the words next to their definitions below. Then, find and circle the words in the puzzle. The words are written forwards or backwards in either a horizontal, vertical, or diagonal direction.

```
t f s r o p t l c o u r t i n g b e h a v i o r p
c m b r c k r o e z y x a b n c f m p s t u s a h
e s b o l m k l s u l u m i t s f k n p g h r j e
s k l i a u r t s v z x h k m n t p k l b e d f r
n c d v r t t b e f u a k n c d e i t i n s t u o
i n n a t e b e h a v i o r l c d o n t c k m k m
l r s h m f l e f r k s n b a k l e a c s k u v o
a w l e a r n e d b e h a v i o r l r s t b a c n
i d w b x l x a p m o n t t s c l t r k j h i e
c a l l f g e f l m o t z h r a r m b d f h l z s
o z o t a k l r b n o i t a r g i m d k c w m o e
s e r a k g j k l e t b d e c d m r s o t z a x t
```

1. a chemical that changes the behavior of animals of the same species

   _____

2. behavior that must be taught

   _____

3. movement of animals in response to the season of the year

   _____

4. the way an animal acts

   _____

5. adults giving food, protection, and warmth to eggs or young

   _____

6. behavior that does not require learning

   _____

7. something that causes an animal to react

   _____

8. complex pattern of behavior an animal is born with

   _____

9. used by males and females to attract one another

   _____

10. lives in a group in which each individual does a certain job

   _____

Name _____ Date _____ Class _____

AN INTRODUCTION TO DRUGS

In Section 18:1 of your textbook, read about drugs and drug labels.

1. Complete this outline by writing in the correct definition below each word.

Drug _____   Legal _____   Two   Prescription
                                                       types
_____   _____   _____

_____   _____   _____

_____   _____   Over-the-counter

_____   Controlled   _____

                          _____   _____

                          _____

                          _____

2. Examine the drug label below. Notice that parts of the label are marked with letters. Choose the lettered part of the label that best matches each of the items below and write the correct letter on the blank.

(A) Provides temporary relief from the symptoms of allergies, hay fever, and the common cold.	(D) May cause drowsiness. Alcohol may increase this effect. Avoid alcohol while taking this drug. Use caution while driving a motor vehicle or operating machinery. If you are pregnant or nursing a baby, ask your doctor before using this drug.
(B) Directions: *Adults:* 1 to 2 tablets every 4 to 6 hours not to exceed 12 tablets in 24 hours. *Children 6 to under 12 years:* 1 tablet every 4 to 6 hours, not to exceed 6 tablets in 24 hours. *For children under 6:* ask your doctor.	(E) Keep this and all medicines out of the reach of children.
(C) Do not take this drug if you have asthma, glaucoma, emphysema, or shortness of breath unless directed by your doctor. May cause excitability, especially in children.	(F) In case of accidental overdose, contact your doctor or a Poison Control Center immediately.
	(G) Each tablet contains 25 mg rhinamine.

a. dosage ____   e. warnings ____

b. cautions ____   f. drug contained in tablets ____

c. main use of drug ____   g. what to do in case of overdose ____

d. possible side effects ____

AN INTRODUCTION TO DRUGS

In Section 18:1 of your textbook, read about drug dose and overdose.

3. Examine the drug label below and answer the questions that follow.

> DIRECTIONS: Adults—2 tablets every 4 hours as needed. Do not take more than 8 tablets in 24 hours.
> Children (6-12)—½ adult dosage
>
> CAUTION: Do not give to children under 6 years. Do not use for more than 5 days. If problem continues, see a physician.
>
> WARNING: THIS DRUG MAY CAUSE DROWSINESS

a. Define drug dosage. _____

b. What is the adult dose of this drug? _____

c. What is the proper dose of this drug for a child under the age of six?

_____

d. What warning is given on this label? _____

4. The drawings below can be compared to drugs entering and leaving the body in proper drug dose and drug overdose.

a. What is meant by a drug overdose?

_____

_____

b. Which drawing (A or B) is more like a

drug overdose? _____

c. Why? _____

_____

_____

_____

d. Which drawing (A or B) is more like a correct dose? _____

e. Why? _____

_____

Name _____ Date _____ Class _____

HOW DRUGS AFFECT BEHAVIOR

In Section 18:2 of your textbook, read about stimulants, depressants, and psychedelic drugs.

1. Complete the following table about stimulants.

Definition	
Examples, controlled	
Examples, not controlled	
Two ways nervous system may be affected	
Effects on body	

2. Complete the following table about depressants.

Definition	
Examples, controlled	
Two ways nervous system may be affected	
Effects on body	

3. Complete the following idea map about psychedelic drugs. Use these words or phrases: natural, PCP and LSD, inhalant, synthetic, glue and paint, marijuana and certain cacti and mushrooms.

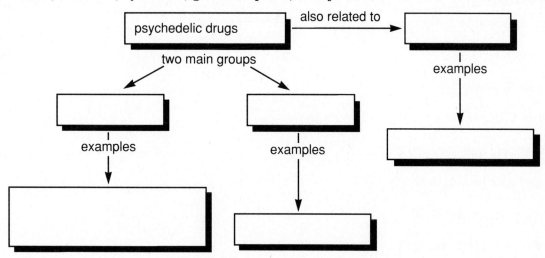

Name _____ Date _____ Class _____

USES OF OVER-THE-COUNTER DRUGS

In Section 18:3 of your textbook, read about antihistamines, cough suppressants, and antacids.

1. Explain how an antihistamine works. _____

_____

2. Explain how a cough occurs. _____

_____

_____

_____

_____

3. What does a cough suppressant do to help stop coughing? _____

_____

4. Use the diagrams below to answer the questions. Some answers will require more than one letter.

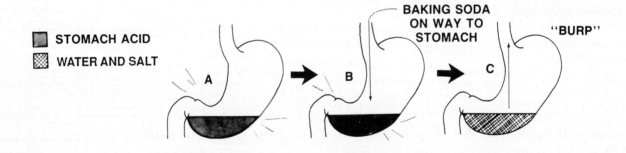

a. Sodium bicarbonate is being added to the stomach. _____

b. Person has heartburn. _____

c. Heartburn is gone. _____

d. Antacid is being taken. _____

e. Carbon dioxide gas is given off. _____

f. Water and salt are in stomach. _____

g. Acid is present in stomach. _____

h. Acid was chemically changed. _____

Name _____ Date _____ Class _____

CARELESS DRUG USE

In Section 18:4 of your textbook, read about careless drug use.

Place a checkmark in front of those sentences that are true.

_____ **1.** It is safe to use the drugs that a physician has told someone else to use.

_____ **2.** The dose of a drug prescribed by a physician for someone else is always the same as the dose that you would need.

_____ **3.** A drug allergy means that you are sensitive to a particular drug.

_____ **4.** Allergic drug reactions can never cause death.

_____ **5.** Drug abuse is the incorrect or improper use of a drug.

_____ **6.** Drug abuse can never lead to drug dependence.

_____ **7.** Codeine, alcohol, and heroin are examples of drugs that may cause dependence.

8. Complete the following table by placing checkmarks in the correct columns.

	Cocaine	Caffeine	Nicotine	Alcohol
May cause breathing or heart to stop suddenly				
Causes feeling of alertness and difficulty in falling asleep				
Stimulant				
Depressant				
Leads to dependence				
When BAC is 0.4-0.5, unconsciousness or coma can occur				
Causes cancer and linked to heart disease				
One form, crack, can cause death with first use				
Can lead to withdrawal symptoms if stopped after dependent use				

Name _____ Date _____ Class _____

VOCABULARY

Review the new words in Chapter 18 of your textbook. Then, write the term that each of the phrases below describes on the blank that follows the phrase.

1. a drug that slows messages in the nervous system _____

2. too much of a drug _____

3. will form carbon dioxide in the stomach _____

4. a drug in cigarettes _____

5. a chemical that changes the way a living thing functions when it is taken into the body _____

6. a drug that speeds up body activities controlled by the nervous system _____

7. the incorrect or improper use of a drug _____

8. a change that is not expected caused by a drug _____

9. drug that relieves a stuffy nose _____

10. a drug you can buy legally without a prescription _____

11. a change that takes place in the body due to disease _____

12. needing a certain drug in order to carry out normal daily activities _____

13. a drug in cola, tea, and coffee _____

14. a drug that a doctor must tell you to take _____

15. drug made from the leaves of the coca bush _____

16. drugs that are controlled by law _____

17. how much and how often to take a drug _____

18. drug that changes the signals from the sense organs _____

19. drug breathed in through the lungs _____

20. drug found in alcoholic drinks _____

Name _____ Date _____ Class _____

THE STRUCTURE OF LEAVES

In your textbook, read about leaf traits in Section 19:1.

1. Label the following parts of this diagram: stalk, midrib, blade, smaller vein.

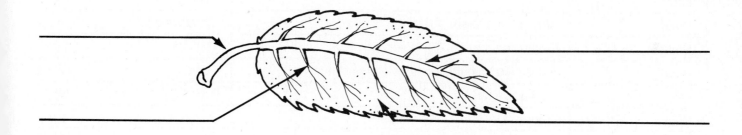

In your textbook, read about the cells in a leaf in Section 19:1.

2. Label the following parts of this diagram of a leaf section: air spaces, upper epidermis, lower epidermis, wax layer, guard cell, wax layer, vein, stoma, spongy layer, palisade layer.

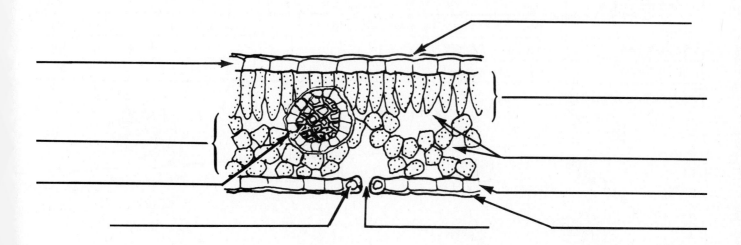

3. Using these colors, shade in the following parts on the diagram above:
   Green—leaf cells that make food   Blue—leaf cells that carry water and food
   Red—leaf cells that protect   Yellow—waterproof layer

Name _____ Date _____ Class _____

THE STRUCTURE OF LEAVES

4. *The chart below describes several different kinds of leaves and gives an example of each. Read each description and example. Examine the diagrams carefully. Then, write the letter of the leaf type on the blank next to the diagram that it best matches.*

Shape	Other traits	Example	
Fan		Ginkgo	(a)
Heart	Edges have teeth.	Cottonwood	(b)
Heart	Edges are smooth. Tip is very pointed.	Catalpa	(c)
Heart	Edges are smooth. Tip is not very pointed.	Redbud	(d)
Oval	Edges are smooth.	Magnolia	(e)
Oval	Edges have a few large teeth.	Holly	(f)
Oval	Edges have many small teeth.	Elm	(g)
Needle	Needles are in twos.	Virginia pine	(h)
Needle	Needles are in threes.	Pitch pine	(i)
Needle	Needles are in fives.	White pine	(j)
5-part	All leaflets attach at same point.	Buckeye	(k)
5-part	Three leaflets attach at top, two near bottom.	Shagbark hickory	(l)
More than 5-parts	Edges have teeth. Leaflets are oppositely attached.	Sumac	(m)
More than 5-parts	Edges are smooth. Leaflets are oppositely attached.	White ash	(n)
Oval	Edges are toothed. Tip is very pointed.	Hackberry	(o)
Wavy lobed	Lobes are pointed.	Pin oak	(p)
Wavy lobed	Lobes are rounded.	White oak	(q)

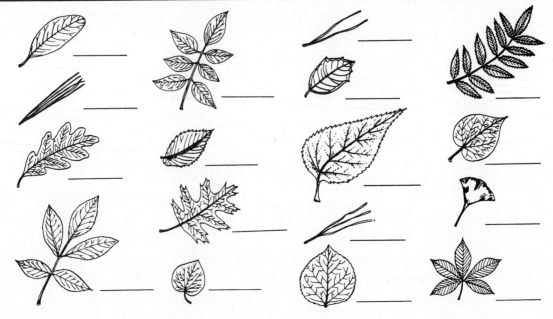

Name _____ Date _____ Class _____

THE STRUCTURE OF LEAVES

In your textbook, read about water loss in plants in Section 19:1.

5. The path of water movement through a plant is shown below. Complete the diagram by writing each of these sentences in the place that best shows what is stated.

    Water moves into the leaves where some is used in photosynthesis.
    Water enters roots through the root hairs.
    Water escapes from stomata into the air during transpiration.
    Tubelike cells (xylem) carry water through the stem to the leaves.

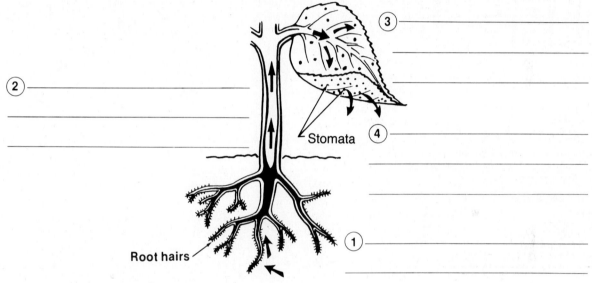

6. Circle the conditions under which a plant will lose much water through its stomata.

    a. Hot, dry days   **b.** Cool, damp days   **c.** In humid greenhouse

7. Circle the conditions under which a plant will lose little water through its stomata.

    a. Hot, dry days   **b.** Cool, damp days   **c.** In humid greenhouse

8. **a.** The diagram below shows the outline of a plant in two conditions. Assume the plant receives no water through its roots and its stomata are open. Complete the diagram by drawing over the dashed lines that best show what the plant would look like.

    b. Which of the following words best describes what has happened to the plant from position A to position B? (Circle one.)

    transpiration, wilting, respiration,

    photosynthesis

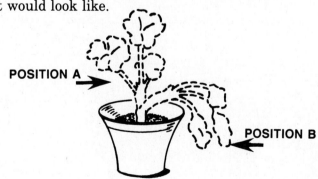

POSITION A

POSITION B

Name _____ Date _____ Class _____

LEAVES MAKE FOOD

In your textbook, read about photosynthesis in Section 19:2.

The two columns of pictures below relate a carpenter's building a house to a leaf's making food. For each step in both processes, fill in the blanks with the name of what is being produced or used.

being
used

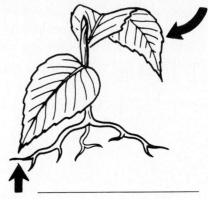

_____

_____

being
used

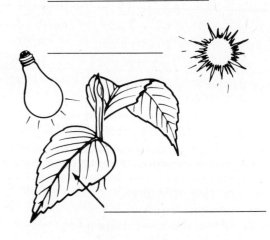

_____

_____

being
produced

$6CO_2$

$6H_2O$

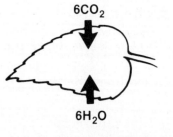

_____

being
produced

_____

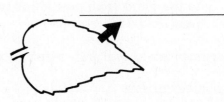

_____

LEAVES FOR FOOD

In your textbook, read about leaf color changes in Section 19:3.

1. These two diagrams show sections of a leaf. The left leaf has been in the light for 10 days. The right leaf has been in the dark for 10 days. Color the cells of the leaves either green or yellow depending on what they would look like to us. Color only those cells within the brackets.

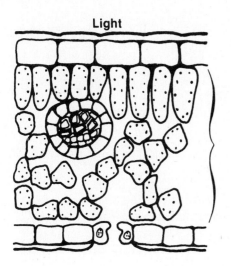
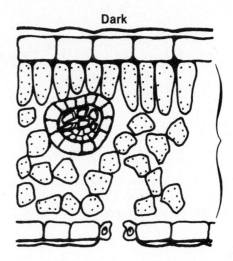

2. Label the two diagrams with the leaf parts you can see. Use colored pencils to shade in what color a red oak leaf will be during each season shown.

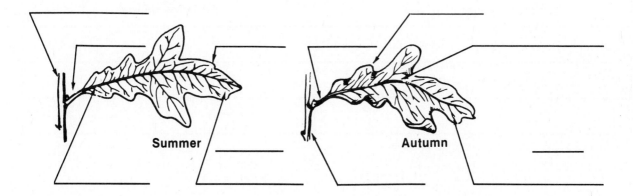

Name _____ Date _____ Class _____

VOCABULARY

Review the new words used in Chapter 19 of your textbook. Then complete this puzzle.

1. On the diagram below, label the following leaf structures: blade, midrib. Then write a sentence describing each structure.

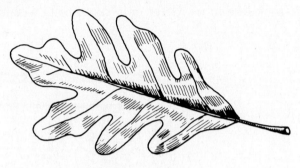

   a. The blade is the _____

   b. The midrib is the _____

2. Tell which of the following processes is helpful for the plant and which is harmful.

   a. wilting _____

   b. transpiration _____

3. Write these words in the proper places in this table: palisade layer, stoma, spongy layer, epidermis, guard cell.

Parts on outside of leaf	Parts inside leaf

Name ____________________ Date __________ Class __________

STEM STRUCTURE

In your textbook, read about herbaceous and woody stems in Section 20:1.

1. Use the letters of the correct words or parts from the following chart to complete the table below.

	A	B	C
Outer covering	Soft	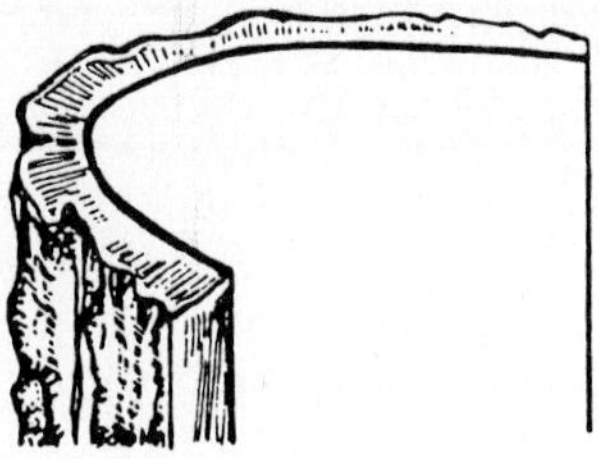	Epidermis
Outer color	Brown	Yellow	Green
Xylem and phloem	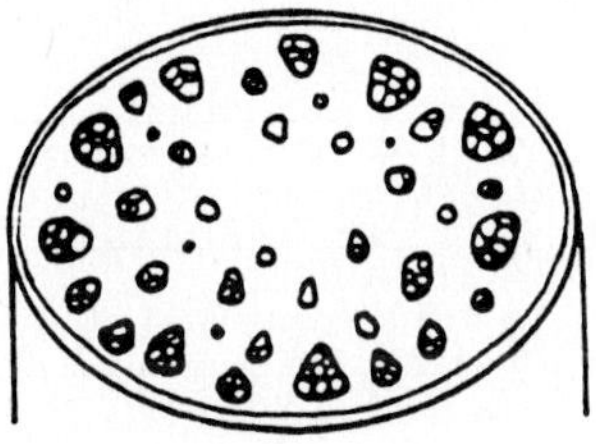	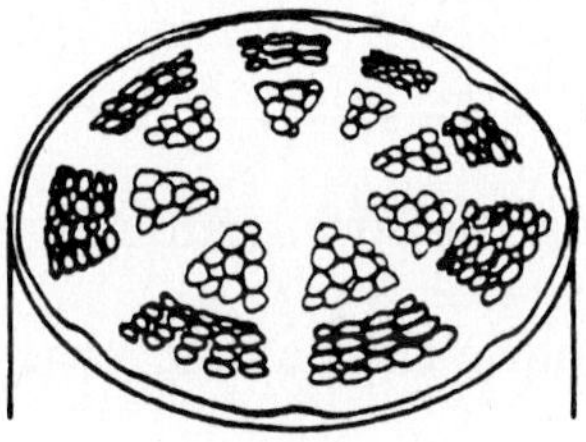	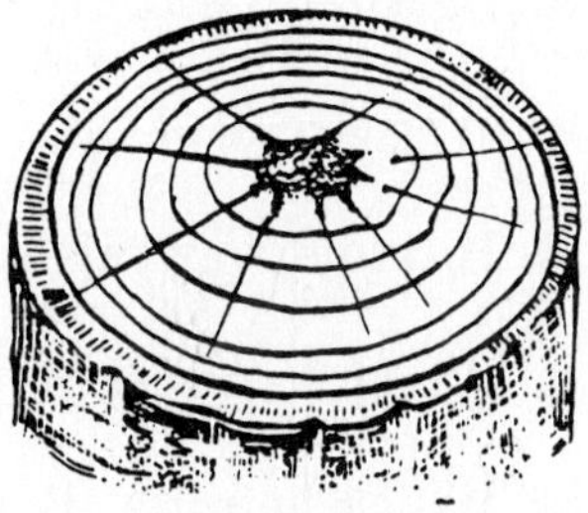
Example of stem type	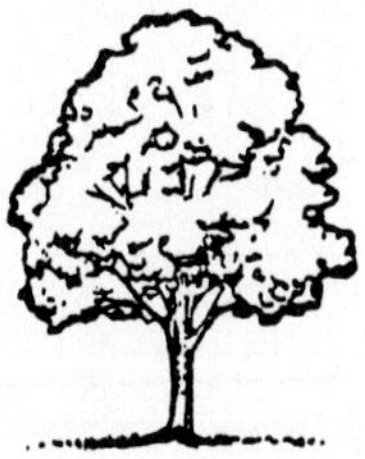	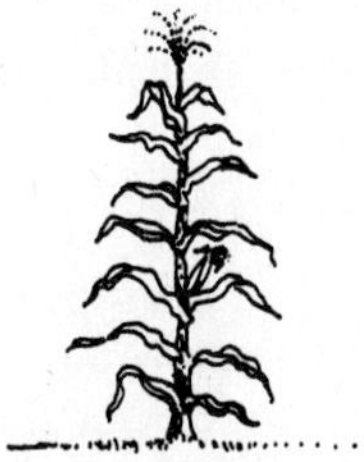	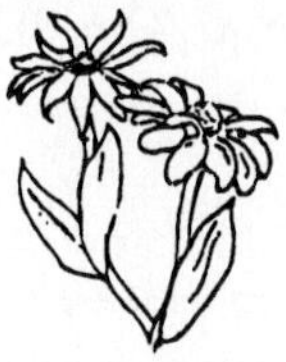

	Woody stem	Herbaceous stem
Outer covering		
Outer color		
Xylem and phloem		
Example of stem type		

Name _____ Date _____ Class _____

STEM STRUCTURE

In your textbook, read about stem growth in Section 20:1.

2. Examine the diagram of a core sample taken from a tree. Then, answer the following questions.

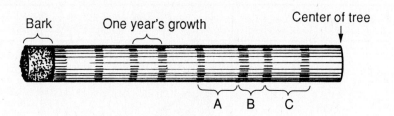

a. What is counted to determine the age of a tree? _____

b. In what part of the year do the dark bands form? _____

c. Why are they dark? _____

d. In what part of the year do the light bands form? _____

e. Why are they light? _____

f. How old was this tree when the core sample was taken? _____

g. Which band (A, B, or C) shows the poorest year of growth? _____

h. Which band (A, B, or C) shows the year with the most rainfall? _____

3. Examine the diagram below of a core sample taken in 1991.

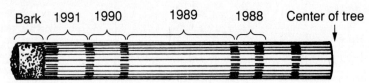

a. How old was this tree in 1991? _____

b. What year was rainfall the least where this tree was growing? _____

c. What year did the tree grow the least? _____

d. What year was rainfall the most where this tree was growing? _____

e. What year did the tree grow the most? _____

<table>
<tr><td>

STUDY **G**UIDE</td><td>**C**HAPTER **20**</td></tr>
</table>

Name _____ Date _____ Class _____

THE JOBS OF STEMS

In your textbook, read about transport and storage in Section 20:2.

1. How do leaves get the water and minerals they need? _____

_____

_____

2. How does new water enter the roots? _____

3. How is the movement of water through a plant like a thread being pulled through a straw?

_____

_____

4. In what form is sugar stored in plants? _____

5. **a.** What kind of cells allow the transport of water upward in a plant?

_____

b. What kind of cells allow the transport of food downward in a plant?

_____

6. Examine the diagrams below. Which one (A or B) best shows the path water takes through a

stem? _____

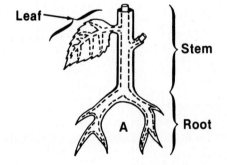
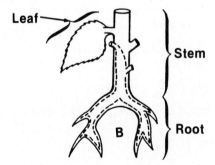

7. Explain what is wrong with the diagram that you did not choose as the answer to the last

question. _____

_____

Name _____ Date _____ Class _____

ROOT STRUCTURE

In your textbook, read about root cells and growth in Section 20:3.

1. Label the drawing below using these labels: root hair, cortex, xylem, phloem, epidermis, endodermis.

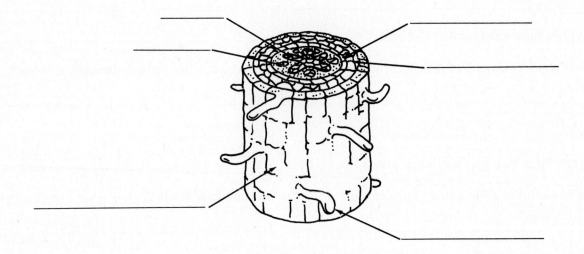

2. Label the diagram below using these labels: primary root, secondary root, root hairs.

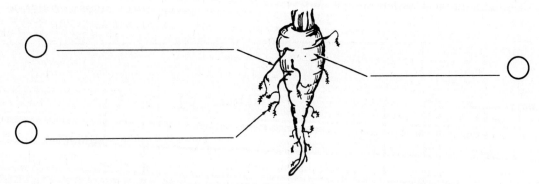

3. From the diagram above, put the correct letters on the blanks below.

   a. largest root of plant ____

   b. absorb water and minerals ____

   c. first root to form in plants ____

   d. would measure greatest distance if put in line ____

   e. forms from primary root ____

Name _____ Date _____ Class _____

ROOT STRUCTURE

In your textbook, read about taproots and fibrous roots in Section 20:4.

4. Examine the drawings below. Then, put A or B on the blank after each phrase or word.

 a. taproot _____

 b. fibrous roots _____

 c. often spreads out _____

 d. often grows very deep _____

A   B

THE JOBS OF ROOTS

In your textbook, read about absorption, anchorage, and storage in Section 20:4.

Examine the pictures below. Beside each picture write a sentence describing what the object pictured does. Then, write a sentence describing a similar job of roots. The first one is done for you.

Sponge

1. A sponge absorbs water. Roots absorb water and minerals from the soil.

Suitcase

2. _____

_____

Hair net

3. _____

_____

Paper clip

4. _____

_____

Anchor

5. _____

_____

Paper towels

6. _____

_____

Stapler

7. _____

_____

Silo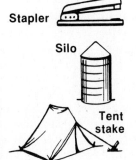

8. _____

_____

Tent stake

9. _____

Name _____ Date _____ Class _____

VOCABULARY

Review the new words used in Chapter 20 of your textbook. Use the glossary in your textbook if you need help.

Complete each sentence using the words below to fill in the blanks. Do not use any words more than once.

lateral buds	root hairs	woody stems
fibrous roots	herbaceous stems	endodermis
annual rings	terminal bud	cortex
cork	taproot	cambium

1. There are two main kinds of roots. A large, single root is called a _____.

   Many-branched roots that grow in clusters are _____.

2. Tiny threadlike _____ are cells of the epidermis. They absorb

   water and minerals for the plant.

3. Inside the root and stem, a layer of large, loosely packed _____

   cells are present. They are used mainly for food storage.

4. Trees and shrubs have _____. Tree stems have an outer

   covering called _____. It is made up of dead cells and protects the stem.

5. _____ is a thin layer of cells in a stem that divide to form

   new phloem and xylem cells.

6. The cross section of a tree trunk shows that the trunk is made up of a series of

   _____ , made up of dark and light bands of cells.

7. Soft, green stems are called _____.

8. Inside the cortex of a root is a ring of waxy cells called the _____.

9. The _____ is responsible for a plant's growth in length.

   The _____ give rise to new branches, leaves, or flowers.

Name _____ Date _____ Class _____

PLANT RESPONSES

In your textbook, read about growth and flowering in Section 21:1.

Look at the pictures of the plants below. Then, answer the questions that follow.

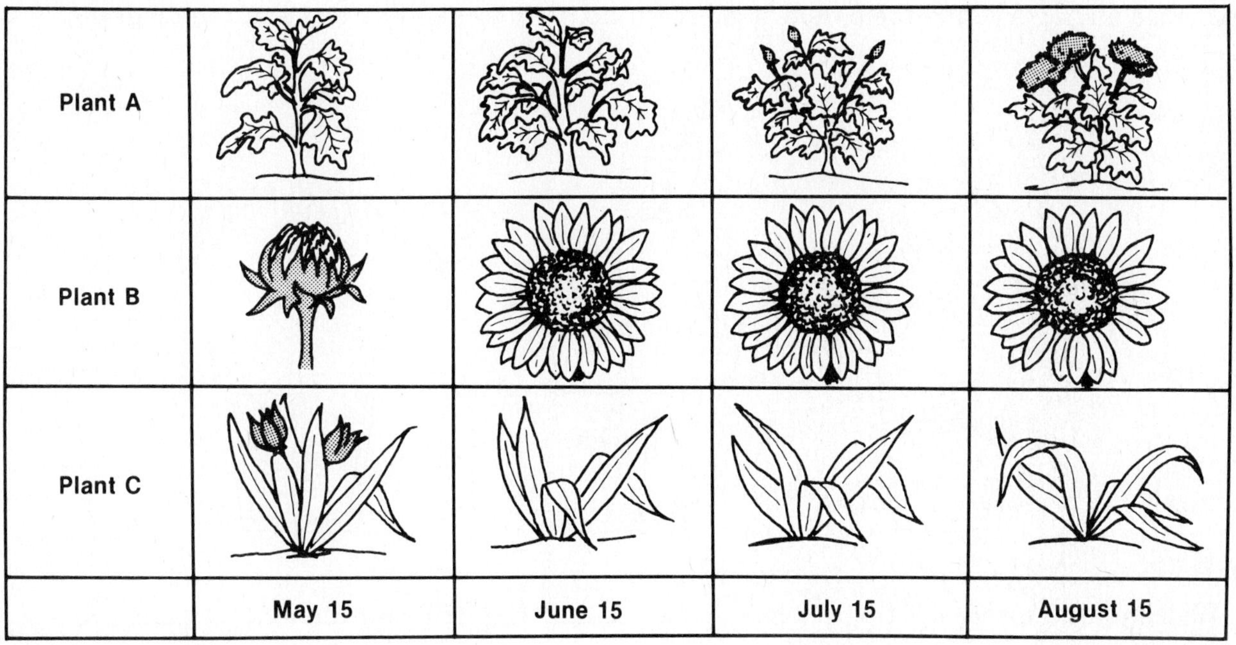

	May 15	June 15	July 15	August 15
Plant A				
Plant B				
Plant C				

1. Which plant is called a short-day plant? _____

   Explain your answer. _____

   _____

2. Which plant is called a long-day plant? _____

   Explain your answer. _____

   _____

   _____

3. Which plant is called a day-neutral plant? _____

   Explain your answer. _____

   _____

Name _____ Date _____ Class _____

PLANT RESPONSES

In your textbook, read about tropisms in plants in Section 21:1. Then, read the description below and answer the questions that follow.

Some plants in a greenhouse were tipped over and not set upright for several weeks. When the greenhouse manager found them, and stood them up, they looked like those in the diagram.

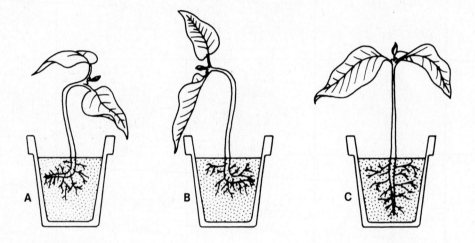

4. Which plant(s) were not tipped over? _____ Explain your answer. _____

_____

_____

5. Which plant(s) were tipped over? _____ Explain your answer. _____

_____

_____

6. What is the name of the tropism that describes how the roots are responding? _____

7. What is the name of the tropism that describes how the stem is responding? _____

8. Define each tropism. _____

_____

9. Which part of the plant responds to gravity? _____ How can you tell? _____

_____

10. Which part of the plant responds to light? _____ How can you tell? _____

_____

Name _____ Date _____ Class _____

GROWTH REQUIREMENTS

In your textbook, read about growth requirements of plants in Section 21:2. Then, read the following description of a set of experiments on plant growth.

Experiments were done to find what effects the amount of water, light, minerals, and soil had on some plants. In each experiment, the amounts of light, water, minerals, soil, and temperature were kept the same except where shown in the figure on the next page. The plants were grown for nearly two months. Answer the questions after you have studied the diagrams.

1. In experiment 1, which plant grew best? _____ How often was this plant

   watered? _____

2. What would happen to the plant in answer 1 if it were planted in an area where it rained four

   days each week? _____

3. Does the kind of plant used in experiment 1 grow well with a great amount of water? _____

   Explain your answer. _____

   _____

4. What growth requirement is being tested in experiment 2? _____

5. In experiment 2, which plant grew best? _____ How much sun did the plant

   receive? _____

6. Suppose you bought several of these plants to put in your flower beds. Where would you *not*

   plant them? _____ Why? _____

   _____

7. What growth requirement is being tested in experiment 3? _____

8. In experiment 3, which plant grew best? _____ What type of soil was this plant

   grown in? _____

9. Could the type of plant in experiment 3 be grown in the desert? _____ Why or

   why not? _____

   _____

Name _____ Date _____ Class _____

GROWTH REQUIREMENTS

Plant A	Plant B	Plant C	
 watered 3 times a day	 watered 1 time a day	 watered every 3 days	Experiment 1
 full sun	 partial sun	 shade	Experiment 2
 clay and sand	 potting soil	 sand	Experiment 3

Name _____ Date _____ Class _____

PLANT DISEASES AND PESTS

In your textbook, read about factors that can slow down or stop plant growth in Section 21:3.

1. List two ways that bacteria can enter a plant. _____

_____

2. Once inside, how do bacteria harm plants? _____

_____

3. What can happen to the leaves of plants infected by viruses? _____

_____

4. How are diseases that are caused by fungi carried to plants? _____

_____

5. How do insects infect plants with diseases? _____

_____

_____

_____

6. How else can insects be harmful to plants? _____

_____

_____

7. Complete the table below by placing checkmarks in the correct columns.

Condition in plants	Cause		
	Bacteria	Viruses	Fungi
Corn smut			
Mosaic disease			
Dutch elm disease			
Blister spots on fruit and leaves			
Wheat rust			

VOCABULARY

Review the new words in Chapter 21 of your textbook. Then, complete this puzzle.

Across

6. response of a plant to light
7. substance made of minerals that makes soil productive for plant growth
8. plant that needs two years to complete growth and produce seeds
9. plant that flowers when the length of day rises above 12 to 14 hours
10. plant that completes its life cycle in one year
11. response of a plant to contact

Down

1. plant that doesn't depend on the number of hours of light to flower
2. response of a plant to gravity
3. plant that lives longer than two years
4. growth response of a plant to a stimulus
5. plant that flowers when the day falls below 12 to 14 hours

Name _____ Date _____ Class _____

MITOSIS

In your textbook, read about the steps of mitosis in Section 22:1.

1. The following steps of mitosis are out of order. Place the numbers *1-5* in the blanks to show the correct order.

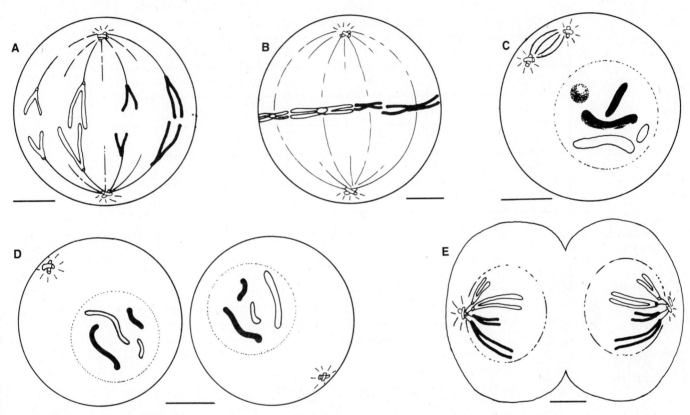

2. In the blanks below, write the letter of the diagram above that is being described.

a. Two new identical cells are formed. _____

b. Cytoplasm begins to separate. _____

c. Sister chromatids are first pulled apart. _____

d. Chromosomes are completely separated and at opposite ends of the cell. _____

e. Sister chromatids can be seen for the first time. _____

f. This is what cells look like before going through mitosis. _____

g. Nuclear membrane begins to break down. _____

h. Sister chromatids move to the cell's center and line up on fibers. _____

i. A nuclear membrane begins to form around chromosomes. _____

Name _____ Date _____ Class _____

MEIOSIS

In your textbook, read about meiosis in Section 22:2.

1. Examine the table below. Fill in the missing information based on the numbers that are given.

Organism	Body cell chromosome number	Chromosome number sex cell
Human	46	23
Cat	38	
Onion		8
Rye	14	
Guinea pig		
Chicken		39

2. Graph the data in the table above on the graph below. Follow the example on the graph.

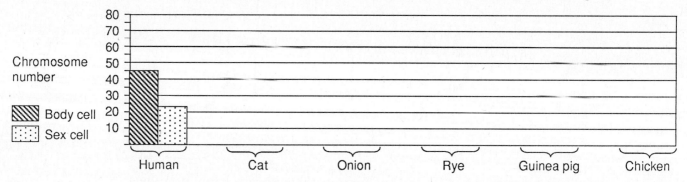

3. Using the information above, complete the following table. The first one is done for you.

Organism	Sperm chromosome number	Egg chromosome number	Fertilized egg chromosome number	Chromosome number in each body cell of offspring
Human	23	23	46	46
Cat				
Onion				
Rye				
Guinea pig				
Chicken				

Name _____ Date _____ Class _____

MEIOSIS

In your textbook, read about mitosis and meiosis in Section 22:2.

4. The chart below shows the steps of mitosis and meiosis in the correct order. Complete the chart by answering the questions beside the diagrams.

Mitosis   **Meiosis**

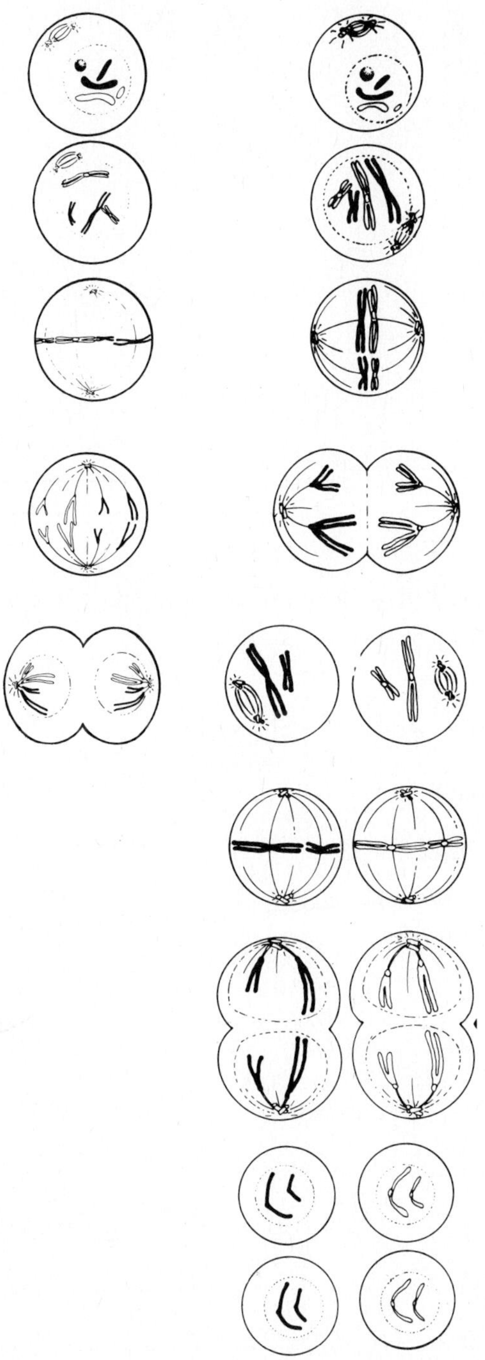

a. Where are the chromosomes? _____

b. How many are present in each cell? _____

c. What happened to the chromosomes in each cell? _____

d. Where are the sister chromatids? _____

e. What is happening to the sister chromatids?

_____

_____

_____

f. How many cells are formed in mitosis? _____

g. Are the chromosomes single or double? _____

h. Are the chromosomes single or double now in meiosis?

_____

i. What happens in meiosis now? _____

_____

j. How many cells are formed in meiosis? _____

Name _____ Date _____ Class _____

MEIOSIS

In your textbook, read about the steps of meiosis in Section 22:2.

5. Match each of the following steps of meiosis with the statements below. Letters may be used more than once. Write the correct letter on each blank. Note: The statements describing the steps of meiosis are not in the correct order.

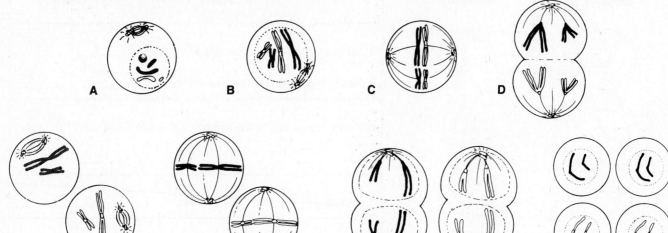

a. Matching chromosomes come together to form pairs. ____

b. Each chromosome has two strands of sister chromatids. Pairs of sister chromatids are lined up near cell's center; original and copy still together. ____

c. One cell division completed and two new cells formed. ____

d. Each chromosome becomes doubled, forming sister chromatids. ____

e. Original and copy chromosome move to opposite ends of cell. ____

f. Centrioles move again to opposite ends of cells. ____

g. Pairs of sister chromatids move to center of cell. ____

h. Four new cells have formed from original. ____

i. Nuclear membrane begins to fade away. ____

j. Sister chromatid pairs move to opposite ends of cell. ____

k. Four single chromosomes are present in cell. ____

l. Each cell is now a sex cell. ____

m. Nuclear membrane is reappearing. ____

Name _____ Date _____ Class _____

MEIOSIS

In your textbook, read about sperm, eggs, and fertilization in Section 22:2.

6. Look at the drawing below. Label the parts as egg, sperm, or chromosomes.

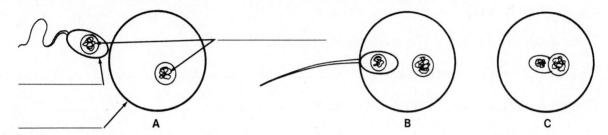

_____   A   B   C

    a. How many chromosomes are in each human sex cell? _____

    b. How many pairs of chromosomes are in each sex cell? _____

    c. What process has occurred between diagram B and C? _____

    d. How many chromosomes are in the human egg cell in diagram C? _____

CHANGES IN THE RATE OF MITOSIS

In your textbook, read about aging and cancer in Section 22:3.

1. What happens to fingernail growth as a person ages? Explain your answer. _____

_____

_____

2. Why is the heart weaker and less able to pump blood as a person ages? _____

_____

_____

3. How are cancer cells different from normal cells? _____

_____

_____

4. List three causes of cancer. _____

_____

Name _____ Date _____ Class _____

VOCABULARY

Review the new words used in Chapter 22 of your textbook. Then complete this exercise.

1. Match one of these choices to each of the following statements. Write the proper choice on each blank: mitosis, meiosis.

   a. Four new cells are formed from each original. _____

   b. This process makes sperm cells. _____

   c. Two new cells are formed from each original. _____

   d. New skin cells are made this way. _____

   e. This type of cell reproduction helps you grow. _____

   f. This type of cell reproduction makes egg cells. _____

   g. This makes cells with half the original cell chromosome number. _____

   h. This makes cells with the same chromosome number as the original. _____

2. Match one of the choices to each of the following phrases. Write the proper choice on each blank: testes, ovaries, cancer, polar body, puberty, sex cells, body cells, sister chromatids

   a. stage when person produces sex cells _____

   b. organs that produce eggs _____

   c. small cell formed and then dies during meiosis in female _____

   d. organs that produce sperm _____

   e. egg and sperm _____

   f. cells that make up the skin, blood, bones, and stomach _____

   g. the two strands of a doubled chromosome _____

   h. a disease in which body cells reproduce faster than normal _____

Name _____ Date _____ Class _____

ASEXUAL REPRODUCTION IN PLANTS

In your textbook, read about reproduction by roots, leaves, and stems in Section 23:1.

1. Complete the table below.

Plants	Plant part being used	Egg or sperm cells needed? (yes or no)	Number of parents needed	Mitosis or meiosis occurring
African violet 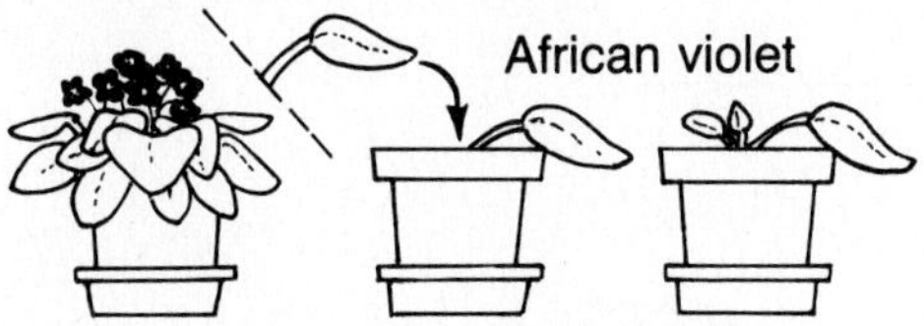				
Tuber (white potato) 				
Tuber (Sweet Potato) 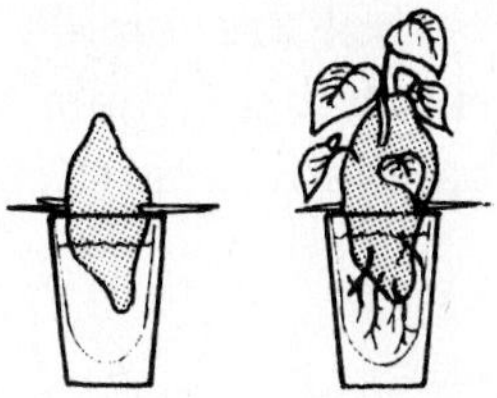				
Onion bulb 				
Delicious apple Macintosh apple 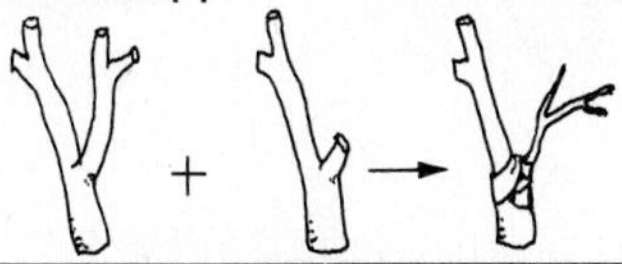				
Strawberry 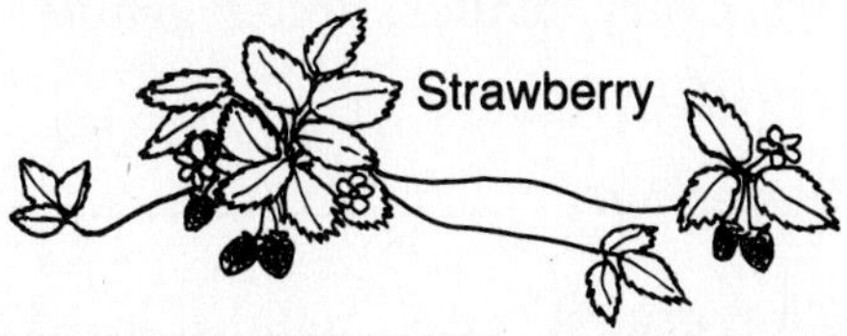				

2. Were sex cells or fertilization involved in any of the situations shown above? _____

Name _____ Date _____ Class _____

SEXUAL REPRODUCTION IN PLANTS

In your textbook, read about flowers and sexual reproduction in Section 23:2.

1. Label these four parts: pistil, petal, stamen, sepal.

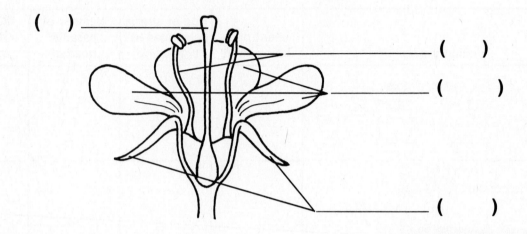

( ) _____
( ) _____
( ) _____
( ) _____

2. Use the following colors to shade in the above drawing.
   a. yellow, for parts that attract insects   c. red, for parts that are female
   b. green, for parts that protect flower in bud stage   d. blue, for parts that are male

3. Label the parts shown here. Use these choices: sticky tip, pollen grains, pistil, ovary, stamen, ovule, saclike part, stalk.

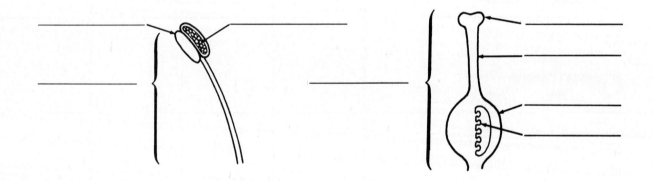

4. Name the part being described. Use these choices: saclike part, ovary, ovules, **pollen grains**, sticky tip, pistil, stamen.

   a. contains ovules   _____   e. female flower part   _____

   b. male flower part   _____   f. traps pollen grains   _____

   c. contains pollen   _____   g. hold female   _____
                                                     reproductive cells

   d. will form sperm   _____

134

Name _____ Date _____ Class _____

SEXUAL REPRODUCTION IN PLANTS

In your textbook, read about pollination and fertilization in plants in Section 23:2.

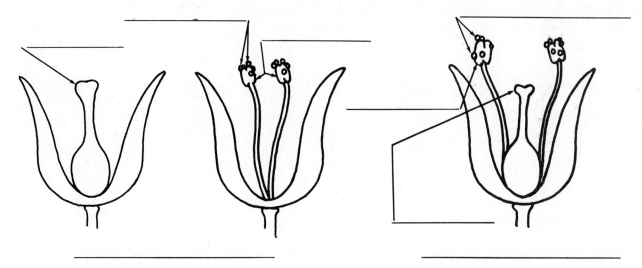

5. Examine the pictures shown above.
   a. Label the saclike part, pollen grains, and sticky tip in both diagrams.
   b. Use arrows to draw the pathway that pollen grains take in order for pollination to occur.
   c. On the line below each diagram, label the process self-pollination or cross-pollination.
6. The diagrams below show pollination and fertilization of a flower. However, the diagrams are out of order. Put the letter of each step below the diagram that it best matches.

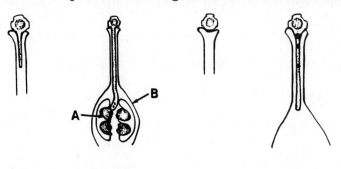

   a. A pollen grain lands on the sticky tip of the pistil.
   b. A tube from the pollen grain grows down into the stalk.
   c. Two sperm nuclei and a tube nucleus travel down the tube.
   d. One sperm fertilizes the egg in the ovule. One sperm fertilizes a nucleus to form a food supply.
7. Examine the diagram above that has labels A and B on it.

   a. Which part (A or B) becomes the seed? _____

   b. Which part (A or B) becomes the fruit? _____

   c. Which part (A or B) contains the embryo? _____

Name _____ Date _____ Class _____

PLANT DEVELOPMENT

In your textbook, read about the formation of seeds and fruits in Section 23:3.

1. The diagrams below show 60 days in the life of a bean flower. Pollination takes place on Day 10.
    Examine the pictures and then answer the questions.

    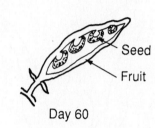

Ovary
Egg

Day 1   Day 10   Day 15   Day 45   Day 60

Seed
Fruit

   a. How many ovaries are present in the bean flower? _____

   b. How many ovules are present in the bean flower? _____

   c. What are the little dots shown on Day 10? _____

   d. What happens to the petals, pollen sacs, and stalk after Day 10? _____

       _____

   e. Explain what happens to the ovary from Day 10 to Day 60. _____

       _____

   f. Explain what happens to the ovules from Day 10 to Day 60. _____

2. The diagram shows a sliced peach.

    a. Which part (A or B) was the ovary from the flower? _____

    b. Which part was the ovule? _____

    c. Which part is the fruit? _____

    d. Which part is the seed? _____

3. Are tomatoes, green peppers, and cucumbers fruits? Explain your answer. _____

    _____

4. List four ways that seeds may be carried before they land in the place where they eventually

    grow. _____

    _____

Name _____ Date _____ Class _____

PLANT DEVELOPMENT

In your textbook, read about plant development from seeds in Section 23:3.

5. What is germination? _____

6. Examine these diagrams of a developing plant. Then, fill in the blanks with the following labels: main root appears, leaves spread out and trap sunlight, secondary roots, first leaves and stem appear aboveground, seed halves drop off plant.

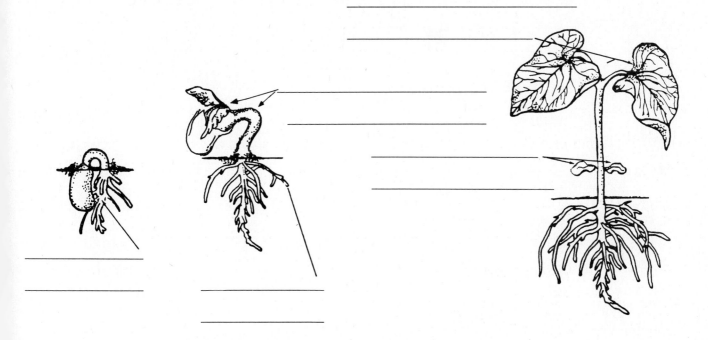

7. How does asexual reproduction help a plant? _____

_____

_____

8. How does sexual reproduction help a plant? _____

_____

_____

_____

_____

Name _____ Date _____ Class _____

VOCABULARY

Review the new words used in Chapter 23 of your textbook. Then, complete this puzzle.

Across
6. green, leaflike, protective part of flower
7. enlarged ovary containing seeds
8. pollen from stamen of one flower carried to pistil of another flower
9. underground root or stem swollen with stored food
10. short, underground stem surrounded by fleshy leaves
11. brightly colored, scented part of flower
12. first growth of young plant from a seed

13. joining the stem of one plant to the stem of another
14. small section of plant stem that is removed and planted

Down
1. tiny, round part containing egg cell
2. pollen from stamen of flower carried to pistil of same flower
3. stem that grows along the ground or in air
4. female flower part
5. male flower part

15. What is the process by which pollen goes from stamens to pistils? _____ _____

Name _____ Date _____ Class _____

ASEXUAL REPRODUCTION

In your textbook, read about asexual reproduction in Section 24:1.

1. Identify the type of asexual reproduction shown in each picture.

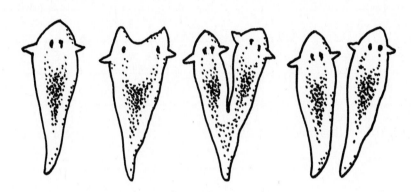 

    a. _____   b. _____

2. On each blank write T if the statement is true or F if the statement is false.

_____ **a.** During asexual reproduction animals reproduce by meiosis.

_____ **b.** A hydra forms buds in its ovaries.

_____ **c.** An offspring produced by sexual reproduction is identical to its parent.

_____ **d.** Complex animals reproduce by sexual reproduction.

_____ **e.** Regeneration occurs when an organism separates into pieces and each piece forms a new organism.

_____ **f.** Organisms produce eggs and sperm when they reproduce asexually.

_____ **g.** A planarian regenerates by mitosis.

_____ **h.** A hydra is a simple animal.

_____ **i.** Asexual reproduction requires two parents.

_____ **j.** When a planarian regenerates, it can form two heads.

_____ **k.** All the offspring of a hydra are different from each other when formed by budding.

3. Answer the question below.

What is a clone? _____

_____

Name _____ Date _____ Class _____

SEXUAL REPRODUCTION

In your textbook, read about external and internal fertilization in Section 24:2.

1. Define external and internal fertilization.

   a. external fertilization: _____

   _____

   b. internal fertilization: _____

   _____

2. Where do most animals that have external fertilization live? _____

   _____

3. What would happen to sperm and eggs if land animals had external fertilization? _____

   _____

4. List two advantages of internal fertilization. _____

   _____

   _____

In your textbook, read about breeding seasons in Section 24:2.

5. What is a breeding season? _____

   _____

6. How does the breeding season of frogs help them? _____

   _____

   _____

7. How does the breeding season of large mammals such as deer help them? _____

   _____

   _____

   _____

8. What is an estrous cycle? _____

   _____

Name _____ Date _____ Class _____

REPRODUCTION IN HUMANS

In your textbook, read about the human reproductive systems in Section 24:3.

1. Label the diagram below using these words: oviduct, ovary, uterus, egg, vagina.

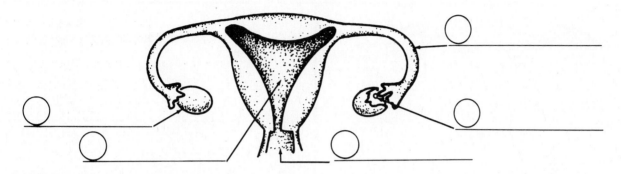

2. In each circle on the diagram, write the letter of the job listed below that the body part does.
  A. Muscular organ where fertilized egg develops.
  B. Cell formed in the ovary.
  C. A place where the egg is formed.
  D. Receives sperm during mating.
  E. Tubelike parts that connect ovary to uterus.

3. Fill in the blanks below with the correct numbers.

  a. Ovaries in a human female ____   **c.** Eggs usually produced by human at one time ____

  b. Testes in a human male ____

4. Label the diagram below using these words: testes, penis, vas deferens, urethra, scrotum, glands.

5. In each circle on the diagram, write the letter of the job listed below that the body part does.

  A. Sperm pass out of the body here.
  B. Sperm are made here.
  C. Sperm move from the testes to the penis here.
  D. Provides liquid for sperm.
  E. Carries sperm out of body.
  F. Sac that holds testes.

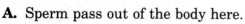

REPRODUCTION IN HUMANS

In your textbook, read about stages of reproduction in Section 24:3.

6. Examine the diagrams below and label the parts. Then, answer the questions.

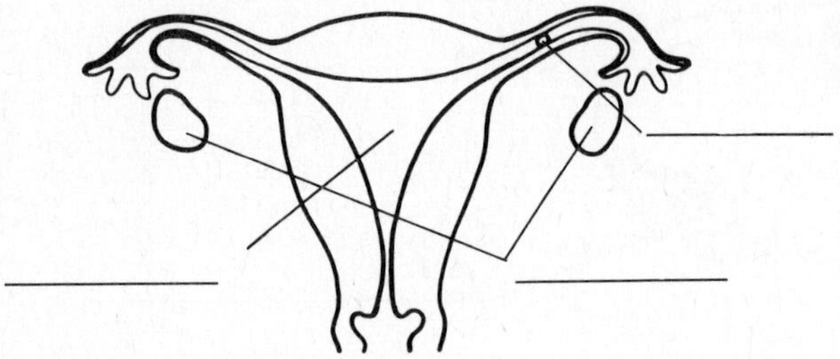

a. Why will fertilization not take place in this diagram?

_____

_____

_____

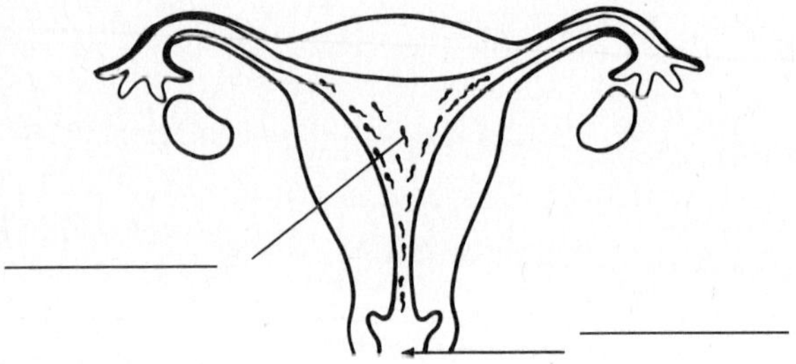

b. Why will fertilization not take place in this diagram?

_____

_____

_____

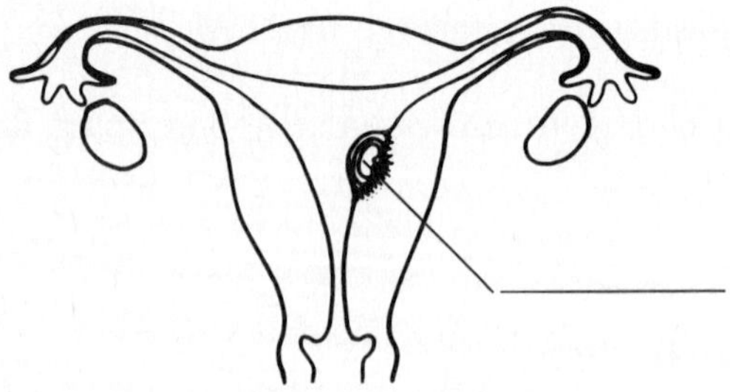

c. Why will fertilization not take place in this diagram?
(HINT: Note that an embryo is already present.)

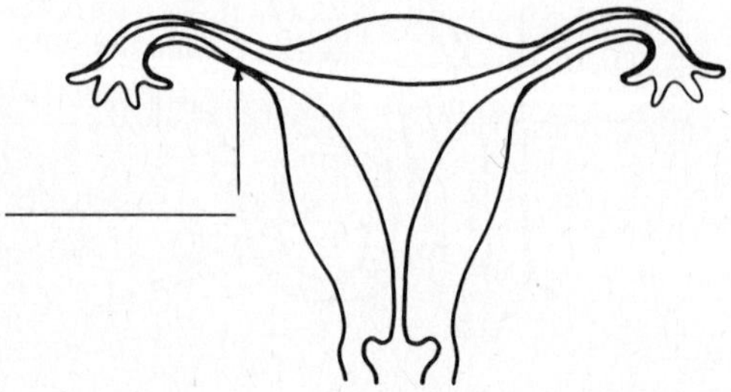

_____

_____

_____

d. Why will fertilization not take place in this diagram?

_____

_____

_____

Name _____ Date _____ Class _____

REPRODUCTION IN HUMANS

In your textbook, read about the menstrual cycle in Section 24:3.

7. The following chart shows the changes in a female's reproductive system in 28 days. These changes take place when an egg is not fertilized.

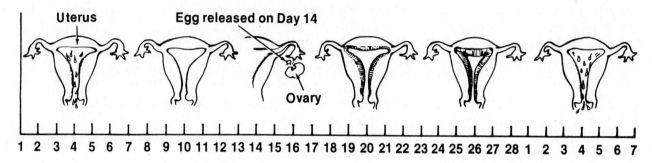

a. What is the cycle on the chart called? _____

b. What are the changes that take place on days 1 to 4 (loss of the lining of the uterus) called?

_____

c. When is the egg released from the ovary? _____

d. Describe the changes that take place in the uterus from day 5 through day 28. _____

_____

e. What happens to an egg that is not fertilized? _____

8. Match the following diagrams with their places on the chart by writing each letter on the chart below the proper diagram. A is done for you.

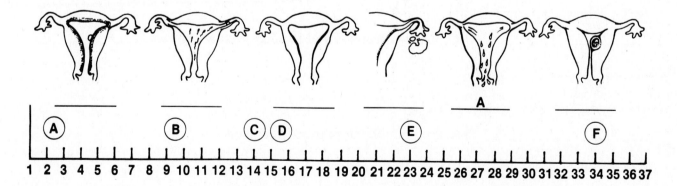

a. How many of the days in this chart match those in the chart in question 7? _____

b. How long (in months) will step F last? _____

VOCABULARY

Review the new words used in Chapter 24 of your textbook. Then, fill in the blank next to each definition with the word or phrase it defines.

_____ 1. male reproductive organ that deposits sperm inside a female

_____ 2. sac that holds testes

_____ 3. organ in which a fertilized egg will develop

_____ 4. tube leading from outside the female's body to the uterus

_____ 5. tubelike organs that connect the ovaries to the uterus

_____ 6. reproduction in which parent separates into two or more pieces, each of which forms a new organism

_____ 7. loss of the uterine lining

_____ 8. cycle in which the female will mate only at certain times

_____ 9. joining of egg and sperm outside the body

_____ 10. monthly cycle that takes place in female reproductive organs

_____ 11. joining of egg and sperm inside the female's body

_____ 12. a female hormone

_____ 13. diseases transmitted through sexual contact

_____ 14. system used to produce offspring

Name _____ Date _____ Class _____

DEVELOPMENT INSIDE THE FEMALE

In your textbook, read about early stages of development in Section 25:1.

1. Arrange the following events in their proper order by placing the numbers 1-7 in the spaces provided.

   a. _____ The embryo forms a solid ball of cells.

   b. _____ An egg is fertilized.

   c. _____ About three days later, the embryo is sixteen cells in size.

   d. _____ The embryo attaches itself to the lining of the uterus.

   e. _____ The fertilized egg undergoes mitosis to form two cells.

   f. _____ The embryo, now a hollow ball of cells, moves out of the oviduct into the uterus.

   g. _____ Mitosis continues and two cells form four cells, four cells form eight cells.

In your textbook, read about the needs of the embryo in Section 25:1.

2. Complete the diagram below by coloring the correct end of each arrow to show the proper direction the material takes.

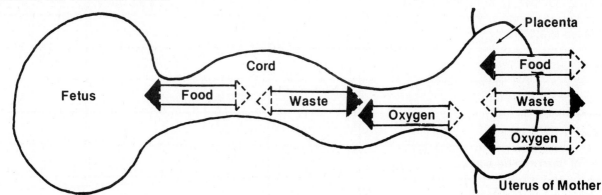

3. Place the numbers from the diagram on the right next to the correct statements below.

   a. _____ The *umbilical cord* connects the young to the placenta.

   b. _____ The young is protected by a *liquid-filled sac.*

   c. _____ Wastes are carried away by the *placenta.*

   d. _____ The *fetus* grows in the uterus.

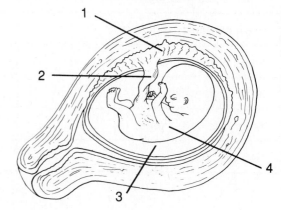

Name _____ Date _____ Class _____

DEVELOPMENT INSIDE THE FEMALE

4. Why are proper nutrition and good health important during pregnancy? _____

_____

_____

5. How does the amniotic sac help the developing embryo? _____

_____

In your textbook, read about human development in Section 25:1.

6. Complete the following table by placing a checkmark in the column that tells when the traits listed form.

Trait	Month			
	1	2	3	4 to birth
Muscles and bones form.				
Liver and ears appear.				
Kicking, bending, and turning occurs.				
Embryo is 1.0 gram.				
Arms and legs form.				
Stomach starts to form.				
Fetus is 3000 grams.				
Sex of child can be seen.				
Eyes begin to develop.				
Fingers and toes appear.				
Brain and heart start to form.				
Fetus is 100 grams.				
Eyes have eyelids.				
Embryo is 0.02 grams.				
Heart is beating.				

Name _____ Date _____ Class _____

DEVELOPMENT INSIDE THE FEMALE

In your textbook, read about human births in Section 25:1.

7. Study the diagrams of a human before and during birth. Then, complete the table below by writing *yes* or *no* in the blanks.

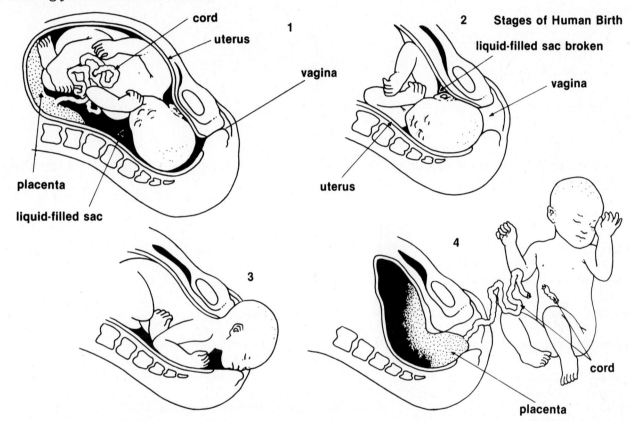

Diagram	1	2	3	4
Time	Three days before birth	Three hours before birth	During birth	A few minutes after birth
Is baby in vagina?				
Is bottom of uterus closed?				
Is baby inside liquid sac?				
Is liquid sac broken?				
Is baby attached to umbilical cord?				
Is umbilical cord attached to placenta?				
Is placenta attached to uterus?				

Name _____ Date _____ Class _____

DEVELOPMENT OUTSIDE THE FEMALE

In your textbook, read about eggs and the needs of the young before hatching in Section 25:2.

1. Write the names of the parts of the developing chicken in the correct blank.

   A. _____

   B. _____

   C. _____

   D. _____

   E. _____

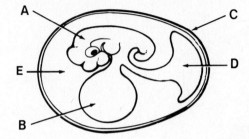

2. Match the terms with their definitions by writing the correct letter from Column II on the blanks after the words in Column I.

I	II
yolk _____	**a.** place where liquid wastes are stored
blood vessels just below shell _____	**b.** the protein in egg white
eggshell _____	**c.** the young chicken
sac within egg _____	**d.** leave the egg through the shell
albumen _____	**e.** pick up oxygen that passes to embryo
embryo _____	**f.** diffuses into shell from air outside
gas wastes _____	**g.** protects embryo from water loss and injury
oxygen _____	**h.** the yellow part of egg containing protein and stored fat

3. How is development in frogs, birds, and reptiles similar to that in humans? _____

   _____

4. How is development in frogs, birds, and reptiles different from that in humans? _____

   _____

   _____

5. How are the eggs of birds and reptiles suited to the environment in which they develop? _____

   _____

   _____

Name _____ Date _____ Class _____

METAMORPHOSIS

In your textbook, read about frog metamorphosis in Section 25:3.

1. Complete the table below showing frog development. Measure the drawings and record your measurements in the second column. (In the tadpole and frog stages, measure from the head to the tip of the tail.) Then, list at least one major trait of each stage.

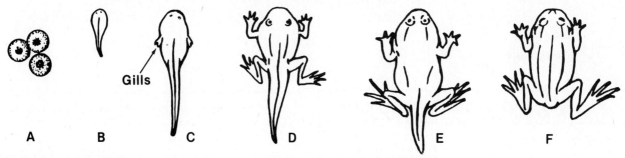

Stage	Size (mm)	Traits of stage
A		
B		
C		
D		
E		

2. Label the stages of metamorphosis shown below.

   a.

   _____   _____   _____

   b.

   _____   _____   _____   _____

Name _____ Date _____ Class _____

VOCABULARY

Review the new words in Chapter 25 of your textbook. Then, complete this puzzle.

Below are five tables. List the following words in every table in which they are correct. Some words are used more than once.

amniotic sac breaks   incomplete   metamorphosis   placenta
complete   metamorphosis   navel   pupa
  metamorphosis   labor   nymph   umbilical cord
fetus   larva
cleavage

A change that takes place in all living things

Changes or stages that take place in insects

Changes or stages that take place in frogs

Parts or stages in humans

Changes that occur during a human birth

Name _____ Date _____ Class _____

GENETICS, HOW AND WHY

In Section 26:1 of your textbook, read about genes and how they are passed to offspring.

1. Examine the drawings of horsefly chromosomes below. Complete the table by filling in the information about the chromosomes.

	Body cell	Sex cell
	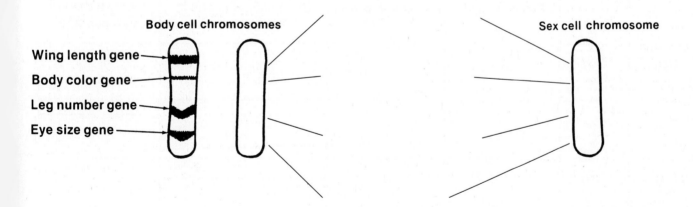	
Number of chromosomes present		
Can the chromosomes be put in pairs? (yes or no)		

2. **a.** Genes are often shown as lines on a chromosome. Examine the diagrams below of a pair of body cell chromosomes and a sex cell chromosome of a horsefly. Complete the diagrams by drawing the genes on the unmarked chromosomes and labeling them by trait.

Body cell chromosomes   **Sex cell chromosome**

Wing length gene
Body color gene
Leg number gene
Eye size gene

   b. How many genes for wing length are present in this body cell? _____

   c. How many genes for wing length are present in this sex cell? _____

3. In dogs, black fur is dominant to brown fur. Write the color each dog will be if the dog is:

   pure dominant _____ pure recessive _____ heterozygous _____

STUDY GUIDE

CHAPTER 26

Name _____ Date _____ Class _____

EXPECTED AND OBSERVED RESULTS

In Section 26:2 of your textbook, read about possible combinations of eggs and sperm.

1. Here are six dogs. In the small box below each dog, write the genes present in the body cells of that dog. Use the letters *B* for black and *b* for brown.

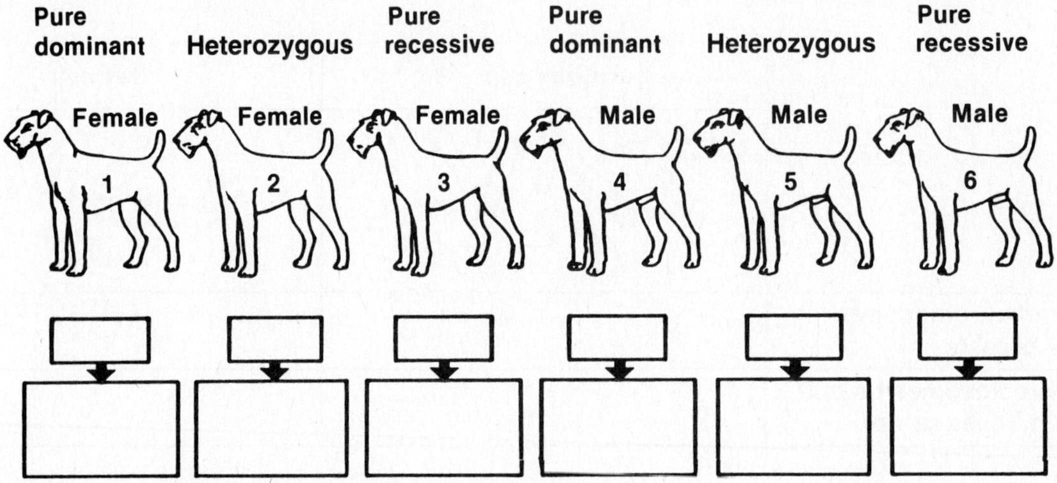

Pure dominant	Heterozygous	Pure recessive	Pure dominant	Heterozygous	Pure recessive
Female 1	Female 2	Female 3	Male 4	Male 5	Male 6

In the large boxes in the diagrams, draw 2 sex cells below each dog. Draw sperm like this.
Draw eggs like this.
Complete the drawings by marking the genes *B* or *b* on the sex cells you have drawn.

2. The following table shows possible results of mating the dogs. Complete the table.

Mother	Father	Possible gene in eggs	Possible gene in sperm	Gene combinations in fertilized eggs	Likely fur color of 4 puppies
Dog 1	Dog 4				
Dog 1	Dog 5				
Dog 2	Dog 4				
Dog 2	Dog 5	(B) (b)	(B)~ (b)~	(BB) (Bb) (Bb) (bb)	3 black 1 brown
Dog 3	Dog 5				
Dog 3	Dog 6				

152

Name _____ Date _____ Class _____

EXPECTED AND OBSERVED RESULTS

In Section 26:2 of your textbook, read about solving genetics problems using the Punnett square.

3. Examine the diagrams below. Each is a step in the Punnett square method. Put the steps in order by writing the numbers 1 to 4 below them on the correct blanks.

	D	d
D		
d		

_____

	D	d
D	D	d
D	D	d

_____

_____

	D	d
D	DD	Dd
d	Dd	dd

_____

4. What do the letters outside the Punnett square stand for? _____

_____

What do the letters inside each box stand for? _____

_____

5. Examine the following Punnett squares and circle those that are correct.

	D	d
d	Dd	dd
d	Dd	dd

	D	D
d	Dd	DD
d	Dd	Dd

	D	d
D	DD	Dd
d	Dd	Dd

	D	D
D	DD	DD
d	Dd	Dd

	A	a
A	AA	Aa
a	Aa	aa

	A	a
A	AA	aa
a	Aa	Aa

	A	a
a	Aa	aa
a	Aa	aa

	A	a
A	AA	AA
A	AA	a

6. Complete the following to determine the expected offspring.

	T	t
T		
T		

	e	e
E		
e		

	R	r
R		
r		

	S	S
S		
s		

EXPECTED AND OBSERVED RESULTS

7. In corn plants, normal height H is dominant to short height h. Complete those four Punnett squares showing different crosses. Then, shade red all the pure dominant offspring. Shade green all the heterozygous offspring. Leave all the pure recessive offspring unshaded.

8. In flies, long wings L are dominant to short wings l. Complete these four Punnett squares showing different crosses. Then, shade red all the offspring that will have long wings. Leave all the shortwinged offspring unshaded.

9. In guinea pigs, short hair S is dominant to long hair s. Complete the following Punnett squares according to the directions given. Then, fill in the blanks beside each Punnett square with the correct numbers.

   a. One guinea pig is Ss and one is ss.

   Offspring expected (number)

   ____ Short hair

   ____ Long hair

   b. Both guinea pigs are heterozygous for short hair.

   Offspring expected (number)

   ____ Short hair

   ____ Long hair

Name _____ Date _____ Class _____

EXPECTED AND OBSERVED RESULTS

In Section 26:2 of your textbook, read about the work done by Gregor Mendel in genetics.

10. Mendel made the following crosses with pea plants. Complete the Punnett squares and answer the questions about each cross.

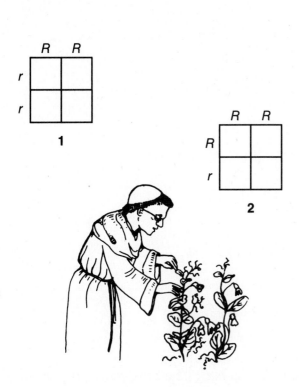

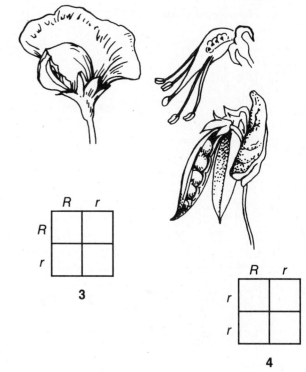

a. He crossed a red flowered *R* plant with a white flowered *r* plant. His results were 126 red flowered plants and 122 white flowered plants. Which of the Punnett squares above best shows the parents

and offspring that could give these results? _____

b. He crossed a red flowered plant with a white flowered plant. His results were 307 red flowered plants and 0 white flowered plants. Which of the Punnett squares above best shows the parents

and offspring that could give these results? _____

c. He crossed a red flowered plant with a red flowered plant. His results were 306 red flowered plants and 110 white flowered plants. Which of the Punnett squares above best shows the parents and

offspring that could give these results? _____

d. He crossed a red flowered plant with a red flowered plant. His results were 300 red flowered plants and 0 white flowered plants. Which of the Punnett squares above best shows the parents and

offspring that could give these results? _____

Name _____ Date _____ Class _____

VOCABULARY

Review the new words used in Chapter 26 of your textbook. Then, answer these questions.

1. Below each of the following words are choices. Circle the choices that are examples of each of those words.

   a. Dominant gene

      D   e   k   L   N   o   R   S

   b. Recessive gene

      M   n   d   F   G   i   k   P

   c. Pure dominant

      AA   Gg   KK   ll   pp   Rr   TT

   d. Pure recessive

      ee   Ff   HH   Oo   qq   Uu   ww

   e. Offspring combinations in which dominant gene *must* show

      AA   Dd   EE   ff   Jj   RR   Ss

   f. Offspring combinations in which recessive gene *must* show

      aa   Gg   Ff   KK   Oo   PP   ss   tt

2. Fill in the blanks below using these choices: dominant, genes, genetics, heterozygous, pure, recessive, chromosomes, Punnett square.

   a. Chromosomes have parts that determine traits. These parts are _____.

   b. A person having two genes that are alike is said to be _____.

   c. A gene that prevents others from showing is said to be _____.

   d. A gene that may not show up even though it is there is said to be _____.

   e. Long rod-shaped bodies inside a cell's nucleus are called _____.

   f. One who studies how traits are passed on is studying _____.

   g. A person with one dominant and one recessive gene for a trait is _____.

   h. A way to show which genes can combine when an egg and sperm join is a _____
   _____.

Name _____ Date _____ Class _____

THE ROLE OF CHROMOSOMES

In your textbook, read about sex—a genetic trait in Section 27:1.

1. Examine the chromosomes shown below from two people. Then, answer the questions that follow.

A

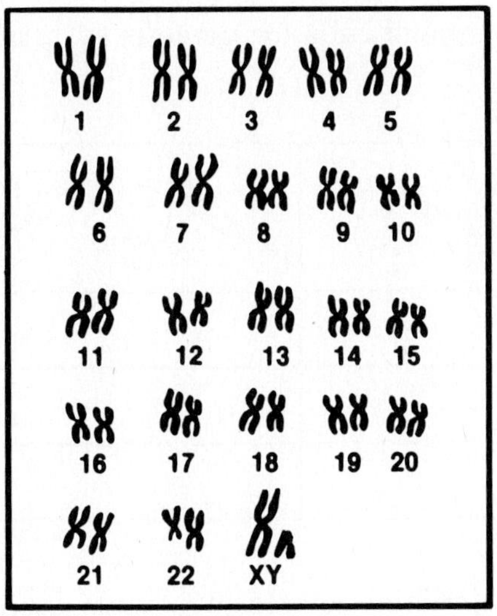

1	2	3	4	5	
6	7	8	9	10	
11	12	13	14	15	
16	17	18	19	20	
21	22	XY			

B

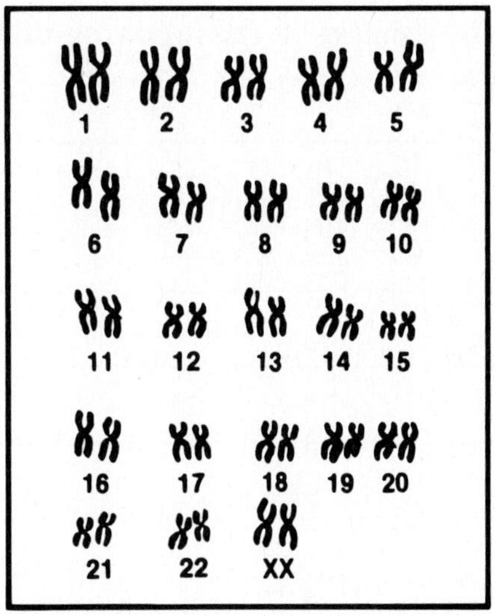

1	2	3	4	5	
6	7	8	9	10	
11	12	13	14	15	
16	17	18	19	20	
21	22	XX			

   a. Is person A male or female? _____ How do you know? _____

   _____

   b. Is person B male or female? _____ How do you know? _____

   _____

   c. Circle the sex chromosomes of each of the above people.

2. Complete the Punnett square.
   Then, answer the questions below.

   a. Out of four children, how many are expected to be female? _____

   b. Out of four children, how many are expected to be male? _____

   c. Which sex chromosome do both males and females have? _____

   d. Which sex chromosome do only males have? _____

   e. Shade the female offspring in the above Punnett square. Leave the male offspring unshaded.

Name _____ Date _____ Class _____

HUMAN TRAITS

In your textbook, read about incomplete dominance in Section 27:2.

1. Red blood cell shape shows incomplete dominance in humans. R is the gene for round cell shape and R' is the gene for sickle cell shape.

   a. Put checkmarks in the following table to show the shape of cells for persons with the genes listed.

$R'R'$			
RR'			
RR			

   b. Which gene, R or R', is dominant? _____ Which is recessive? _____

2. **a.** Describe the condition that a person with $R'R'$ genes has. _____

   _____

   _____

   _____

   b. What is the name of this disease? _____

3. Human blood types show incomplete dominance as well as dominance. Fill in the table at the right showing possible genes a person with each blood type might have.

Blood type	Possible genes
A	or
B	or
O	
AB	

4. Which blood type genes are dominant to other blood type genes? _____

   _____

5. Which blood type genes show incomplete dominance to each other? _____

Name _____ Date _____ Class _____

HUMAN TRAITS

In your textbook, read about color blindness in Section 27:2.

1. Color blindness is a trait carried on the sex chromosomes. Let *C* be normal color vision and *c* be red-green color blindness. Use the diagrams to answer the questions.

   a. What is the sex of each of these people? Write either male or female on the blank below each.

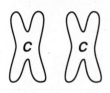   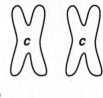

   A _____ B _____ C _____ D _____ E _____

   b. Which are red-green color blind? _____

   c. Which have normal color vision? _____

   d. Which has normal color vision even with the gene for color blindness? _____

2. **a.** Complete the following Punnett squares. The first one has been done for you.

   b. Using these colors, shade the following parts of the Punnett squares.
   Blue—normal females   Red—color blind females
   Yellow—normal males   Green—color blind males

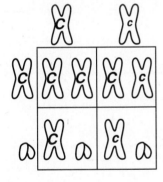 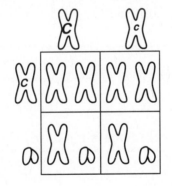 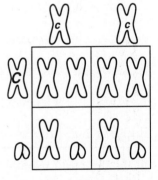

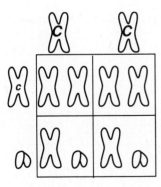 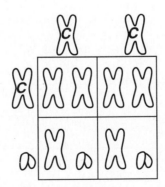

Name _____ Date _____ Class _____

GENETIC DISORDERS

In your textbook, read about errors in chromosome number in Section 27:3.

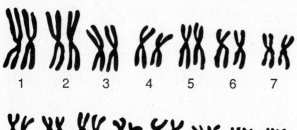

Figure 1

Figure 2

1. Suppose a child was found to have the chromosome pattern shown in Figure 1 above.

   a. Is the child a male or female? _____

   b. Explain your answer. _____

   c. Down syndrome is caused by one extra autosome in each cell. What pair of chromosomes has an

   extra chromosome? _____

   d. How did this child get an extra chromosome? _____

   _____

2. Suppose a child was found to have the chromosome pattern shown in Figure 2 above.

   a. Is the child a male or female? _____

   b. Explain your answer. _____

   _____

   c. Which chromosome is the extra chromosome, an X or Y? _____

   d. How did the child get an extra chromosome? _____

   _____

   _____

   _____

   _____

Name _____ Date _____ Class _____

GENETIC DISORDERS

In your textbook, read about hemophilia in Section 27:3.

1. In the boxes below each of these people, draw the sex chromosomes. Then, on the chromosomes write the genes they have for hemophilia. The dominant gene is *H*. The recessive gene is *h*.

Normal, pure dominant female	Female with hemophilia	Normal male	Male with hemophilia	Normal, heterozygous female

2. Complete the following Punnett squares. Then, match the correct Punnett square with each one of the following expected results. Write the letter of the Punnett square on the line next to the expected result it matches.

Expected results
2 normal females 1 normal male 1 male with hemophilia
1 normal female 1 normal male 1 female with hemophilia 1 male with hemophilia
2 normal females 2 males with hemophilia

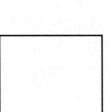
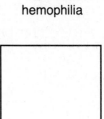
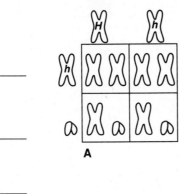
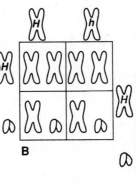

3. Circle the Punnett squares that show individuals with hemophilia.

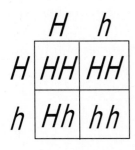
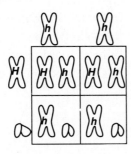
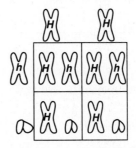

4. Describe the condition of hemophilia. _____

_____

Name _____ Date _____ Class _____

VOCABULARY

Review the new words in Chapter 27 of your textbook. Then, complete this puzzle.

Across	**Down**
5. Use of genetics to predict and explain traits in children	1. Genetic disorder called word blindness
6. Condition in which neither gene is dominant	2. Disorder in which some colors are not seen as they should be
7. Chromosome that does not determine sex	3. Way of looking at chromosomes of a fetus
8. Disorder in which red blood cells are not round	4. Sex chromosomes of a male
9. Sex chromosomes of the female	
10. Chromosomes that determine if child is male or female	
11. Diagram that can show how a trait is passed along in a family	

Name _____ Date _____ Class _____

THE DNA MOLECULE

In your textbook, read about the structure of DNA in Section 28:1.

1. What do the letters *DNA* stand for? _____

2. Where is DNA found? _____

   _____

3. Label the following parts of a DNA model: nitrogen bases, sugar, acid, upright side, ladder rung.

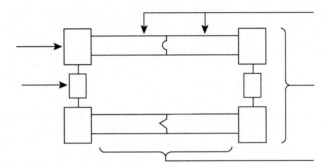

4. Use the parts shown below to draw a section of DNA in the box provided. You design the order in which the bases appear, but remember that they only join in certain ways.

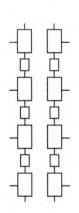 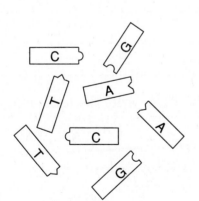 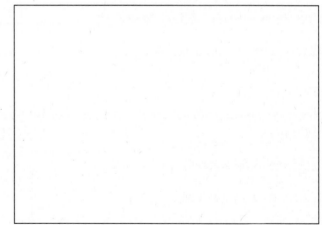

In your textbook, read about DNA and chromosomes in Section 28:1.

5. Define a gene in three ways. _____

   _____

   _____ _____

THE DNA MOLECULE

In your textbook, read about proof that DNA controls traits in Section 28:1.

6. Study Figure 28-4 and page 590 of your textbook. Then, explain why you would expect a mouse to:

   a. live if given an injection of living harmless bacteria. _____

   _____

   b. die if given an injection of living harmful bacteria. _____

   _____

   c. live if given an injection of dead harmful bacteria. _____

   _____

   d. die when given a mixture of living harmless bacteria and dead harmful bacteria. _____

   _____

   _____

In your textbook, read about making proteins in Section 28:1.

7. What do the letters *RNA* stand for? _____

8. Why is RNA called a messenger? _____

   _____

9. Examine the diagram of a cell and some of its parts. Then, write the letter of the labeled part that shows:

   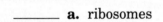

   _____ **a.** ribosomes

   _____ **b.** the nucleus

   _____ **c.** a chromosome

   _____ **d.** DNA

   _____ **e.** RNA

   _____ **f.** cytoplasm

   _____ **g.** the worktable for making proteins

   _____ **h.** DNA's helper molecule

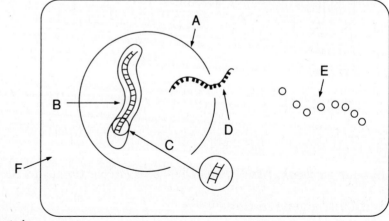

Name _____ Date _____ Class _____

THE DNA MOLECULE

In your textbook, read about how DNA copies itself in Section 28:1.

10. The model of DNA on the left is ready to be copied. The copies on the right labeled 1-3 show the resulting molecules as drawn by several students.

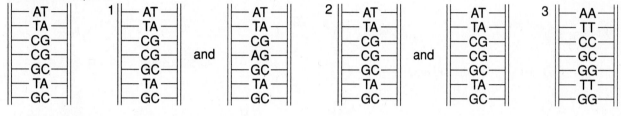

   a. Explain why number 1 is incorrect. _____

   _____

   b. Explain why number 2 is correct. _____

   _____

   c. Explain why number 3 is incorrect. _____

   _____

11. How does the genetic message compare in the original cell and the two new cells that form after

   the cell reproduces? _____

HOW THE GENETIC MESSAGE CHANGES

In your textbook, read about mutations in Section 28:2.

1. Complete the diagram on the left. Then, circle the areas in the diagram on the right that show a mutation.

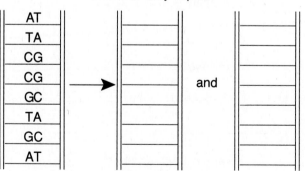
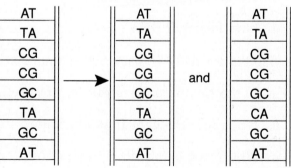

2. List three causes of mutations. _____

   _____

   _____

Name _____ Date _____ Class _____

HOW THE GENETIC MESSAGE CHANGES

In your textbook, read about cloning in Section 28:2.

3. A mother has four children. Children A and B were born at the end of her first pregnancy. Children C and D were born at the end of her second pregnancy. Which of her children:

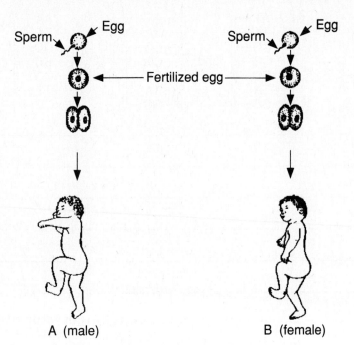
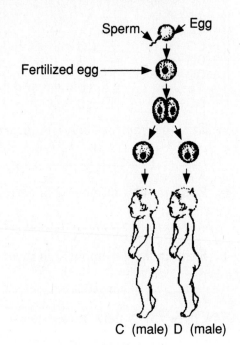

A (male) B (female) C (male) D (male)

a. are identical twins? _____

b. were formed from two different eggs and sperm? _____

c. are clones? _____

d. have identical DNA? _____

e. are fraternal twins? _____

f. have different genes? _____

g. were formed from one egg and one sperm? _____

4. Use Figure 28-12 on page 599 of your textbook to answer the following questions.

a. In the cloning process shown, what cell part does the dark frog contribute? _____

b. What does the light frog contribute? _____

c. Which frog is contributing its DNA? _____ Explain your answer. _____

_____

d. Why does the cloned frog resemble the dark parent instead of the light parent? _____

_____

Name _____ Date _____ Class _____

HOW THE GENETIC MESSAGE CHANGES

In your textbook, read about breeding of plants and animals and splicing genes between organisms in Section 28:2.

5. This diagram shows two bulls. Below each is a description of that bull's traits.

Bull A

Sleek, clean, solid-colored fur
Long tail, long legs
Milk production of his offspring
is low.

Bull B

Rough, spotted fur
Short tail, short legs
Milk production of his offspring
is high.

a. Which bull would you choose to breed with a cow to produce a herd of cows that would supply

a lot of milk? _____ Why? _____

b. Which bull would you choose for breeding to produce "beautiful" offspring? _____ Why?

_____

c. Which bull would you choose for breeding to produce offspring that would not jump over

fences? _____ Why? _____

d. Explain the value of plant and animal breeding. _____

_____

_____

6. What is recombinant DNA? _____

_____

7. Why does gene splicing work? _____

_____

8. List four ways that gene splicing is of value to humans now or may be of value in the future.

_____

_____

_____

Name _____ Date _____ Class _____

VOCABULARY

Review the words used in Chapter 28 of your textbook. Then, complete this exercise.

Each word listed here has at least three statements after it. Place a checkmark in front of all the statements that are either correct or are examples of the word.

1. DNA

   _____ makes up chromosomes

   _____ are proteins in cells

   _____ deoxyribonucleic acid

   _____ controls the traits of living things

2. Breeding

   _____ the act of bringing oxygen into the lungs

   _____ can be done with plants and animals

   _____ can result in better crops

3. Genetic message

   _____ order of bases in DNA

   _____ used for computers

   _____ is copied

4. Fraternal twins

   _____ form from different egg and different sperm

   _____ are not clones

   _____ DNA is different

   _____ have different genes

5. Radiation

   _____ can cause mutations

   _____ is a form of energy

   _____ released by the sun

6. Identical twins

   _____ form from one egg and one sperm

   _____ have exactly the same genes

   _____ a brother and a sister

   _____ have the same DNA

7. Mutation

   _____ any change in the DNA message

   _____ error in base pairing

   _____ a computer card error

8. Nitrogen bases

   _____ A, C, G, T

   _____ join only in certain ways

   _____ present in the cell nucleus

9. RNA

   _____ ribonucleic acid

   _____ carries DNA message from nucleus to ribosome

   _____ directs the forming of protein

   _____ rung of the DNA ladder

10. Recombinant DNA

    _____ formed by splicing of DNA

    _____ occurs in wires

    _____ has produced human insulin

    _____ adding human DNA to bacteria

Name _____ Date _____ Class _____

CHANGES IN LIVING THINGS

In your textbook, read about adaptations and natural selection in Section 29:1.

1. Circle the adaptations below that aid survival in water.

2. Circle the adaptations below that aid survival on land or in the air.

3. Suppose a bird eats moths that land on tree trunks. Circle the moths on each of these tree trunks that would probably be eaten by the bird. Then, answer the following questions by filling in the blanks with the words *dark* or *light*.

Which moths in picture:

   a. A blend well with the color of the tree trunk? _____

   b. B blend well with the color of the tree trunk? _____

   c. A will be eaten first by the birds? _____

   d. B will be eaten first by the birds? _____

   e. A have the best chance to survive and reproduce? _____

   f. B have the best chance to survive and reproduce? _____

Name _____ Date _____ Class _____

CHANGES IN LIVING THINGS

In your textbook, read about mutations in Section 29:1.

4. These two polar bears are alike except for their fur color. Answer the following questions about the polar bears.

A   B

   a. Which has a trait that could be harmful to survival? _____

   Explain your answer. _____

   _____

   b. Suppose all polar bears had fur like A, and suddenly a bear with fur like B is born. Could the

   change be the result of a mutation? _____

   c. Would the mutation have produced an adaptation? (Is the change helpful to the bear?)

   _____ Explain your answer. _____

   _____

5. Below are several mutations. After each, write how the trait could be harmful. Then, write how each trait could be helpful.

	How trait could be harmful	How trait could be helpful
Albino squirrel		
Hornless cattle		
Short-legged dog		
Long eyelashes in humans		

170

Name _____ Date _____ Class _____

CHANGES IN LIVING THINGS

In your textbook, read about species formation in Section 29:1.

6. a. How can the word *species* be defined as it relates to the classification of living things? _____

_____

   b. How can the word *species* be defined as it relates to breeding? _____

_____

_____

7. Use Figure 29-5 on page 611 of your textbook to help you do this exercise. The following statements involve events that can result in the formation of a new species. Number them from 1-6 in the proper order. Number one is done for you.

_____ **a.** animals are separated into two groups and must now live apart

_____ **b.** environments on either side of the river change with time

___1___ **c.** animals of the same species living on either side of a stream can move from one side to the other

_____ **d.** the stream changes into a river

_____ **e.** animals, due to natural selection, undergo change

_____ **f.** after thousands of years, two different species of animals form

8. In the example in Figure 29-5, what three events led to the formation of new species? _____

_____

_____

_____

9. How do the finches of the Galapagos Islands differ? _____

_____

10. Describe how a single finch ancestor probably evolved into many different species. _____

_____

_____

_____

_____

Name _____ Date _____ Class _____

EXPLANATIONS FOR EVOLUTION

In your textbook, read about Darwin's work in Section 29.2.

1. The four diagrams below each show a main point in Darwin's theory of evolution. Below each, write the sentence from this list that is best shown.

Living things overproduce.   There is a struggle to survive.
There is variation among the offspring.   Natural selection is always taking place.

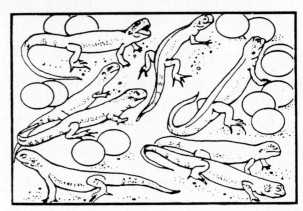

_____   _____

_____   _____

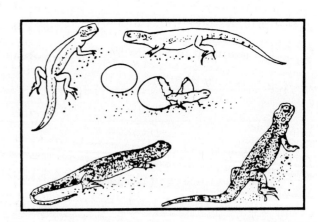

_____   _____

_____   _____

2. What phrase describes the hawk choosing the light lizard? _____

3. What is evolution? _____

_____

Name _____ Date _____ Class _____

EXPLANATIONS FOR EVOLUTION

In your textbook, read about evidence of evolution in Section 29:2.

4. List five examples of fossils. _____

_____

_____

5. a. You are on an expedition digging down through Earth's crust. You uncover the materials shown below. Put an X through those objects that are *not* fossils.

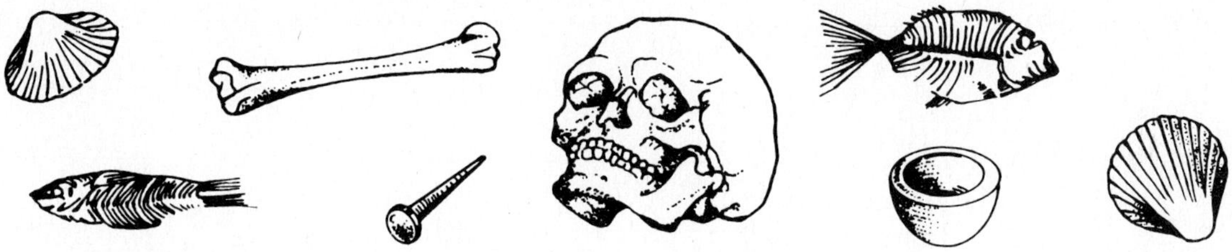

b. What made you decide that the objects you put an X through in part *a* were not fossils?

_____

6. Examine the diagram of a side view of sedimentary rocks in the Earth's crust. Which layer:

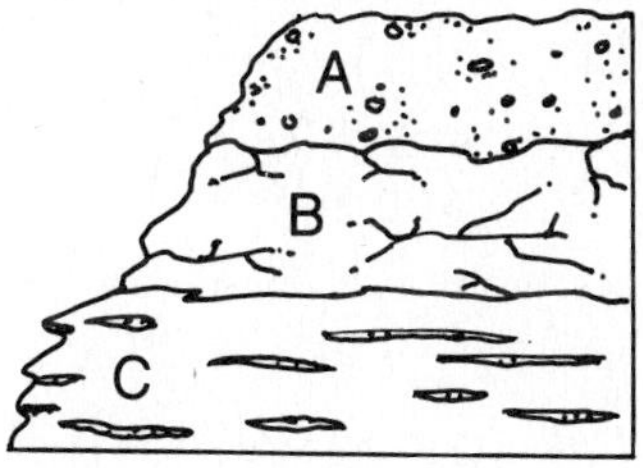

a. is the oldest? _____   **d.** was formed first? _____

b. was formed last? _____   **e.** is the youngest? _____

c. has life forms most like those   **f.** has life forms least like those

of today? _____   of today? _____

7. How does Figure 29-3 on page 620 of your textbook provide evidence of evolution. _____

_____

_____

_____

8. How is the genetic code similar in early and modern forms of life? _____

_____

9. a. What is a vestigial structure? _____

b. How do vestigial structures provide evidence of evolution? _____

_____

_____

Name _____ Date _____ Class _____

VOCABULARY

Review the new words in Chapter 29 of your textbook. Then, write a sentence defining each word.

1. species _____
   _____

2. old-world monkeys _____
   _____

3. natural selection _____
   _____

4. vestigial structure _____
   _____

5. sedimentary rocks _____
   _____

6. primate _____
   _____

7. evolution _____
   _____

8. new-world
   monkeys _____

9. extinct _____

10. competition _____
    _____

11. fossils _____
    _____

12. fertile _____
    _____

13. variation _____
    _____

Name _____ Date _____ Class _____

POPULATIONS

In your textbook, read about population size in Section 30:1.

1. Make a population count of the crabs in the diagram below. Place a checkmark on the shell of each crab to avoid counting any twice. Keep track of how long it takes you to do it.

Total number = _____ Time it took = _____

2. A faster way to count a population is to sample it. Count the number of crabs in the small square on the right below.

Total number = _____

Time it took = _____

This square is ⅛ the size of the large square above. Therefore, you need to multiply the number you counted by 8 to get the total population size.

 × 8 = _____

3. **a.** Were the results from counting about the same regardless of which method was used to count?

_____

b. What is the advantage of counting a population by sampling it? _____

_____

Name _____ Date _____ Class _____

POPULATIONS

In your textbook, read about population changes in Section 30:1.

4. Many things change the numbers of individuals in a population. One important factor is food supply. For example, foxes eat mice. The table below shows how their numbers change.

Year	Number of mice	Number of foxes
1983	1050	200
1984	800	425
1985	426	581
1986	730	300
1987	980	153
1988	620	399
1989	380	548
1990	680	403
1991	1010	255

   a. Plot the number of mice on the graph below and connect all the points with a black line.
   b. Plot the number of foxes on this graph. Connect all the points with a red line.
   c. In the boxes at the right of the graph, indicate which animal is the predator and which is the prey by writing *predator* and *prey* in the correct box.

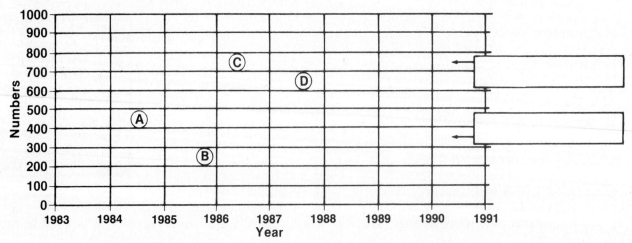

5. After each of the phrases below, write the letter from the graph (A, B, C, or D) that best matches.

   a. Fox population increasing _____   **c.** Mouse population increasing _____

   b. Fox population decreasing _____   **d.** Mouse population decreasing _____

Name _____ Date _____ Class _____

COMMUNITIES

In your textbook, read about the parts of a community in Section 30:2.

1. This picture of a community shows many different kinds of living things. Using these colors, shade the following parts.

   Green—producers
   Red—primary consumers

   Yellow—secondary consumers
   Blue—decomposers

2. What is the habitat of the deer? _____

3. What is the niche of the deer? _____

4. List two decomposers in this community. _____

5. What producers are present in this community? _____

6. List two secondary consumers and tell what they eat. _____

   _____

Name _____ Date _____ Class _____

ENERGY IN A COMMUNITY

In your textbook, read about energy and food chains in Section 30:3.

 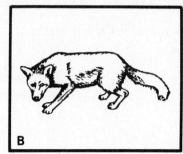 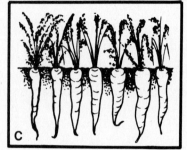

1. Write the letter of the diagram above that best matches each of these words or phrases.

   needs sun's energy to make food ____   producer ____

   consumers ____ and ____   primary consumers ____

   secondary consumer ____   gets the least energy available ____

2. **a.** Count the number of living things in each of the pictures above and record the numbers in

   the blanks. rabbits ____ foxes ____ carrots ____

   b. Complete the diagram below by following these steps.
   1) On the blanks at the left, write the names of the living things in correct order.
   2) On the right side, write each of these terms on the correct blank: producer, secondary consumer, primary consumer.

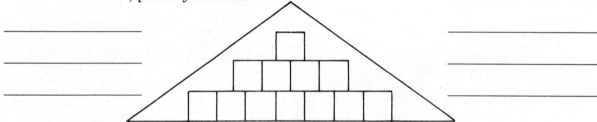

3. Explain why the picture has fewer living things at the top of the pyramid.

   _____

   _____

   _____

4. **a.** Explain why the top of an energy pyramid does not have an arrow showing energy going back

   down to the bottom. _____

   b. Where does the energy go? _____

   _____

Name _____ Date _____ Class _____

RELATIONSHIPS IN A COMMUNITY

In your textbook, read about relationships in a community in Section 30:4.

1. This picture shows an example of parasitism. This boy has a condition called elephantiasis (el uh fun TI uh sus). The condition is caused by a small roundworm in his body. The worm reproduced and the many worms blocked small blood vessels in his body. Fluids then became trapped in his leg. The swelling resulted from the fluid buildup.

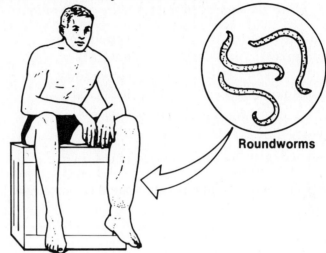

Roundworms

Define parasitism. _____

_____

2. The picture below shows an example of mutualism. This living thing, called a lichen (LI kun), is made of an alga and a fungus. The alga cells make food for themselves and the fungus. The fungus holds water and minerals that they both use. They live better together than either could live alone.

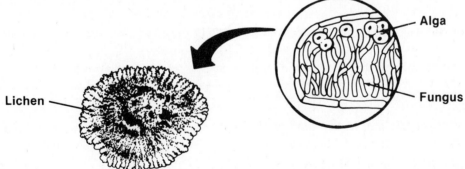

Alga

Fungus

Lichen

   a. Define mutualism. _____

   _____

   b. Circle the correct answers.

   The alga in a lichen supplies food, water.

   The fungus in a lichen supplies food, water.

Name _____ **Date** _____ **Class** _____

VOCABULARY

Review the new words used in Chapter 30 of your textbook. Then complete this puzzle. Use the words listed below to fill in the blanks in the sentences that follow.

commensalism	population	immigration
energy pyramid	habitat	emigration
niche	community	limiting factor
primary consumers	food chain	secondary consumers
prey	food web	predator
predation	parasitism	

A group of organisms of the same species make up a _____.

The size of this group of organisms can change because new organisms enter and leave. This is

called _____ and _____.

A condition that keeps the size of a population from increasing is a _____.

Living things of different kinds live together in a _____. The

place where a plant or animal lives is its _____. The job of the

organism is its _____. Animals that eat only plants are

_____. Animals that eat other animals are

_____.

Energy and materials are passed from one living thing to another in a community through a

_____. A _____ shows

how food chains are connected in a community. An _____ is a

diagram that shows energy loss in the food chain.

Living things depend on each other in several ways. In _____,

one organism is helped and the other is not affected. In _____,

one organism is helped and the other is harmed but not usually killed. In _____,

one animal hunts and kills another animal. The _____ is the

animal that is eaten. The _____ is the animal that hunts and

kills the other animal.

Name _____ Date _____ Class _____

ECOSYSTEMS

In your textbook, read about cycles in an ecosystem in Section 31:1.

1. The incomplete diagram below shows the water cycle. Complete the diagram by following these steps.

    a. Use blue to shade the arrow that shows evaporation of water into air from ground or streams.

    b. Use green to shade the arrow that shows evaporation of water into air from plants.

    c. Leave unshaded the arrow that shows water falling from the clouds.

2. Complete the diagram below of the oxygen and carbon dioxide cycle by following these steps. Write the symbols for the gases in all the spaces marked A. Use O_2 as the symbol for oxygen and CO_2 as the symbol for carbon dioxide. Then, identify the process that takes place in all the spaces marked B. Use P as the symbol for photosynthesis and R as the symbol for respiration.

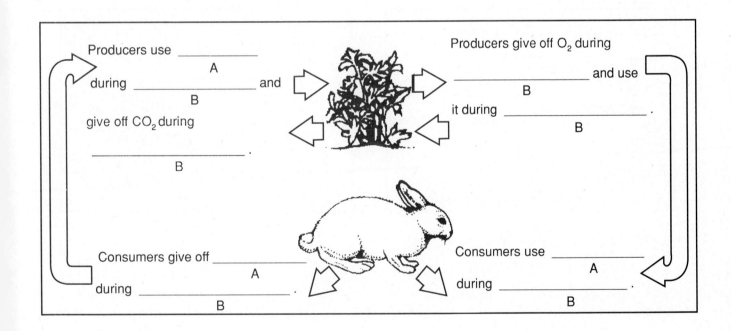

Name _____ Date _____ Class _____

SUCCESSION

In your textbook, read about succession in a land community in Section 31:2.

1. These diagrams of succession are not in the correct order. Show the correct order by writing the numbers 1 to 4 on the blanks below the diagrams.

_____   _____

_____   _____

2. Match each diagram to the phrases below. Write the correct number of the diagram on each blank.

   a. Climax community _____   d. Few primary consumers _____

   b. Weeds begin to appear _____   e. Most animals present _____

   c. Soil good for larger plants _____   f. Rabbits, mice, and fox might be here _____

Name _____ Date _____ Class _____

SUCCESSION

In your textbook, read about succession in a water community in Section 31:2.

3. Examine the diagrams below and the one on the next page. Measure the width and depth of the pond from the center of the X's in each diagram and record your measurements on the table on page 184. Then, answer the questions that follow.

Stage A 1883

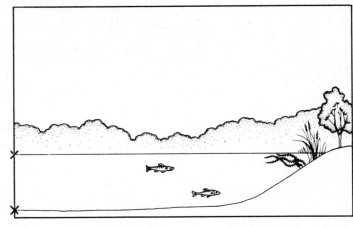

Stage B 1899

Stage C 1945

Name _____ Date _____ Class _____

SUCCESSION

Stage D   1991

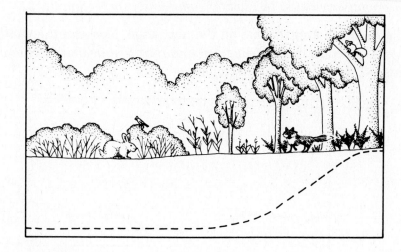

Stage	Year	Pond depth (mm)	Pond width (mm)
A			
B			
C			
D			

4. Describe the changes that take place in pond depth and width as the pond ages. _____

_____

5. How have the numbers and types of animals changed from stage A to stage B? _____

_____

6. a. What has happened to the pond by stage C? _____

_____

b. How has this event affected the types of animals that are living in the pond? _____

_____

7. What has replaced the pond in stage D? _____

8. What word describes these changes in the pond? _____

Name _____ **Date** _____ **Class** _____

HOW LIVING THINGS ARE DISTRIBUTED

In your textbook, read about biomes in Section 31:3.

1. The picture below shows the major world biomes. Using colored pencils, shade in the biomes described.

   a. Use blue for the biome that has an almost constant temperature.

   b. Use brown for the biome that has temperatures from $-28°$ to $15°C$.

   c. Use green for the biome that has evergreen trees, moose, weasels, and mink.

   d. Use purple for the biome that has grasses.

   e. Use yellow for the biome that has less than 25 cm of rainfall each year and whose common plants are cacti and small bushes.

   f. Use red for the biome that has trees such as hickory, maple, beech, and oak.

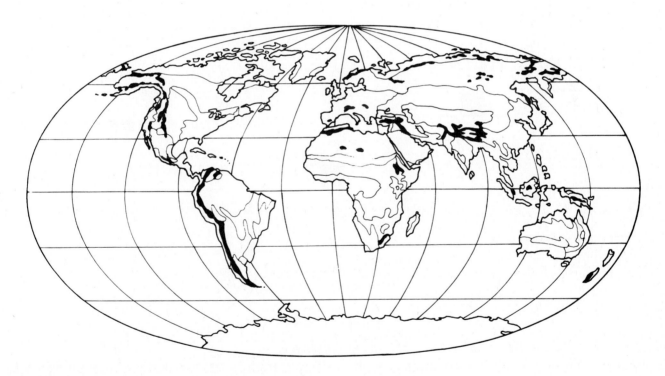

2. In which biome do you live? _____

3. Which biome makes up most of the United States? _____

4. **a.** Which two biomes have the least amount of rainfall? _____

   b. Why do no trees grow in these two biomes? _____

   _____

Name _____ Date _____ Class _____

VOCABULARY

Review the new science words used in Chapter 31 of your textbook. Then, complete this puzzle.

Across

6. changes that take place in a community as it ages

7. water in the air that falls to Earth

8. study of how organisms interact with each other and the environment

9. last stage in succession

Down

1. community interacting with the environment

2. an area with a distinct climate and organisms

3. reusing of nitrogen in an ecosystem

4. path that water takes through an ecosystem

5. average temperature and precipitation in an area

Name _____ Date _____ Class _____

RESOURCES AND HUMAN ACTIVITIES

In your textbook, read about natural resources in Section 32:1.

1. Each year during the five years from 1986 through 1990, millions of square kilometers of rain forests were cut down and cleared in Africa and Asia to make room for farmland. Use the information in the table below to help you answer the questions that follow.

Year	Number of square kilometers of forest removed	
	Africa	Asia
1990	24 000	16 000
1989	24 000	16 000
1988	24 000	16 000
1987	24 000	16 000
1986	24 000	16 000

2. **a.** How many square kilometers of forests were destroyed in Africa during the last five years? _____

   b. How many square kilometers of forests were destroyed in Asia during the last five years?

   _____

3. What happens to the soil when all of the plants are removed from the forests? _____

   _____

4. What happens to this soil when it is washed into a stream? _____

   _____

5. How does clearing the forests affect the level of gases in the air? _____

   _____

6. How does the removal of the forest environments affect the extinction of organisms? _____

   _____

Name _____ Date _____ Class _____

PROBLEMS FROM POLLUTION

In your textbook, read about air and water pollution in Section 32:2.

1. Fill in the boxes of the pollution table below with the correct words or phrases: burning coal, oil, gasoline, and natural gas; PCBs; harmful gases; heavy metals; pesticides and weed killers; tiny particles; sulfur dioxide. Several are already done for you.

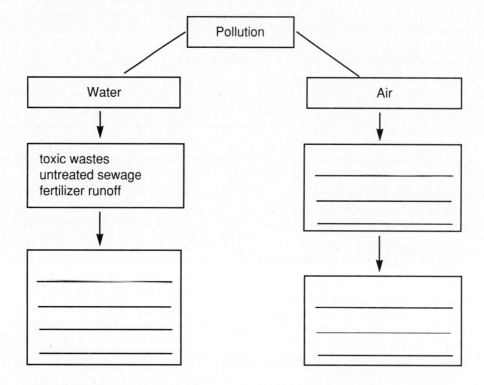

2. How is smog produced? _____

_____

3. What is the greenhouse effect? _____

_____

_____

_____

4. Why are chemicals such as PCBs and DDT so harmful to the environment? _____

_____

_____

Name _____ Date _____ Class _____

PROBLEMS FROM POLLUTION

In your textbook, read about acid rain in Section 32:2.

1. Study the map below.

U. S. Acid-Sensitive Areas

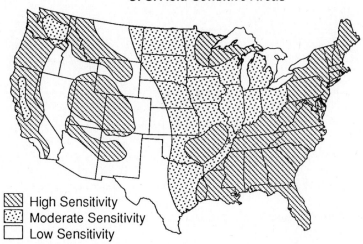

▨ High Sensitivity
▧ Moderate Sensitivity
☐ Low Sensitivity

2. Using an atlas and the map above, list the states that have a high sensitivity to acid rain. Place a checkmark by those states that have only small areas of high sensitivity to acid rain.

      West   **East**

_____

_____

_____

_____

_____

_____

_____

_____

_____

_____

_____

_____

Name _____ Date _____ Class _____

PROBLEMS FROM POLLUTION

3. What are two reasons that the eastern part of the United States has a greater acid rain problem than other parts?

   a. _____

   _____

   b. _____

   _____

4. What does the pH scale measure? _____

   _____

5. What are some examples of acids? _____

6. What are some examples of bases? _____

7. What pH do acids have? _____

8. What pH do bases have? _____

9. What is the pH of pure water? _____

10. What is the pH of normal rain? _____

11. What is the pH of acid rain? _____

12. How is acid rain formed? _____

   _____

13. List three results of acid rain in the United States.

   a. _____

   _____

   b. _____

   c. _____

14. What things other than lakes does acid rain damage? _____

   _____

15. Why must countries work together to solve the acid rain problem? _____

   _____

Name _____ Date _____ Class _____

WORKING TOWARD SOLUTIONS

In your textbook, read in Section 32:3 about conserving our resources and keeping our environment clean.

1. How do National Wildlife Refuges help endangered animals? _____

_____

2. What is the Endangered Species Act of 1973? _____

_____

_____

_____

3. What can be done to slow down or prevent erosion? _____

_____

4. What can you do to help conserve water? _____

_____

5. Since Congress passed laws to help clean up the air, what are industries required to do? _____

_____

6. Instead of using coal or oil for energy, what cleaner sources of energy can be used to make

electricity? _____

7. How have scientists been able to destroy insect pests without the use of pesticides?

_____

_____

8. What things can you do to conserve resources and prevent pollution? _____

_____

_____

_____

_____

VOCABULARY

Review the new words in Chapter 32 of your textbook. Use the terms below to fill in the blanks of the sentences that follow.

acid	biodegradable	endangered	radon	smog
base	greenhouse effect	fossil fuel	recycling	threatened
erosion	natural resource	pesticide	sediment	toxic
ozone	acid rain	pollution		

1. A _____ has a pH value greater than 7.

2. _____ makes surroundings unclean.

3. Any part of the environment used by humans is a _____ .

4. An _____ is in danger of becoming extinct.

5. A _____ is one that is close to being endangered.

6. _____ is material on the bottom of a stream.

7. Any poisonous material is _____ .

8. A _____ is a chemical used to kill rodents or insects.

9. A combination of smoke and fog is called _____ .

10. Something is _____ if it can be broken down by microbes into harmless chemicals.

11. _____ is the wearing away of soil by wind and water.

12. _____ causes living things to die in lakes and ponds.

13. Vinegar and lemon juice are _____ that have pH values lower than 7.

14. A _____ is the remains of organisms that lived millions of years ago.

15. The _____ is caused by a carbon dioxide layer around Earth that traps heat.

16. _____ is a molecule made of three oxygen atoms.

17. _____ is found naturally in the ground and might cause cancer.

18. _____ is the reusing of resources.

STUDY GUIDE

Name _____ Date _____ Class _____

BIOLOGY IN USE

In your textbook, read about the tools of biology in Section 1:1.

3. Biologists use many tools when they study living things. You may use some of the same tools. Label the tools shown below. Fill in the blanks below each picture.

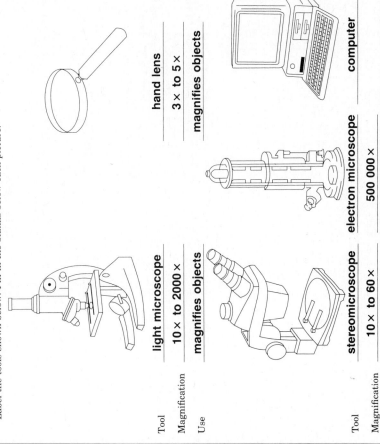

	hand lens
	3 × to 5 ×
	magnifies objects

Tool	light microscope
Magnification	10 × to 2000 ×
Use	magnifies objects

	computer
	to store, find, and
	process information

Tool	stereomicroscope	electron microscope
Magnification	10 × to 60 ×	500 000 ×
Use	viewing large	viewing things that
	objects through	cannot be seen
	which light	with the light
	cannot pass	microscope

STUDY GUIDE

Name _____ Date _____ Class _____

BIOLOGY IN USE

In your textbook, read about people who use biology in Section 1:1. Then, answer the questions below.

1. Many people use biology every day. What do the people shown below need to know about biology?

A florist needs to know how to care for plants.

A coach needs to know about bones and muscles.

A pharmacist needs to know how medicines affect the body.

A farmer needs to know how to raise plants and animals.

A veterinarian needs to know how to keep animals healthy.

A lifeguard needs to know about lungs and breathing.

2. Many people use biology in their hobbies. The column on the right lists ways biology can be used in hobbies. In front of the hobbies on the left, write the letter or letters of the way people use biology in each hobby.

a, c	1. growing houseplants	a. know about different kinds of plants
d	2. jogging	b. know about the habits of birds
b, e	3. bird watching	c. know how to make plants grow
d	4. swimming	d. know about bones and muscles
a, e	5. identifying wild flowers	e. know about classifying things

193

CHAPTER 1

Name _____ Date _____ Class _____

MEASUREMENTS USED IN BIOLOGY

In your textbook, read about measurements used in biology in Section 1.2.

1. Examine the recipe below and answer the questions. Circle all the measurements on the recipe card.

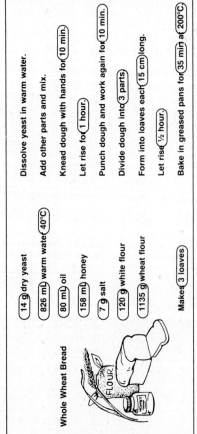

Whole Wheat Bread

14 g dry yeast

826 mL warm water 40°C

80 mL oil

158 mL honey

7 g salt

120 g white flour

1135 g wheat flour

Makes 3 loaves

Dissolve yeast in warm water.

Add other parts and mix.

Knead dough with hands for 10 min.

Let rise for 1 hour.

Punch dough and work again for 10 min.

Divide dough into 3 parts.

Form into loaves each 15 cm long.

Let rise ½ hour.

Bake in greased pans for 35 min at 200°C.

a. How many milliliters of liquid parts were added together in the recipe? ____ **1064 mL**

b. How many grams of dry parts were added together in the recipe? ____ **1276 g**

c. Complete the following table using the recipe.

Measurement		What is being measured	
Number	Unit	In general	In this recipe
14	g	mass	yeast
826	**mL**	volume	**warm water**
80	**mL**	**volume**	oil
1135	**g**	**mass**	wheat flour
40	°C	temperature	water temperature
200	**°C**	**temperature**	**baking temperature**
35	**min**	**time**	baking time

CHAPTER 1

Name _____ Date _____ Class _____

MEASUREMENTS USED IN BIOLOGY

In your textbook, read about measuring volume in Section 1.2.

2. Look at the graduated cylinder on the right. Note the lines and numbers printed on its sides. The graduated cylinder is filled to the 45 mL mark. Read the level of the liquid in each of the graduated cylinders below. Write the correct volume on the line below each graduated cylinder.

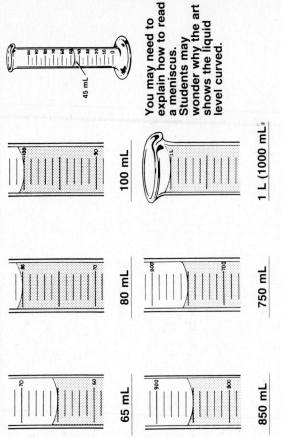

45 mL

You may need to explain how to read a meniscus. Students may wonder why the art shows the liquid level curved.

65 mL   80 mL   100 mL

850 mL   750 mL   1 L (1000 mL)

In your textbook, read about measuring temperature in Section 1.2.

3. In each space, write one of the following phrases that best matches the temperature shown. Use these phrases—water for bath, water freezes, water boils, a cool day, and human with fever.

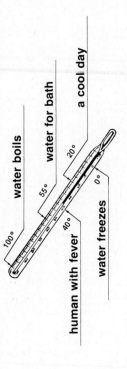

water boils   100°

water for bath   55°

a cool day   20°

human with fever   40°

water freezes   0°

SCIENTIFIC METHOD

In your textbook, read about scientific method in Section 1.3. Then, complete the exercises below.

Long ago, many people believed that living things could come from nonliving things. They thought that worms came from wood and that maggots came from decaying meat. This idea was called spontaneous generation. In 1668, an Italian biologist, Francesco Redi, did experiments to prove that maggots did not come from meat. One of his experiments is shown below.

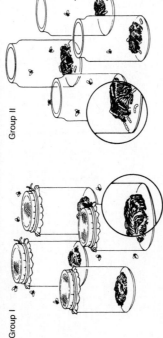

Group I

Group II

Redi placed pieces of meat in several jars. He divided the jars into two groups. He covered the first group of jars with fine cloth. He left the second group of jars uncovered. Redi observed the jars for several days. He saw flies on the cloth of the covered jars, and he saw flies laying eggs on the meat in the uncovered jars. Maggots appeared only on the meat in the group of jars left uncovered.

1. Scientists use a series of organized steps called scientific method to solve problems. List the steps that are often used. **recognizing a problem, researching a problem, forming a hypothesis, testing the hypothesis, drawing conclusions**

2. What was the problem in Redi's experiment? **Do maggots come from decaying meat?**

3. What do you think his hypothesis was? **If maggots come from decaying meat, maggots will appear on the meat in covered and uncovered jars.**

4. How did he test his hypothesis? **He experimented with meat in covered and uncovered jars.**

5. What was the variable in his experiment? **the group of covered jars**

6. What was the control in his experiment? **the group of uncovered jars**

7. What do you think Redi's conclusion was? **Maggots do not come from decaying meat.**

VOCABULARY

Review the new words in Chapter 1 of your textbook. Then, complete this puzzle.

```
 B
 I
H Y P O T H E S I S
 L        C
K I L O G R A M   I
 G        E
 Y        N
          S T E R E O M I C R O S C O P E
         C   I
         M   F    T E C H N O L O G Y
         E   I         V
         T E C H N O L O G Y
               X   P L  O   I
          V A R I A B L E  T H E O R Y
               X   P  L  M  I   G
                R  E  G   H
                I  N  M  T
          C E L S I U S
           D A T A
```

ACROSS

9. a statement that can be tested
10. SI unit of mass—1000 grams
11. a microscope that has an eyepiece lens and an objective lens for each eye
12. use of scientific discoveries to solve every-day problems
13. something that causes changes in an experiment
14. a hypothesis that has been tested over and over again
15. temperature scale used by scientists
16. recorded facts or measurements from an experiment

DOWN

1. study of living and once-living things
2. International System of Units (abbreviation)
3. method used to solve a problem
4. SI unit of length
5. the standard for comparing results in an experiment
6. the amount of space a substance occupies
7. to test a hypothesis
8. microscope used in class

195

LIVING THINGS AND THEIR PARTS

In your textbook, read about the features of living things in Section 2:1.

1. Underline the feature of life that you think each of the following pictures shows best.

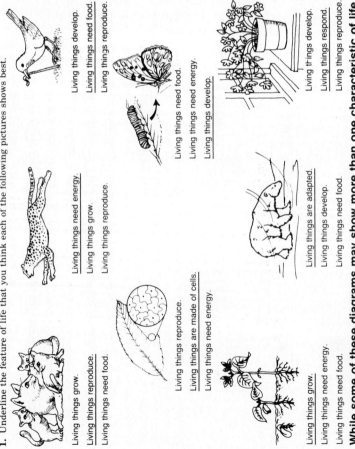

Living things grow.
Living things reproduce.
Living things need food.

Living things need energy.
Living things grow.
Living things reproduce.

Living things reproduce.
Living things are made of cells.
Living things need energy.

Living things need food.
Living things need energy.
Living things develop.

Living things develop.
Living things need food.
Living things reproduce.

Living things grow.
Living things need energy.
Living things need food.

Living things are adapted.
Living things develop.
Living things need food.

Living things develop.
Living things respond.
Living things reproduce.

While some of these diagrams may show more than one characteristic of life, each shows one characteristic best.

2. Explain how:

a. developing is different from growing. **Developing is changing in shape or form. Growing is increasing in size.**

b. living things get energy from food. **Food is broken down and energy is released in the process of cell respiration.**

7

LIVING THINGS AND THEIR PARTS

In your textbook, read about the chemistry of life in Section 2:1.

1. Fill in the boxes below with the correct words. What living things are made of:

matter
↓ is made of

atoms — make up → **elements** — 2 or more join to form a → **compound** — smallest part is a → **molecule** — represents a → **formula**

atoms are represented in writing by **symbols** — make up a chemical → **formula**

elements — examples are → **oxygen** and **hydrogen** — form → **water** — is represented in writing as → **H₂O**

compound — example is → **water**

molecule — example is → **H₂O**

In your textbook, read about the cell theory in Section 2:1.

2. What contribution did each of the following people make to the cell theory?

a. Robert Hooke **saw cell walls in a piece of cork.**

b. Robert Brown **discovered the nucleus.**

c. Schleiden and Schwann **hypothesized that all plants and animals were made of cells.**

3. The major ideas of the cell theory are:

a. **All living things are made of one or more cells.**

b. **Cells are the basic units of structure and function in living things.**

c. **All cells come from other cells.**

8

CELL PARTS AND THEIR JOBS

In your textbook, read about cell parts and their jobs in Section 2:2.

1. Label the parts of these two cells in the spaces provided.

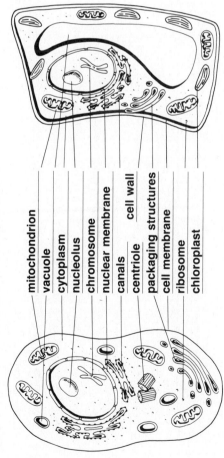

Cell A

Cell B

mitochondrion
vacuole
cytoplasm
nucleolus
chromosome
nuclear membrane
canals   cell wall
centriole
packaging structures
cell membrane
ribosome
chloroplast

2. Read the descriptions of cell parts below and write in the name of the cell part. Use the color indicated to shade the pictures above.

a. Use red for the part that gives the cell shape and holds the cytoplasm. **cell membrane**

b. Use green for parts that make food. **chloroplasts**

c. Use brown for the thick outer covering that protects and supports the cell. **cell wall**

d. Use blue for the part that stores substances. **vacuole**

e. Use black for parts that release energy from food. **mitochondria**

f. Use purple for parts that carry hereditary information. **chromosomes**

g. Use pink for the cell part that helps with cell reproduction. **centriole**

h. Use orange for the parts that package and store chemicals. **packaging structures**

3. List two cell parts found only in a plant cell. **chloroplasts, cell wall**

4. Where in a cell do most chemical reactions take place? **in the cytoplasm**

SPECIAL CELL PROCESSES

In your textbook, read about diffusion and osmosis in Section 2:3.

1. The first picture below, labeled *Before*, shows a cell surrounded by oxygen molecules before diffusion takes place. Each of the small black dots represents an oxygen molecule. Which of the three pictures labeled *After* shows where these oxygen molecules would be found after diffusion takes place? Circle your answer. **Students are being asked to show *net* diffusion. Diffusion continues after equilibrium is reached, but net diffusion does not.**

Before	After	After	After

2. What is diffusion? **the movement of a substance from where there is a large amount of it to where there is a small amount of it**

3. How do molecules get through the cell membrane? **The membrane has pores, or small openings, through which the molecules can pass.**

4. What is osmosis? **Osmosis is the movement of water across the cell membrane.**

5. Which way would the water molecules move in the following situations?

a. cucumber slice is placed in salt water   **out of the cucumber**

b. salt is poured on a snail   **out of the snail**

c. vegetables are sprinkled with water   **into the vegetables**

d. potato slice is placed in pure water   **into the potato**

6. Circle the letter in front of the sentence that best explains the process of osmosis.

(a.) Osmosis is the movement of water into or out of a cell from where it is in large amounts to where it is in small amounts.

b. Osmosis is the movement of water into or out of a cell from where it is in small amounts to where it is in large amounts.

c. Osmosis is the movement of salt into or out of a cell from where it is in large amounts to where it is in small amounts.

SPECIAL CELL PROCESSES

In your textbook, read about the organization of cells, tissues, and organs in Section 2·3.

7. Place a check mark in the correct column for each phrase or diagram on the left.

	Tissue	Organ	Organ system
Groups of cells all doing the same job	✓		
Stomach, mouth, and intestines all working together			✓
Made up of a group of tissues		✓	
[diagram of cells]	✓		
Small intestine		✓	
[diagram of mouse]		✓	
Leaf		✓	
Muscle	✓		
Bark	✓		
Outer surface of a leaf	✓		

8. How is an organ different from a tissue? **A tissue is made up of only one kind of cell. An organ is made up of many different kinds of tissues that work together to perform a job. Because the different tissues in an organ are each made up of a different kind of cell, an organ is made up of different kinds of cells.**

9. What is an organism? **An organism is a living thing.**

10. Compare a one-celled organism with a many-celled organism. **In a one-celled organism, a single cell carries out all the activities of life. In a many-celled organism, cells are organized into groups and the cells of each group do special jobs.**

198

VOCABULARY

Review the new words in Chapter 2 of your textbook. Then complete the puzzle. The letters in the dark boxes will summarize what you are studying in Chapter 2.

1. CYTOPLASM
2. CHLOROPLAST
3. REPRODUCE
4. MITOCHONDRIA
5. TISSUE
6. NUCLEAR MEMBRANE
7. CELLULAR RESPIRATION
8. PRODUCER
9. DIFFUSION
10. CELL MEMBRANE
11. ORGAN SYSTEM
12. CELL
13. OSMOSIS
14. VACUOLE
15. CENTRIOLE
16. DEVELOPMENT
17. ORGANISM
18. CELL WALL
19. ADAPTATION
20. CHROMOSOME
21. RIBOSOME
22. NUCLEUS
23. ORGAN
24. CONSUMER
25. NUCLEOLUS

1. clear jellylike material in cells
2. cell part that contains chlorophyll
3. form offspring similar to parents
4. cell parts that release energy
5. group of similar cells carrying out a job
6. structure that surrounds the nucleus
7. process by which food is broken down and energy is released
8. living thing that makes its own food
9. movement of a substance from where there is a large amount to where there is a small amount of it
10. controls what moves into cells
11. group of organs working together
12. basic unit of all living things
13. movement of water across a membrane
14. stores water, food, and minerals
15. part near the nucleus that helps with reproduction
16. all the changes that occur as a living thing grows
17. living thing
18. thick outer covering of a plant cell
19. trait that helps a living thing survive
20. cell part with information that determines a living thing's traits
21. cell part where protein is made
22. controls the activities of the cell
23. group of tissues that work together
24. living thing that eats other living things
25. smaller body inside the nucleus that helps make ribosomes

11

12

Name _____ Date _____ Class _____

WHY THINGS ARE GROUPED

In your textbook, read about why things are grouped in Section 3:1.

1. Separate the items pictured into two groups. Put the letters of the items in the proper section of the chart below. **You may need to explain to your students what some of these articles are and how they are used.**

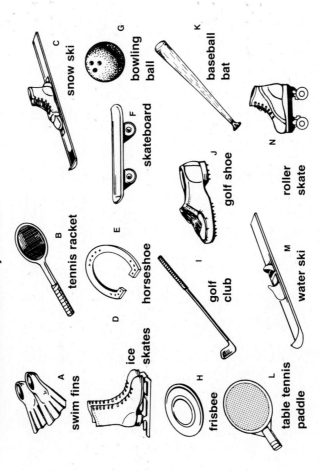

A swim fins
B tennis racket
C snow ski
D ice skates
E horseshoe
F skateboard
G bowling ball
H frisbee
I golf club
J golf shoe
K baseball bat
L water ski
M table tennis paddle
N roller skate

Items for feet	Items held in hand(s)
A C D F J M N	B E G H I K L

2. Regroup the items using the chart below.

Used only indoors	Used indoors or outdoors
G	A B D L N

Used only outdoors
C E F H I J M K

13

STUDY GUIDE

Name _____ Date _____ Class _____

WHY THINGS ARE GROUPED

3. Which of the two ways of grouping these items might be used by a sporting goods store? Either grouping might be used.

4. Why do different people classify the same things in different ways? **Different groupings show relationships better to different people.**

5. List two reasons why humans group things. **Humans group things to put things in order so they become easier to find and to show how things are alike.**

6. A certain student grouped the items in the pictures on page 13 as follows:

Group 1	Group 2
D N	A B C E F G H I J K L M
skates	not skates

a. What trait was used for Group 1?
b. What trait was used for Group 2?

7. Of the three ways to classify these items you have seen, which is the right way? the wrong way? **There is no right way. There is no wrong way.**

8. Group the items again using a different set of traits. Write the traits used on the lines. **Student answers will vary. A possible answer is given below.**

Trait wheels	Trait spikes	Trait no wheels or spikes
F N	J	A B C D E G H I K L M

9. Group the items again using a set of traits that has not been used. Write the traits used on the lines. **Student answers will vary. A possible answer is given below.**

Trait for water sports	Trait for snow/ice sports	Trait for other sports
A M	C D	B E F G H I J K L N

The point of the questions on this page is to make students see that there is no single way to classify things. As long as classification rules are consistently applied in the grouping, the classification is "correct."

14

199

STUDY GUIDE

Name _____ Date _____ Class _____

METHODS OF CLASSIFICATION

In your textbook, read about early and modern methods of classification in Section 3.2.

1. Study Figure 3-2 of Aristotle's classification in your textbook and look at the pictures of living things shown below. Then, answer the questions that follow.

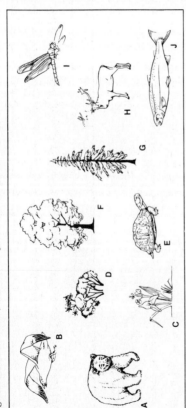

a. Why did Aristotle place E and J in the same group? **They both live in water.**

b. Why were B and I placed together? **They both fly in the air.**

c. Why were A and H placed in the same group? **They both live on land.**

d. What were Aristotle's two main groups? **plants and animals**

e. What characteristic did Aristotle use to divide animals into groups? **where they lived**

f. What characteristic did Aristotle use to divide plants into groups? **size and pattern of growth**

2. What were three important changes Linnaeus made in Aristotle's system of classification?
He classified plants and animals into more groups.
He based his system on specific traits.
He gave organisms names that described their traits.

3. Number these classification divisions in order from the smallest (1) to the largest (7).

1 species	**6** phylum	**3** family
7 kingdom	**4** order	**2** genus
	5 class	

STUDY GUIDE

Name _____ Date _____ Class _____

HOW SCIENTISTS CLASSIFY

In your textbook, read about how scientists classify today in Section 3.3. Then, examine the classification of the three animals in the chart below.

	Animal A	Animal B	Animal C
Kingdom	Animal	Animal	Animal
Phylum	Chordate	Chordate	Chordate
Class	Mammal	Aves	Aves
Order	Primates	Passeriformes	Passeriformes
Family	Pongidae	Fringilidae	Fringilidae
Genus	Pan	Spizella	Serinus
Species	troglodytes	passerina	canarius

1. Comparing Animals A and B, how many groups are the same? **2**

2. Comparing Animals A and C, how many groups are the same? **2**

3. Comparing Animals B and C, how many groups are the same? **5**

4. Which two animals (A and B, A and C, or B and C) are most alike in classification? **B and C**

5. Which two animals have more of the same traits? **B and C**

6. Which two animals have more of the same body parts? **B and C**

7. Which two animals are most closely related? **B and C**

8. What is the scientific name of Animal A? **Pan troglodytes**

9. What does the first word of the scientific name represent? **genus**

10. What does the second word of the scientific name represent? **species**

11. What are three reasons for using scientific names? **No mistake can be made about what living thing is being described. Scientific names of living things seldom change. Scientists throughout the world use the same language to name living things.**

Name _____ Date _____ Class _____

HOW SCIENTISTS CLASSIFY

In your textbook, read about the evidence used in classifying in Section 3:3.

1. The diagrams below compare the forelimbs of a human, a dog, a horse, a bird, a bat, and an organism that lived long ago. Use the numbers shown on the human arm to label similar parts on the forelimbs of the other animals. Then complete the statements that follow.

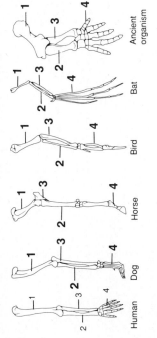

Human   Dog   Horse   Bird   Bat   Ancient organism

a. Each limb is similar in _____ **structure** _____.

b. This similarity is evidence of a _____ **common ancestor** _____.

In your textbook, read about the five-kingdom system of classification in Section 3:3.

2. The names of each of the five kingdoms are found in the column on the left below. List the traits of each group in the space provided on the right.

a. monerans   **are one-celled organisms, do not have a nucleus, lack most cell parts that other cells have**

b. protists   **are one-celled organisms with a nucleus and other cell parts**

c. fungi   **have many cells, each with a nucleus and a cell wall, do not have chlorophyll, cannot make their own food**

d. plants   **have many cells, have chlorophyll, can make their own food, do not move**

e. animals   **have many cells, cannot make their own food, can move**

17

Name _____ Date _____ Class _____

VOCABULARY

Review the new words used in Chapter 3 of your textbook. Then, complete the puzzle and definitions below.

1. Use these words to fill in the blanks of the puzzle.

class   scientific name   species
genus   traits   phylum
order   kingdom   family

Animal   K I N G D O M
Chordate   P H Y L U M
Mammal   C L A S S
Carnivore   O R D E R
Felidae   F A M I L Y
Felis   G E N U S
domesticus   S P E C I E S

Felis domesticus is the S C I E N T I F I C N A M E of the house cat. The name comes from the T R A I T S that the animal has.

2. Define each of the following words or phrases.

a. trait   **feature that a thing has**

b. order   **largest group within a class**

c. classify   **to group things together based on similarities**

d. family   **largest group within an order**

e. class   **largest group within a phylum**

f. species   **smallest group of living things**

g. phylum   **largest group within a kingdom**

h. genus   **largest group within a family**

3. A kingdom is the largest group of living things. List the five kingdoms into which scientists classify living things today. **moneran, protist, fungus, plant, animal**

18

STUDY GUIDE — CHAPTER 4

Name ______ Date ______ Class ______

VIRUSES

In your textbook, read about viruses in Section 4:1.

1. Use the words *chromosome-like part* and *protein coat* to label the bacterial virus shown below.

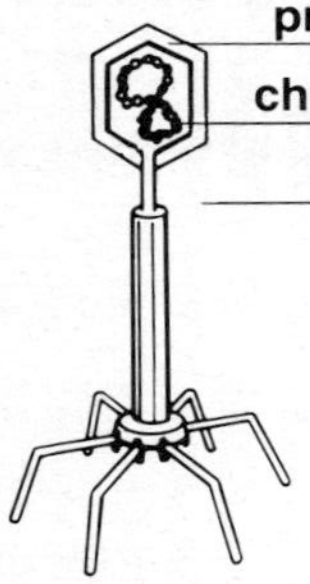

protein coat

chromosome-like part

2. List six traits of viruses.

a. Viruses are so small they can only be seen with an electron microscope.

b. Viruses have different shapes.

c. Viruses are made of a chromosome-like part surrounded by a protein coat.

d. Viruses are not cells and have no cell parts.

e. Viruses reproduce only in living cells.

f. Viruses act like parasites.

3. Study the incorrect statements about viruses below. Change the underlined word or words to make each sentence correct. Write the correct new word or words on the line to the right.

a. Viruses cause disease only in humans. — in plants, animals, and humans

b. Each kind of virus infects many hosts. — only certain

c. The rabies virus will infect only the digestive system of mammals. — nervous

d. Cold sores are caused by a virus that remains active. — hidden

e. Viruses are always larger than cells they infect. — smaller

f. Viruses reproduce outside of living cells. — inside

g. Viruses do not change the hereditary material in the host cell. — change

STUDY GUIDE — CHAPTER 4

Name ______ Date ______ Class ______

VIRUSES

4. The stages of a virus infecting a bacterial cell shown below are out of order. Label the diagrams 1 through 5 to show the correct order. Then, describe what is happening in each stage.

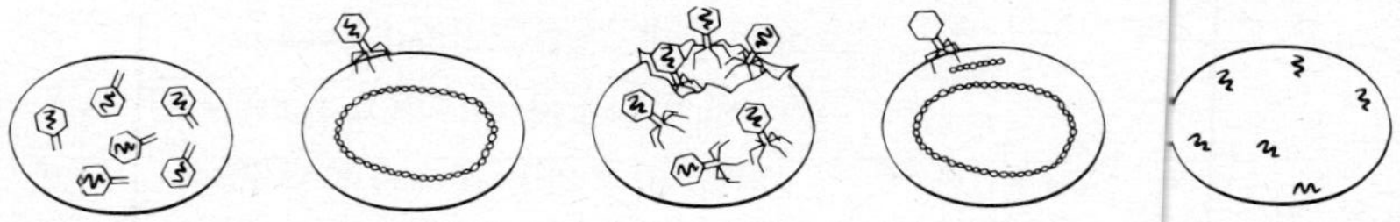

4 — 1 — 5 — 2 — 3

Stage 1 The virus attaches itself to the host cell.

Stage 2 The chromosome-like part enters the host cell.

Stage 3 The chromosome-like part takes over the cell.

Stage 4 The host cell produces more viruses.

Stage 5 The cell breaks open and new viruses are released.

5. The following diseases are caused by viruses: Newcastle disease, curly top, AIDS, distemper, dwarfism, herpes, mosaic disease, cowpox, measles, cold, bushy stunt, rabies, foot-and-mouth disease, chickenpox, dwarf mosaic. Fill in the chart below by placing the diseases under the proper headings.

Plant	Animal	Human
curly top	Newcastle disease	AIDS
dwarfism	distemper	herpes
mosaic disease	cowpox	measles
bushy stunt	rabies	cold
dwarf mosaic	foot and mouth disease	mumps

6. Humans and other animals can be protected against some viruses in several ways. List four methods of protection.

a. white blood cells b. antibodies

c. interferon d. vaccines

7. How are viruses spread in humans? Viruses are spread by insects, air, water, food, and other people.

MONERA KINGDOM

In your textbook, read about the traits of bacteria in Section 4:2.

1. In the space below, draw and label the three different groups of bacteria.

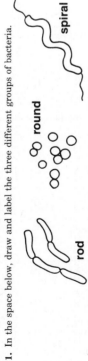

rod

round

spiral

2. Answer the following questions about bacteria in complete sentences.

a. Where are they found? **Bacteria are found almost everywhere, in air, soil, and food.**

b. What conditions do they need to survive? **They need moisture, a certain temperature, and food.**

c. How do they reproduce? **They reproduce by fission—the division of one organism into two organisms.**

d. How can some bacteria withstand extreme conditions? **They withstand extreme conditions by forming endospores.**

e. What do they use as food? **Some bacteria use other living things or dead things as food. Others can make their own food.**

In your textbook, read about bacteria and disease in Section 4:2.

3. What are Koch's postulates? **a set of steps for proving that a disease is caused by a certain microscopic organism**

4. What are communicable diseases? **diseases that can be passed from one organism to another**

5. How are communicable diseases spread? **by air, by touching anything an infected organism has touched, by drinking water that contains bacteria, by sexual contact, by insects that carry disease organisms**

6. What are two sexually transmitted diseases? **syphilis and gonorrhea**

MONERA KINGDOM

In your textbook, read about helpful bacteria in Section 4:2.

7. In the blank below each drawing, tell how bacteria are helpful.

  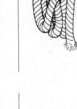 

break down grass in cow's stomach | **give taste and texture** | **give flavor**

recycle materials in dead matter | **produce antibiotics** | **break down plant fibers**

8. How are bacteria used in biotechnology? **to produce natural gas, detergents, and human insulin**

In your textbook, read in Section 4:2 about controlling bacteria.

9. Tell how each of the following controls bacteria.

a. canning **Food is heated to a high temperature to destroy bacteria. Containers are sealed so other bacteria cannot enter.**

b. pasteurization **Heating kills harmful bacteria in milk.**

c. cooling **Bacterial growth is slowed.**

d. freezing **Bacterial growth is slowed.**

e. dehydration **Water is removed from food, and bacteria cannot live.**

f. antiseptics **Bacteria on living things are killed.**

g. disinfectants **Bacteria are destroyed on objects that are not living.**

h. vaccines **Bacterial infections are prevented from starting.**

i. antibiotics **Bacteria are killed.**

MONERA KINGDOM

In your textbook, read about bacteria and blue-green bacteria in Section 4:2.
Below are pictures of monerans drawn by students.

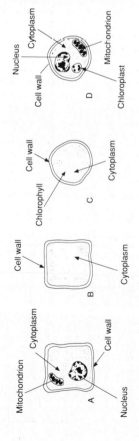

10. a. Which drawing of the bacterial cell is correct, A or B? __A bacterial cell does not have a__
    b. List two things wrong with the other drawing. __nucleus. A bacterial cell does not have mitochondria.__

11. a. Which drawing of the blue-green bacteria is correct, C or D? __C Blue-green bacteria do not have__
    b. List two things wrong with the other drawing. __nuclei. Blue-green bacteria do not have mitochondria or chloroplasts.__

12. List two ways bacteria and blue-green bacteria differ. __Blue-green bacteria contain__
    __colored pigments; bacteria do not. Blue-green bacteria have chlorophyll__
    __and can make their own food; bacteria cannot.__

13. How are bacteria and blue-green bacteria alike? __They have a similar cell structure.__
    __They do not have nuclei or most other cell parts.__

14. How are blue-green bacteria helpful? __They are food for animals that live in the__
    __water. They produce oxygen. They recycle nitrogen, which is used by__
    __plants.__

15. How are blue-green bacteria harmful? __They grow rapidly in ponds and kill other__
    __living things. They make water unfit for drinking and swimming.__

VOCABULARY

Review the new words used in Chapter 4 of your textbook. Then, complete the puzzle below.
Write the correct term in the space provided next to the definitions. Find the same word in the letter
grid and circle it. Words may be written on horizontal, vertical, or diagonal lines.

host	
virus	
interferon	
fission	
saprophyte	
communicable	
disease	
endospore	
pasteurization	
antibiotic	
biotechnology	
flagellum	
vaccine	

1. organism that provides food for a parasite
2. chromosome-like part surrounded by protein coat
3. chemical that interferes with how viruses reproduce
4. one organism divides into two organisms
5. organism that uses dead material for food
6. disease passed from one organism to another
7. protective structure with a thick wall that some bacteria form
8. process of heating milk to kill bacteria
9. drug that kills or slows growth of bacteria
10. use of living things to solve practical problems
11. whiplike thread used for movement
12. substance made from weakened viruses or bacteria

```
B C D L E R T L A O P O R O A L S I S P   N Y C
G A N T I B M W S T A M E N D O S P O R E R Z N
V X N Z O W S L V K N S T R X C Q Y L E B V A W
P D T T O S M P A V I R U S L E O S C W A W N O
A A O L I K B W T A D R L T M R S T O Q P C N J
R N N S S P N S U C C S R O I N A P L P R A I R
A N T I B I O T I C V N T I M A P M O L D P N K
O X D T Q T G A B I N T E R F E R O N S P T G L
I O F Z C O M Z O N H D R L T Y M V T Y H O S M
T S F L Y R U S T E O T Y O O P A H Y N Y A T V
E V L L E C P Q X C M X Z T A L S T A R T R T S
N P A S T E U R I Z A T I O N S C A P S E S E T
S C G N V O L F E T P R S D M L P A V S R E C R
W T E N H S N A B C W B I O T E C H N O L O G Y
X B L U J O O G R E E T A C R T Y L C O C F M B P
Q S L R S Y C N S N R W F I S S I O N C E S R Q
J M U O T S I L S T M Z W X V T M R P L T R O S
C O M M U N I C A B L E D I S E A S E L V C J D
```

Left page

Name _____ Date _____ Class _____

PROTIST KINGDOM

In your textbook, read about animal-like protists in Section 5:1.

1. Label the following parts of an amoeba: nucleus, cytoplasm, food vacuole, cell membrane, false foot.

cell membrane

nucleus

food vacuole

cytoplasm

false foot

2. Label the following parts of a paramecium: large nucleus, small nucleus, cytoplasm, vacuole, cell membrane, cilia, mouth. Then, answer the question.

vacuole

cilia

cytoplasm

mouth

cell membrane

large nucleus

small nucleus

Explain how paramecia feed. **Food is swept into a mouthlike opening of the body by cilia. A food vacuole forms around the food and digests it.**

In your textbook, read about plantlike protists in Section 5:1.

3. Write the phrase *like plants* or *like animals* after each of the following protist traits.

a. can move about **like animals**

b. have chlorophyll **like plants**

c. have no cell wall **like animals**

d. are producers **like plants**

e. can make their own food **like plants**

f. give off oxygen **like plants**

25

Right page

Name _____ Date _____ Class _____

PROTIST KINGDOM

4. Write the following phrases under the correct headings in the table below.

have a flagellum   cell covering made of two parts   red or brown color
green color   form thick layers when they die   used in toothpaste
cause red tide   boat, rod, disk, or triangle shape
have two flagella   found mostly in fresh water

Euglena	Diatoms	Dinoflagellates
have a flagellum	cell covering made of two parts	have two flagella
green color	form thick layers when they die	cause red tide
found mostly in fresh water	boat, rod, disk, or triangle shape	red or brown color
	used in toothpaste	

In your textbook, read about funguslike protists in Section 5:1.

5. How do slime molds differ from plantlike protists? **Slime molds are consumers.**

6. At what stage(s) in their life cycle are slime molds like animal-like protists? **at the first stage, when they look like a slimy amoeba, and at the third stage when they form amoebalike cells with flagella**

7. At what stage(s) in their life cycle are they like fungi? **at the second stage, when they stop growing and moving and begin to produce spores**

FUNGUS KINGDOM

In your textbook, read about fungi in Section 5:2.

1. Complete the following sentences about fungi.

a. Fungi cannot make their own **food**

b. Hyphae are usually divided by **cross walls**

c. The bodies of most fungi are made up of a network of threadlike **hyphae**

d. Fungi reproduce by forming **spores**

e. Fungi can also reproduce from pieces of **hyphae**

26

FUNGUS KINGDOM

2. Review the following words from Chapter 4. Then, define them in the spaces below.

   a. saprophyte organism that uses dead material for food

   b. parasite organism that lives in or on another living thing

3. Next to each picture, on the first line write the word *parasite* or *saprophyte*, to describe the kind of fungus shown. On the lower line, explain how you know that the fungus is a saprophyte or a parasite.

saprophyte

feeds off dead material

saprophyte

feeds off dead material

parasite

feeds off living things

parasite

feeds off living things

4. Put a check mark in the correct place on the table that indicates which traits are found in the different kinds of fungi.

Trait	Sporangium fungi	Club fungi	Sac fungi
reproduce by spores	✓	✓	✓
spores made in a saclike part			✓
cause Dutch elm disease			✓
spores made in a sporangium	✓		
mushrooms belong here		✓	
yeast belongs here			✓
spores made in club-shaped part		✓	

FUNGUS KINGDOM

5. Label the parts and identify the jobs of this bread mold by putting the correct letters in the circles provided.

   Parts
   A = hyphae
   B = sporangium
   C = spores

   Jobs
   D = develops into new molds
   E = produces spores
   F = takes in food and water

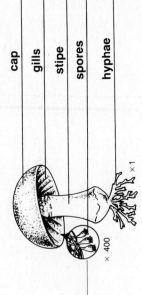

6. Label the parts of a mushroom shown below. Use the following table as a guide.

Part	Appearance
spores	at ends of club-shaped part, can be seen only with microscope
hyphae	threadlike, form networks underground
stipe	stemlike part
cap	top of mushroom, like an umbrella
gills	underside of cap, like ribs of umbrella
club-shaped part	found on underside of gills, very small in size

cap

gills

stipe

spores

hyphae

club-shaped part

×400

×1

206

STUDY GUIDE

Name _____ Date _____ Class _____

CHAPTER 5

FUNGUS KINGDOM

7. Refer to Table 5-3 on page 107 of your textbook, and fill in the following blanks. **Student answers may vary, but**

  a. List three ways in which fungi can be helpful. **Student answers may vary, but may indicate that fungi are used as food, in making food, to make medicine, or to enrich the soil.**

  b. List ways fungi can be harmful to things you own. **Fungi can destroy plants, leather, fabric, and plastic.**

  c. List ways fungi can be harmful to people. **They can cause food to spoil and can cause diseases in humans.**

In your textbook, read about lichens in Section 5.2.

8. What is mutualism? **Mutualism is a living arrangement in which the things living together benefit.**

9. What is a lichen? **A lichen is a fungus and an organism with chlorophyll that live together.**

  a. List two examples of lichens. **British soldier, reindeer moss**

  b. What is the role of the organism with chlorophyll? **It provides food for the fungus.**

  c. What is the role of the fungus? **It provides support and holds water and minerals for the other organism.**

10. Where do lichens live? **on bare rocks, on trees, and on Arctic ice**

  a. How do they help form soil? **Lichens release acids that break down rock. The broken down rock and the dead lichens form soil.**

  b. How do lichens help some animals? **Lichens provide food for some animals.**

29

STUDY GUIDE

Name _____ Date _____ Class _____

CHAPTER 5

VOCABULARY

Below is a list of pronunciations of words related to protists and fungi. Find the word in Chapter 5 and write it on the first blank to the right of the pronunciation. In the remaining space, write a definition of the word.

1. HI fee _____ **hyphae** threadlike structures

2. AL jee _____ **algae** Algae are plantlike protists.

3. SPOR _____ **spore** A spore is a special cell that develops into a new organism.

4. SIHL ee uh _____ **cilia** Cilia are short, hairlike parts.

5. spuh RAN jee uh _____ **sporangia** tips of special hyphae that produce spores.

6. spor uh ZOH uhnz _____ **sporozoans** protozoans that reproduce by forming spores.

7. slime mohld _____ **slime mold** A slime mold is a fungus-like protist that is a consumer.

8. LI kun _____ **lichen** A lichen is a fungus and an organism with chlorophyll that live together.

9. proht uh ZOH uhnz _____ **protozoans** one celled animal-like organisms with a nucleus

10. BUHD ing _____ **budding** reproduction in which a small part of the parent grows into a new organism

11. MYOOCH uh wuh LIZ uhm _____ **mutualism** living arrangement in which both living things benefit

12. MUHL tee SEL yuh luhr _____ **multicellular** an organism that has many different cells that do special jobs.

30

207

PLANT CLASSIFICATION

In your textbook, read about plant features in Section 6:1.

1. Shade green those parts of the living things shown below that are usually green.
2. Draw an X through each living thing that does not contain chlorophyll.
3. Circle each living thing that can make its own food.

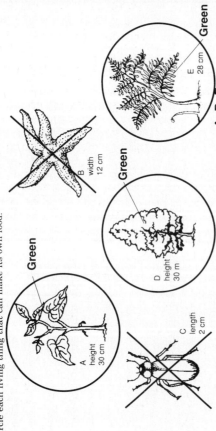

Green — A height 30 cm

Green — D height 30 m

B width 12 cm

C length 2 cm

Green — E 28 cm

4. Which of the diagrams (A, B, C, D, or E) are plants? __A, D, E__

5. List four features of plants that are different from the features of animals.
a. __Plants have green parts called chloroplasts that contain chlorophyll.__
b. __Plants carry on photosynthesis.__
c. __Plants can't move about.__
d. __Plants have stiff cell walls.__

6. What is the main difference between plants and animals? __Plants can make their own food, animals can't.__

7. What is photosynthesis? __Photosynthesis is a process in which plants use energy from the sun, carbon dioxide, and water to make food.__

8. Where does photosynthesis occur in plants? __Photosynthesis occurs in the chloroplasts.__

PLANT CLASSIFICATION

9. Fill in the blanks below with the following words or phrases.

light energy   chloroplasts   photosynthesis
green color   chlorophyll   plants

plants —— have cell parts called —→ **chloroplasts**
that contain a chemical called →
chlorophyll
that gives plants their →
green color
—— and traps —— **light energy**
for use in the process of →
photosynthesis
a process which separates animals from ←

10. What are vascular plants? __Vascular plants are plants that have tubelike cells in their roots, stems, and leaves to carry food and water.__

11. What are nonvascular plants? __Nonvascular plants are plants that don't have tubelike cells in their roots, stems, or leaves.__

12. Why must nonvascular plants grow close to the ground? __They depend on osmosis to move water to all parts of the plant.__

13. Define the following words.
a. root __plant structure that anchors plants in the ground and takes in water and minerals from the soil__
b. stem __plant structure that carries water to all parts of the plant and holds leaves up to the sunlight__
c. leaf __plant structure that makes food__

Name _____ Date _____ Class _____

NONVASCULAR PLANTS

In your textbook, read about mosses and liverworts in Section 6:2. Then answer the following questions.

1. How are mosses and liverworts similar? **They don't have roots, are only a few centimeters tall, and grow in wet or damp places.**

2. How can mosses be classified? **by the shape of their leaves**

3. Describe the leaves and stems of liverworts. **Most have no leaves or stems. Some have two or three flattened rows of leaves on a short, creeping stem.**

4. List three ways that mosses and liverworts are helpful. **They provide food for some animals. They also help hold soil in place, or break down rocks helping to form soil. Sphagnum moss helps increase the amount of water soil can hold. Peat, formed by decayed sphagnum, can be burned as fuel.**

5. Why do mosses and liverworts need water to survive? **The sperm must swim to the eggs to fertilize them. Water is a raw material of photosynthesis.**

6. Where are moss spores produced? **They form in the tip of a stalk that grows from the fertilized egg.**

VASCULAR PLANTS

In your textbook, read about ferns in Section 6:3.

1. Circle the correct word in each sentence.

a. Ferns are vascular plants that reproduce by seeds /(spores)

b. Ferns have special tubelike cells called (xylem)/ phloem that carry water and dissolved minerals from the roots to the leaves.

c. The leaves of a fern grow out of a stem that lies (underground)/ above ground

d. The spore cases of ferns are found on the top /(bottom) side of the leaves.

e. If a spore lands in a (moist) dry place, it grows into a small, heart-shaped plant.

f. The heart-shaped plant produces spores /(sperm and eggs)

g. Ferns (do)/ don't have a vascular system.

Name _____ Date _____ Class _____

VASCULAR PLANTS

In your textbook, read about conifers in Section 6:3.

2. In the blanks provided, place a check mark next to the statements that are true for conifers.

a. ✓ Conifers produce seeds.

b. ✓ Their leaves are green all year.

c. ✓ Many have small, needle shaped leaves.

d. ___ Conifers are nonvascular plants.

e. ✓ They have woody stems.

f. ___ They have thin, broad leaves.

g. ___ Conifers are the smallest group of cone-bearing plants.

h. ✓ They are often called evergreens.

3. Using Figure 6-10 in your textbook as a guide, write in the blank the part of a conifer described below.

a. produces pollen — **male cone**

b. grains in which sperm form — **pollen**

c. produces eggs — **female cone**

d. contains a young plant — **seed**

e. protects developing embryos — **female cone**

4. How does pollen reach the female cone? **by the wind**

5. How do seeds escape from within a cone? **When seeds are ripe, cones become dry, they open, and seeds fall to the ground.**

6. In what ways are conifers important to humans? **They supply three-fourths of the world's lumber; they are used to make paper, cardboard, turpentine, and fuel.**

VASCULAR PLANTS

7. Decide which of the following sentences are true and which are false. Write the word *true* in the blank next to the sentences that are true. For sentences that are false, replace the underlined word with a word that would make the sentence true. Write that word in the blank.

true   a. Seeds of flowering plants are formed inside a <u>flower</u>.

vascular   b. Flowering plants are <u>nonvascular</u>.

true   c. The <u>flower</u> is involved in reproduction.

male   d. Sperm cells are formed within <u>female</u> flower parts.

embryo/seed   e. In a flowering plant, a fertilized egg forms a <u>flower</u>.

Female   f. <u>Male</u> flower parts develop into an embryo.

largest   g. Flowering plants make up the <u>smallest</u> group of all types of plants.

true   h. Seeds contain a supply of food for the developing <u>embryo</u>.

8. Complete the following table. Put a check mark in the column of each kind of plant that has the trait listed.

Trait	Moss and liverwort	Fern	Conifer	Flowering plant
Nonvascular	✓			
Vascular		✓	✓	✓
Has no tubelike cells	✓			
Has tubelike cells		✓	✓	✓
Has roots, stems, leaves		✓	✓	✓
Doesn't have roots	✓			
Spores	✓	✓		
Seeds			✓	✓
Cones			✓	
Flowers				✓
Most common of plants				✓
Gives off oxygen	✓	✓	✓	✓

VOCABULARY

Review the new words used in Chapter 6 of your textbook. Then, complete the exercise.
Fill in the blank in each of the sentences below with the correct word from the following list.

chlorophyll	flowers	sexual reproduction	nonvascular plant
xylem	photosynthesis	egg	fertilization
embryo	conifer	phloem	moss
sperm	seed	pollen	flowering plant
vascular plants	fern		

1. The chemical that gives plants their green color is **chlorophyll**.

2. **Nonvascular** plants don't have tubelike cells in their stems and leaves.

3. A small nonvascular plant that has both stems and leaves but no roots is a **moss**.

4. An **egg** is a female reproductive cell.

5. **Vascular plants** have tubelike cells in their roots, stems, and leaves.

6. A **conifer** produces seeds in cones.

7. A male reproductive cell is a **sperm**.

8. A **flowering plant** produces seeds inside a flower.

9. A **fern** is a vascular plant that reproduces with spores.

10. **Phloem** cells carry food from the leaves to all parts of the plant.

11. **Pollen** are the tiny grains of seed plants in which sperm develop.

12. **Flowers** are the reproductive parts of flowering plants.

13. A **seed** contains a new, young plant and stored food.

14. The young plant in a seed is the **embryo**.

15. **Xylem** cells carry water from the roots to the leaves.

16. In **sexual reproduction**, a new organism forms from the union of two reproductive cells.

17. The joining of the egg and the sperm is **fertilization**.

18. **Photosynthesis** is the process in which plants use water, carbon dioxide, and energy from the sun to make food.

Name _____ Date _____ Class _____

SPONGES AND STINGING-CELL ANIMALS

In your textbook, read about sponges and stinging-cell animals in Section 7:2.

1. How do sponges get their food? **Water flowing through the sponges' pores brings small living things into their bodies. There, the living things are trapped by food-getting cells.**

2. How do the different types of cells help a sponge function? **Some cells move water and trap food, some cover and protect the sponge's body, and others produce chemicals that make the skeleton.**

3. Complete the following sentences about stinging-cell animals.

   a. The body of these animals is a hollow, **sock-shaped** structure.

   b. Most of these animals live in **the ocean** .

   c. Their armlike parts are called **tentacles** .

   d. Each armlike part has many **stinging cells** .

   e. The body has an opening called a **mouth** .

   f. The bodies of these animals have **two** cell layers.

   g. These animals use **muscles and nerves** to move their armlike parts.

4. Explain how each of the following parts helps the animal function.

   a. disc **helps fasten the animals to ocean bottom or to rocks**

   b. stinging cells and triggers **shoot out darts from the stinging cells and stun passing animals with poison**

   c. tentacles **push newly-caught meal through mouth and into body cavity**

5. Circle the letter of the animal shown below that is not a stinging-cell animal.

A   B   C   D

6. What traits helped you choose your answer for question 5? **the lack of tentacles and the presence of pores**

Name _____ Date _____ Class _____

ANIMAL CLASSIFICATION

In your textbook, read about how animals are classified in Section 7:1.

1. What is the difference between vertebrates and invertebrates? **Vertebrates have a backbone, invertebrates do not.**

2. What is symmetry? **Symmetry is the balanced arrangement of body parts around a center point or along a center line.**

3. What is the difference between radial and bilateral symmetry? **In radial symmetry, the body parts are arranged in a circle around a center point. In bilateral symmetry, the body can be divided lengthwise into two equal sides, a right side and a left side.**

4. List four traits of animals.

   a. **Animals can't make their own food.**

   b. **Most animals can move from place to place.**

   c. **Animals have many cells.**

   d. **Most animals have symmetry.**

5. The animal kingdom is one of five kingdoms into which scientists group living things. Scientists group animals into nine major groups.

   a. What are these groups called? **phyla**

   b. Which group contains the largest number of different kinds of animals? **animals with jointed legs**

   c. Which group contains the smallest number of different kinds of animals? **sponges and spiny-skin animals**

   d. Which group contains the simplest animals? **sponges**

   e. Which group contains the most complex animals? **chordates**

6. What main group of animals make up the chordate phylum? **vertebrates**

7. What main groups of animals makes up the rest of the animal kingdom? **invertebrates**

Name _____ Date _____ Class _____

CHAPTER **7**

WORMS

In your textbook read about roundworms in Section 7:3.

5. On the blanks provided, label the parts of this roundworm.

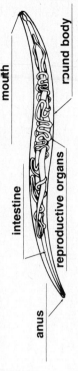

mouth

intestine

reproductive organs

round body

anus

In your textbook, read about segmented worms in Section 7:3.

6. Name a segmented worm that is a parasite. _____ **leech**

7. Name a segmented worm that is not a parasite. _____ **earthworm**

8. On the blanks below, label the parts of this earthworm and briefly describe the job each part does.

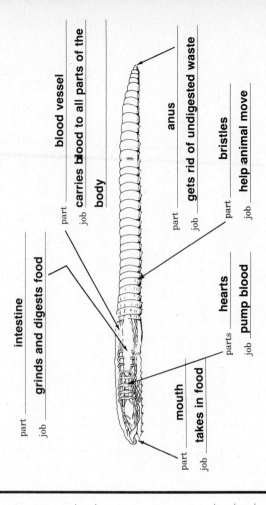

part _____ **blood vessel**
job **carries blood to all parts of the body**

part _____ **anus**
job **gets rid of undigested waste**

part _____ **bristles**
job **help animal move**

part _____ **intestine**
job **grinds and digests food**

parts _____ **hearts**
job **pump blood**

part _____ **mouth**
job **takes in food**

40

Name _____ Date _____ Class _____

CHAPTER **7**

WORMS

In your textbook, read about flatworms in Section 7:3.

1. Study the steps of the pig tapeworm life cycle in Figure 7-9 of your textbook. Then, answer the following questions.

a. What two host animals are part of the tapeworm's life cycle? **pig and human**

b. Which animal will contain cysts of the worm? **pig**

c. In which animal will the worm reproduce? **human**

d. In which animal will the worm's body sections break off and leave the host's body in its solid waste? **human**

e. In which animal will young worms travel to the muscles and burrow into them? **pig**

f. In which animal will worms attach to the inside of the intestines? **human**

2. Why aren't tapeworms common in the United States? **These worms aren't common because in the United States human wastes are treated with chemicals at sewage plants, and meats are inspected for cysts.**

3. On the blanks below, label the parts of this planarian and briefly describe the job each part does.

part _____ **eyespots**
job **detect light**

part _____ **nerve cords**

part _____ **nerve cell mass**
job **respond to environment**

part _____ **intestine**
job **breaks down food**

part _____ **mouth**
job **takes in and gets rid of undigested food from the body**

4. How do planarians differ from most other flatworms? **Most flatworms are parasites. Planarians are free-living.**

39

212

Name _____ Date _____ Class _____

SOFT-BODIED ANIMALS

In your textbook, read about soft-bodied animals in Section 7:4.

1. Match the groups of traits on the left with the pictures of soft-bodied animals on the right. Write the letter of the correct soft-bodied animal on the line following each group of traits.

C no shell
large eyes and a water jet
soft body

E single shell
soft body
glides on a muscular foot

D two shells
soft body
often buried in sand

A soft body
small inside shell
large eyes and a water jet

B soft body
no shell
looks like snail without shell

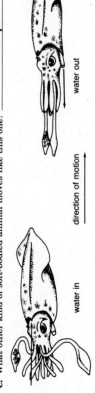

2. List four traits of all soft-bodied animals. **soft bodies usually protected by a hard shell; bodies covered by a thin fleshy tissue called a mantle; have a muscular foot; many have a structure inside the mouth for scraping food**

3. What kind of soft-bodied animal is diagramed below? **squid**

a. Use one arrow to label where water moves into the body in the diagram below. Use another arrow to show where water moves out of the body.

b. Use an arrow to show the direction the soft-bodied animal is moving.

c. What other kind of soft-bodied animal moves like this one? **octopus**

water in ⟶   direction of motion ⟶   water out ⟶

Name _____ Date _____ Class _____

VOCABULARY

Review the new words in Chapter 7 of your textbook. Then, complete the sentences on the right using the words listed below.

anus	invertebrates	roundworm	sponges	tentacles
cysts	mantle	segmented worm	stinging-cell animal	vertebrates
flatworm	planarian	soft-bodied animal	symmetry	tapeworm
hookworm	pores			

1. This animal is a **tapeworm** . It belongs to the **flatworm** phylum.

2. The young worms form **cysts** in muscles.

3. Jellyfish are in the **stinging-cell animal** phylum.
They have armlike parts called **tentacles** .

4. The simplest animals are the **sponges** .
The tiny holes in their bodies are called **pores** .

5. This animal belongs to the **soft-bodied animal** phylum. Its body is covered by thin, fleshy tissue called a **mantle** .

6. Animals that belong to the **roundworm** phylum have round, ropelike bodies. This worm has two openings in its body, a mouth and an **anus** .

7. An animal in this phylum is the **hookworm** .
This worm belongs to the **segmented worm** phylum.

8. This animal is a **planarian** . It belongs to the same phylum as the tapeworms.

9. A few simple animals, such as sponges, do not show **symmetry** .

10. Animals without backbones, like the animals shown above, are **invertebrates** . **Vertebrates** are animals with backbones.

Name _____

INVERTEBRATES

In Section 8:1 of your textbook, read about jointed-leg animals.

1. List three traits of jointed-leg animals. **Student answers will vary, but may include jointed appendages, segmented body, exoskeleton, and molting.**

2. Look at the pictures below. Use the letters A to E to answer the questions that follow.

 A.

 B.

 C.

D. all of the above   E. none of the above

a. Which animal is an invertebrate? **D**
b. Which animal has two pairs of antennae? **C**
c. Which animal is in the insect class? **B**
d. Which animal has an endoskeleton? **E**
e. Which animal has a segmented body? **D**
f. Which animal has eight legs? **A**
g. Which animal has a head, thorax, and abdomen? **B**
h. Which animal has 10 legs? **C**
i. Which animal has two pairs of wings? **B**
j. Which animal has more than 30 legs? **E**

In Section 8:1 of your textbook, read about spiny-skin animals.

3. List three traits of spiny-skin animals. **five-part body design, radial symmetry, spines**

4. Describe how asexual reproduction can occur in a starfish. **If a starfish loses an arm, it can grow a new one. A whole new animal can grow from one arm if the arm is still attached to part of the central body.**

Name _____

VERTEBRATES

In Section 8:2 of your textbook, read about chordates.

1. What trait identifies a chordate? **A chordate is an animal that, at some point in its life, has a tough, flexible rod along its back.**

2. In most vertebrates, what replaces the rod along its back? **a backbone**

In Section 8:2 of your textbook, read about characteristics of fish.

3. Put a checkmark in the column of each kind of fish that has the trait listed.

Trait	Jawless fish	Cartilage fish	Bony fish
have skeletons mostly of bone			✓
have toothlike scales		✓	
are parasites	✓		
group includes perch and trout			✓
have skeletons of cartilage	✓	✓	
group includes lamprey	✓		
have smooth, bony scales			✓
have uncovered gills	✓	✓	
group includes sharks and rays		✓	
have paired fins		✓	✓
most have a swim bladder			✓
have tubelike bodies	✓		

4. Fill in the correct answers in the blanks provided below each picture.

a. Class **bony fish**   b. Class **jawless fish**   c. Class **cartilage fish**
   Phylum **chordate**   Phylum **chordate**   Phylum **chordate**

VERTEBRATES

5. Explain the function of slime and scales in fish. **The slime and scales protect fish from infections and from enemies. The slime also makes it easier for fish to glide through the water.**

6. Explain how a swim bladder works. **It helps fish move up and down in the water. The fish rises when the bladder fills with gases. The fish goes deeper when gases are let out.**

In Section 8:2 of your textbook, read about amphibians.

7. Name the class and phylum to which the animal below belongs. List the major traits of this class.

Class **amphibian** Phylum **chordate**

Major traits of the class **has lungs; has moist skin; young have gills; has two pairs of legs; is cold-blooded**

8. List two reasons why amphibians must live near water. **to prevent skin from drying out; to reproduce—male needs to deposit sperm in water**

9. What is a tadpole? **young frog**

10. Using information from Figure 8-17 on page 169 of your textbook, complete the following table.

Trait	Tadpole	Adult frog
How is the body shaped?	fishlike	body with head and legs with webbed feet
Is a tail present?	yes	no
What part is used for moving?	tail (fin)	legs
What part is used for breathing?	gills	lungs
Where does it live?	in water	in water/on land

VERTEBRATES

11. How are cold-blooded animals affected by the temperature in their surroundings? **The temperature of cold-blooded animals drops as the temperature of their surroundings drop.**

12. How does hibernation help amphibians survive? **Animals that are inactive during cold weather eat no food and use only a little oxygen.**

In Section 8:2 of your textbook, read about reptiles.

13. Name the class and phylum to which the animal below belongs. List the major traits of this class.

Class **reptile** Phylum **chordate**

Major traits of the class **cold-blooded; has dry, scaly skin or hard plates; has lungs; has tough, leathery-shelled egg**

14. List five kinds of reptiles. **snakes, lizards, alligators, crocodiles, turtles**

15. List three reasons why a reptile can live entirely on land. **It has dry, scaly skin that prevents it from drying out, well-developed lungs for breathing air, and a tough, leathery-shelled egg that doesn't need to be laid in water.**

In Section 8:2 of your textbook, read about birds.

16. Compare the following traits of birds with those of reptiles. Using the words *same* or *different*, fill in the blanks provided with the answer that applies.

a. warm-blooded **different**   e. feathers **different**
b. scaly legs **same**   f. lungs **same**
c. shelled eggs **same**   g. beaks **different**
d. toes with claws **same**   h. hollow bones **different**

Name _____ Date _____ Class _____

VERTEBRATES

17. Explain the meaning of *warm-blooded*. **Warm-blooded means controlling the body temperature so that it stays about the same no matter what the temperature of the surroundings.**

18. What do birds have that helps them keep a constant body temperature? **feathers**

19. How are birds well adapted for flying? **They have hollow bones, which makes them light in weight. They have powerful muscles that move their wings.**

20. How are the beaks of birds adapted for getting food? **The kind (shape and size) of beak they have is related to the kind of food they eat.**

In Section 8:2 of your textbook, read about mammals.

21. Name the class and phylum to which the animal below belongs. List the major traits of this class.

Class **mammal**   Phylum **chordate**
Major traits of the class **has hair; is warm-blooded; has mammary glands, nurses young; young are born alive.**

22. a. What is a mammal? **A mammal is an animal that has hair and produces milk for its young.**
    b. Are you a mammal? **yes**

23. a. What are mammary glands? **body parts that produce milk**
    b. How are male mammary glands different from female mammary glands? **Male mammary glands don't produce milk.**

24. List two groups of mammals whose young do not develop inside the mother's body. **pouched mammals, egg-laying mammals**

Name _____ Date _____ Class _____

VOCABULARY

Review the new words used in Chapter 8 of your textbook. Then, fill in the blanks.

Crayfish, insects, and spiders belong to the phylum of **jointed-leg animals**. These animals have **compound eyes** with many lenses. They also have legs, wings, and **antennae** which are used for sensing smell and touch. These body parts are called **appendages**. Animals in this phylum have a skeleton, called an **exoskeleton**, that is outside their bodies. As the animals grow, they shed their outer skeletons. This process is called **molting**.

The phylum of **spiny-skin animals** includes sea urchins, starfish, and sand dollars. These animals use their **tube feet** to move, attach to rocks, and get food.

The phylum of **chordates** includes animals that have a rod along their back at some time in their lives. Their skeleton, called an **endoskeleton**, is inside their body.

Fish live in water and breathe with **gills**. They are **cold-blooded** animals because their body temperature changes with their surroundings. **Jawless fish** have no jaws, scales, or bones. Their skeleton is made of **cartilage**. **Cartilage fish** have jaws, scales, and a cartilage skeleton. **Bony fish** have jaws, scales, and a bony skeleton.

Amphibians live part of their life in water and part on land. **Hibernation** helps animals survive cold weather. **Reptiles** have dry, scaly skin, can live on land and breathe with lungs.

Birds have a beak, wings, and feathers. Their body temperature does not change with the temperature of their surroundings. Thus, they are **warm-blooded** animals. **Mammals** also have a constant body temperature. They have hair on their bodies. The females produce milk from their **mammary glands**.

216

WHAT NUTRIENTS ARE IN FOOD?

In your textbook, read about the nutrients found in food in Section 9:1.

1. The following diagram shows the percentage of nutrients present in males and females. The nutrients, however, are not labelled. Mark the diagrams as follows:
   (a) Pencil shading—nutrient used to build and repair body parts,
   (b) Dots—nutrient that is body's main source of energy,
   (c) xxxx—nutrient that makes up largest percent of body, and
   (d) No marking—nutrient that is body's stored source of energy.

2. Label the nutrients on the blanks in the diagram.

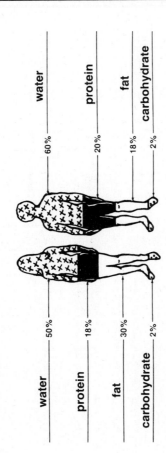

water —— 50%   water —— 60%
protein —— 18%   protein —— 20%
fat —— 30%   fat —— 18%
carbohydrate —— 2%   carbohydrate —— 2%

3. Using the above information from the diagram, label the bar graphs below as *male* or *female*.

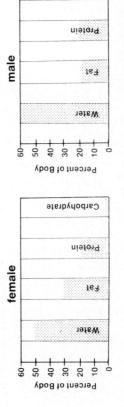

female   male

4. What nutrients were not included in the above diagram? __vitamins and minerals__

5. Do males or females usually have more fat in their bodies? __females__

6. List three reasons why water is important for good health. __Water cools the body. Many chemical changes take place in water. Water helps carry away body wastes.__

WHAT NUTRIENTS ARE IN FOOD?

8. Complete the following table by putting check marks in the correct columns.

	Fat	Protein	Carbohydrate
Present in butter, oils	✓		
Body's main energy source			✓
Present in bread and fruit			✓
Makes up bone and muscle		✓	
Need the most of daily			✓
Present in meat, fish		✓	
Used most quickly in body			✓
10% of your diet each day		✓	
Found as cell membranes	✓	✓	
Stored under skin	✓		
Stored in blood and liver			✓

9. Examine these food labels. Then, answer the questions below.

Cereal (1 serving)

Nutrient	RDA
Vitamin A	20
Vitamin C	10
Riboflavin	30
Thiamine	10
Niacin	25
Calcium	40
Iron	60
Potassium	1

Breakfast drink (1 serving)

Nutrient	RDA
Vitamin A	30
Vitamin C	5
Niacin	2
Riboflavin	40
Thiamine	5
Calcium	50
Iron	4
Zinc	1
Phosphorus	1

a. Circle the vitamins on each label.

b. Underline the minerals on each label.

c. Which of the two foods supplies more Vitamin C in one serving? __cereal__

WHAT NUTRIENTS ARE IN FOOD?

10. a. In general, how much does the body need of each vitamin each day? _____
   very small amounts

   b. Give an example of the amount needed in one day for any vitamin listed in your textbook in Table 9-1. Then, list the vitamin. **1.7 mg of B₂ (Answers will vary.)**

11. *Use Table 9-1 in your textbook to complete these questions.* Which vitamin is being described?

   a. is found in ham, eggs, and raisins — **B₁**

   b. is also called niacin — **B₃**

   c. you need 60 mg each day — **C**

   d. keeps your membranes healthy — **C (or A)**

   e. may cause night blindness if missing in diet — **A**

   f. may cause bowed legs if missing in diet — **D**

   g. is found in yeast, milk, eggs — **B₂**

   h. allows cells to carry out respiration — **B₃**

12. a. In general, how much does the body need of each mineral each day? — **very small amounts**

   b. Give an example of the amount needed in one day for any mineral listed in your textbook in Table 9-2. Then, list the mineral. **1 g of calcium (Answers will vary.)**

13. *Use Table 9-2 in your textbook to complete these questions.* Which mineral is being described?

   a. you need 0.325 g each day — **magnesium**

   b. may cause anemia if missing in diet — **iron**

   c. found in seafoods, iodized table salt — **iodine**

   d. found in bacon, butter — **sodium**

   e. needed to make muscles contract — **sodium**

   f. found in nuts, sardines, milk, cheese — **calcium**

   g. 1000 mg needed each day — **calcium**

   h. helps form blood cells — **iron**

CALORIES

In your textbook, read about the energy in food in Section 9:2.

1. Define *Calorie*. **A Calorie is a measure of the energy in food.**

2. What does it mean if someone says that a food contains 50 Calories? **It means that if this food were burned, it would give off enough heat to raise the temperature of 1000 g of water 50° C.**

3. What is the energy in food used for in your body? **cell work, moving muscles, pumping blood, sending messages along nerves**

4. Complete the table below by determining the number of Calories in each food sample and writing the number in the column at the right.

Food sample	Amount of water in beaker	Starting temperature of water before burning food	Final temperature of water after burning food	Number of Calories in food
A	1000 g	18°C	19°C	1
B	1000 g	10°C	15°C	5
C	1000 g	0°C	100°C	100
D	1000 g	55°C	72°C	17

5. A student ate the foods in the table below in one day. Complete the table by determining the total Calories taken in. Then, answer the questions on the following page.

Food	Calories	×	Amount eaten	=	Total
Egg	80		2		160
Milk	80		2 glasses		160
Bread	70		4 slices		280
Bologna	60		4 slices		240
Cola	145		4 glasses		580
Hamburger	250		2		500
French fries	100		1 serving		100

Name _____ Date _____ Class _____

CALORIES

6. Which food gave the student the most Calories? **cola**

7. Were the servings and mass of each food equal? **no**

8. When comparing equal masses of food, which nutrient type will provide the most Calories? **fat**

In your textbook, read about using Calories in Section 9:2.

9. Look at Table 9-4 in your textbook. Use the information in the table and in your textbook to help you answer the following questions.

a. How many Calories do you need each day? **Answers will vary.**

b. What two things listed on the graph are important in determining how many Calories a person needs? **age and sex**

c. How do Calorie needs differ as a person ages from 7 to 18? **Calorie needs increase with age.**

d. How do Calorie needs differ between males and females above the age of 10? **Males need more Calories than females.**

e. If a typical female age 18 takes in 1500 Calories each day for one month, will she gain or lose weight? Why? **She will lose weight because she needs 2500 Calories each day. Taking in less Calories than one needs over time will result in weight loss.**

f. If a typical male age 15 takes in 3500 Calories each day for one month, will he gain or lose weight? Why? **He will gain weight because he needs 3000 Calories each day. Taking in more Calories than one needs over time will result in weight gain.**

g. How do Calorie needs vary with different kinds of activities a person does? **The more energy it takes to do an activity, the more Calories a person uses to do that activity.**

Name _____ Date _____ Class _____

VOCABULARY

Review the new words used in Chapter 9 of your textbook. Then, complete this crossword puzzle.

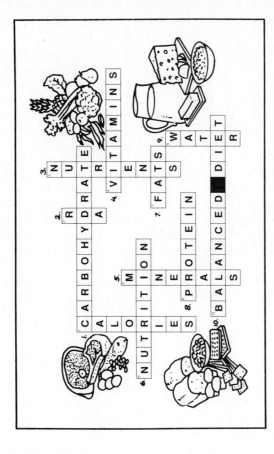

Across
1. nutrient that supplies energy
4. nutrients that help cells carry on daily chemical work
6. study of how body uses food
7. nutrient that supplies energy if body's first energy source is used up
8. main nutrient in meat
10. the right amount of each nutrient (two words)

Down
1. measure of energy in food
2. abbreviation for Recommended Daily Allowance
3. chemicals in food needed by body
5. iron and calcium are examples
9. makes up 50 to 60% of your body

220

STUDY GUIDE

CHAPTER 10

Name _____ Date _____ Class _____

THE PROCESS OF DIGESTION

In your textbook, read about the breakdown of food in Section 10:1.

1. What is the meaning of the word *digestion*? **Digestion is the word used to describe the changing of food into a usable form.**

2. How can the digestive system be compared to a factory? **Food, which is the raw material, is taken into the system and changed into new products.**

3. What is food used for once it is broken down? **Food helps supply cells with energy. It helps in the growth and repair of new cells.**

4. Decide whether the following phrases describe a physical or chemical change. Then, write the word *physical* or *chemical* in the blanks provided.

   chemical a. Food is changed into a form cells can use.

   physical b. Food is ground up in the mouth.

   chemical c. Starch is changed to glucose.

   physical d. Large pieces of food are broken down into small pieces.

   physical e. Food is chewed.

   chemical f. Enzymes speed up chemical changes.

THE HUMAN DIGESTIVE SYSTEM

In your textbook, read about how the digestive system works in Section 10:2.

1. Write the following nutrients under the correct headings in the chart below.

   fats   proteins   water   vitamins   minerals   carbohydrates

Nutrients that have to be digested	Nutrients that do not have to be digested
fats	water
proteins	vitamins
carbohydrates	minerals

55

STUDY GUIDE

CHAPTER 10

Name _____ Date _____ Class _____

THE HUMAN DIGESTIVE SYSTEM

In your textbook, read about a tour through the digestive system in Section 10:2.

2. Label the following parts of the digestive system on the diagram below: stomach, liver, large intestine, small intestine, gallbladder, mouth, esophagus, salivary gland, pancreas, anus, and appendix.

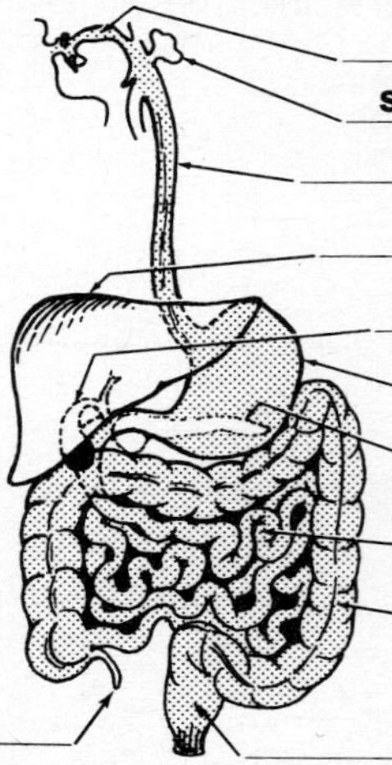

mouth
salivary gland
esophagus
liver
gallbladder
stomach
pancreas
small intestine
large intestine
appendix
anus

3. In the drawing above, shade in with a pencil those organs through which food actually passes.
4. The graph below shows how long food stays in different parts of the digestive system.

Use this graph to answer the questions that follow.

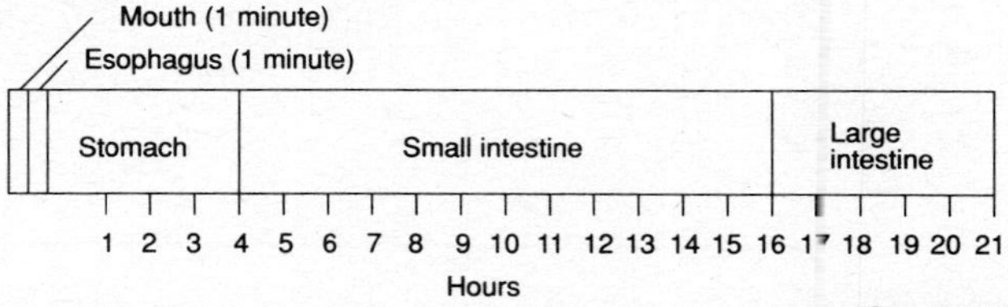

Mouth (1 minute)
Esophagus (1 minute)
Stomach
Small intestine
Large intestine

Hours
1 2 3 4 5 6 7 8 9 10 11 12 13 14 15 16 17 18 19 20 21

a. In which two organs does food stay for the shortest time? **mouth, esophagus**

b. About how long does food stay in the stomach? **4 hours**
   in the large intestine? **12 hours**   in the small intestine? **5 hours**

c. In which organ does food stay for the longest time? **small intestine**

56

THE HUMAN DIGESTIVE SYSTEM

5. Label the diagrams below. Then, color the organs according to this plan:

green—organ that make bile
red—organ that removes water
blue—organ that stores bile
yellow—organ that makes enzymes for digestion

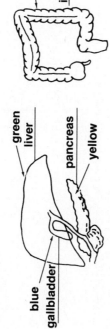

green liver
pancreas yellow
blue gallbladder
red large intestine

In your textbook, read about moving digested food into body cells in Section 10:2.

6. Label the following parts in the diagrams below: blood vessel, villus, small intestine, food molecules.

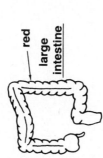

villus
blood vessel
small intestine
food molecules
Blood flow

7. What organ contains the villi? **small intestine**

8. a. By what process does food pass into the blood? **by diffusion**

b. What happens to the food once it enters the blood? **Food is carried by the blood to all body cells.**

c. Explain the importance of villi. **They increase the surface that comes in contact with digested food so that more food can pass into the blood.**

THE HUMAN DIGESTIVE SYSTEM

9. Complete the table below.

Organ	Enzyme formed here? (yes or no)	Food passes through this organ? (yes or no)	Name of nutrient acted upon or digested (fat, protein, carbohydrate, none)	Food absorbed here? (yes or no)	Water absorbed here? (yes or no)	Name of chemical made here
Mouth and salivary glands	yes	yes (mouth)	carbohydrate	no	no	saliva
Esophagus	no	yes	none	no	no	none
Stomach	yes	yes	protein	no	no	hydrochloric acid, enzyme
Liver and gallbladder	no	no	fat	no	no	bile
Pancreas	yes	no	fat, protein, carbohydrate	no	no	enzymes
Small intestine	yes	yes	fat, protein, carbohydrate	yes	no	enzymes
Large intestine	no	yes	none	no	yes	none

10. Decide whether the following statements are true or false. If true, write *true* in the left-hand column. If false, change the underlined word to one that will make the statement true and write the correct word in the blank.

__long__ a. Plant-eating animals usually have <u>short</u> digestive systems.

__two__ b. An earthworm has <u>one</u> opening in its digestive system.

__true__ c. A tapeworm has <u>no</u> digestive system.

__short__ d. Meat-eating animals usually have <u>long</u> digestive systems.

__true__ e. Humans are among the animals that have a <u>complex</u> digestive system.

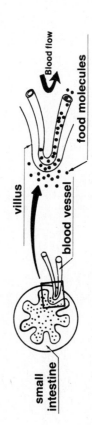

PROBLEMS OF THE DIGESTIVE SYSTEM

In your textbook, read about ulcers and heartburn in Section 10:2.

1. Examine the pictures below. Then, write in the blank the letter of the picture that illustrates the phrase.

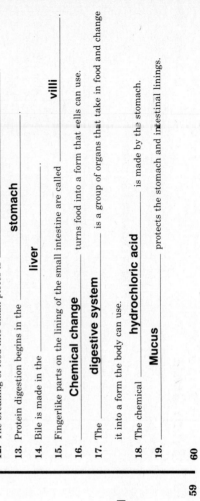

A   B

a. ulcer in stomach lining   **B**   c. results of acid and enzymes working on cells **B**

b. normal stomach lining   **A**

2. a. What causes heartburn? **movement of food from stomach into esophagus**
   .
   b. Why is it called by the name "heartburn"? **Because the esophagus lies behind the**
   heart, the pain seems to be coming from the heart.

3. Label these parts in Diagram A:
   small intestine, esophagus, stomach, proper food amount in stomach

4. Label these parts in Diagram B:
   too much food in stomach, bulging stomach

5. Draw in and label where food can be found if the person in Diagram B has heartburn. Use an
   arrow to show where the food has come from.

esophagus

stomach

proper food
amount in
stomach

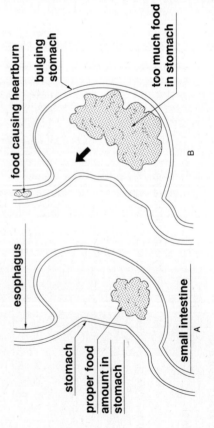

small intestine   A

food causing heartburn

bulging
stomach

too much food
in stomach

B

VOCABULARY

Review the new words used in Chapter 10. Use the terms below to fill in the blanks in the sentences
that follow.

mucus	digestive system	stomach	saliva
villi	physical change	small intestine	enzymes
bile	chemical change	gall bladder	hydrochloric
liver	salivary glands	large intestine	acid

1. Changing of food into a usable form is called ___**digestion**___ .

2. ___**Enzymes**___ speed up the rate of chemical change.

3. ___**Saliva**___ helps digest carbohydrates in the mouth.

4. ___**Bile**___ helps break down fats.

5. The tube that connects the mouth to the stomach is the ___**esophagus**___ .

6. ___**Salivary glands**___ are located under the tongue and behind the jaw.

7. The ___**pancreas**___ is an organ that makes three different enzymes.

8. The ___**gallbladder**___ stores bile.

9. Most digestion and absorption of food takes place in the ___**small intestine**___ .

10. The ___**large intestine**___ removes water from undigested food.

11. The ___**appendix**___ is a small fingerlike part located where the small
    and large intestines meet.

12. The breaking of food into small pieces is ___**physical change**___ .

13. Protein digestion begins in the ___**stomach**___ .

14. Bile is made in the ___**liver**___ .

15. Fingerlike parts on the lining of the small intestine are called ___**villi**___ .

16. ___**Chemical change**___ turns food into a form that cells can use.

17. The ___**digestive system**___ is a group of organs that take in food and change
    it into a form the body can use.

18. The chemical ___**hydrochloric acid**___ is made by the stomach.

19. ___**Mucus**___ protects the stomach and intestinal linings.

Name _____ Date _____ Class _____

THE PROCESS OF CIRCULATION

In your textbook, read about your body's pickup and delivery system in Section 11:1.

Joe Garcia owns a laundry service. Each day his trucks move out onto the streets to pick up dirty laundry from his customers' homes. The trucks also deliver the cleaned clothes that were collected before. The dirty laundry is taken to the store where the washing and cleaning takes place. The cleaned clothes are returned in the trucks to the customers and more dirty clothes are picked up.

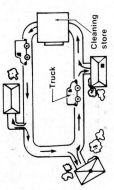

1. Parts of the circulatory system are similar in jobs to objects in the above story. Write the letter of the object in Section I in the space to the left of the part of the circulatory system in Section II that most nearly matches it in function.

Section I

A. Roads
B. Trucks
C. Cleaning store
D. Homes
E. Clean laundry
F. Dirty laundry

Section II

D Body cells   **A** Blood vessels
E Oxygen   **F** Wastes
B Blood   **C** Heart and lungs

In your textbook, read about circulation in animals in Section 11:1.

2. Complete this chart using Yes or No answers.

Animal	Circulatory system present?	Blood present?	Heart present?	Blood vessels present?
Hydra	no	no	no	no
Earthworm	yes	yes	yes	yes
Insect	yes	yes	yes	no
Human	yes	yes	yes	yes

3. a. Define open circulatory system. __An open circulatory system is one in which__ **blood moves about in the body without blood vessels.**

   b. Define closed circulatory system. __A closed circulatory system is one in which__ **blood moves about in the body within blood vessels.**

Name _____ Date _____ Class _____

THE HUMAN HEART

In your textbook, read about the structure of the human heart in Section 11:2.

1. Label the diagram below using these words: right atrium, right ventricle, left atrium, left ventricle, tricuspid valve, semilunar valve (used twice), bicuspid valve, right side of heart, left side of heart

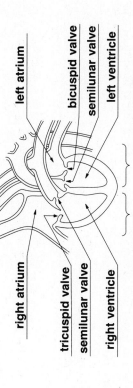

right atrium
tricuspid valve
semilunar valve
right ventricle
right side of heart

left atrium
bicuspid valve
semilunar valve
left ventricle
left side of heart

In your textbook, read about how the heart works as a pump in Section 11:2.

2. Complete the following chart by putting checkmarks in the correct columns.

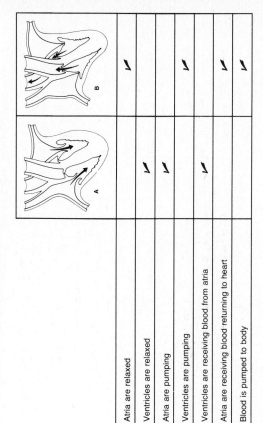

	A	B
Atria are relaxed		✓
Ventricles are relaxed	✓	
Atria are pumping	✓	
Ventricles are pumping		✓
Atria are receiving blood from atria	✓	
Atria are receiving blood returning to heart		✓
Blood is pumped to body	✓	

223

THE HUMAN HEART

In your textbook, read about the jobs of the heart in Section 11.2.

3. Identify the parts lettered A-H in the following diagram. Then, name the parts in the blanks provided.

A _____ pulmonary artery   E _____ vena cava

B _____ pulmonary vein   F _____ aorta

C _____ vena cava   G _____ right ventricle

D _____ aorta   H _____ left ventricle

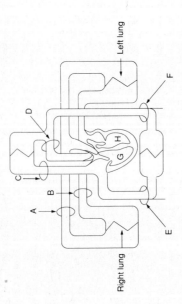

4. Use the diagram to complete the table. Write the letters A-H under the correct headings

Contains blood with much oxygen, little carbon dioxide	Contains blood with much carbon dioxide, little oxygen
B, H, D, F	A, C, E, G

5. Describe the main job of the right side of your heart. __The right side of the heart pumps blood to the lungs to get rid of carbon dioxide and pick up oxygen.__

6. Describe the main job of the left side of your heart. __The left side of the heart pumps blood to all parts of the body to deliver oxygen and pick up carbon dioxide.__

BLOOD VESSELS

In your textbook, read about arteries, veins, and capillaries in Section 11.3.

1. Circle the word or words that make the statement true.

   a. Arteries carry blood toward (away from) the heart.

   b. Arteries carry blood under (high) low pressure.

   c. Arteries have thin (thick) muscular walls.

   d. An example of an artery is the vena cava (aorta).

   e. When your feel your pulse, you are feeling blood moving through your veins (arteries)

2. What is the main job of veins? _____ to carry blood back to the heart

3. Compare the amount of muscle in veins and arteries. __Veins have thin walls with little muscle. Arteries have thick, muscular walls.__

4. Compare the pressure within veins and arteries. __Veins carry blood under low pressure. Arteries carry blood under high pressure.__

5. Explain how the one-way valves in veins help maintain circulation. __Since blood in these vessels is under low pressure, valves help keep blood flowing in one direction toward the heart.__

6. Place a checkmark next to those statements below that are true.

   ___ a. Blood pressure is higher in capillaries than in arteries.

   ✓ b. Capillary walls are only one cell thick.

   ___ c. The human body has more veins than capillaries.

   ✓ d. Capillaries bring blood close to all body cells.

   ✓ e. All the pickups of carbon dioxide and other cell wastes, and all the deliveries of oxygen, food, and other materials, occur in the capillaries.

STUDY GUIDE

Name _____ Date _____ Class _____

CHAPTER 11

PROBLEMS OF THE CIRCULATORY SYSTEM

In your textbook, read about high blood pressure and heart attacks in Section 11:4.

1. The following diagrams show cross sections of three arteries. Choices A, B, and C may be used more than once and in combinations when answering these questions.

A (normal)   B (contracted)   c (filled with cholesterol)

a. Which diagram or diagrams *might* have an upper blood pressure value of 160? **B, C**

   Explain why. **A narrow opening raises blood pressure.**

b. Which diagram or diagrams *might* have an upper blood pressure value of 110? **A**

   Explain why. **Diagram A shows a normal opening through which blood should be able to push at a normal pressure value of 110.**

2. What are coronary blood vessels? **blood vessels that carry blood to and from the heart**

3. What can happen if these vessels become clogged? **Since blood can't reach a part of the heart, that part begins to die due to lack of nutrients and oxygen. This can result in a heart attack.**

In your textbook, read about preventing heart problems in Section 11:4.

4. How can diet help prevent heart problems? **Eating a balanced diet can prevent becoming overweight and can reduce cholesterol intake.**

5. Why is a smoker more likely to have heart problems than a nonsmoker? **Nicotine in tobacco smoke causes blood vessels to narrow in size. This causes the heart to work harder to pump blood.**

65

STUDY GUIDE

Name _____ Date _____ Class _____

CHAPTER 11

VOCABULARY

Review the new words used in Chapter 11 of your textbook. Then, read the statements below.

For each statement, write TRUE or FALSE on the first blank. Make a false statement true by changing the underlined term. Write the correct term on the second blank.

1. **TRUE** _____ Valves are flaps in the heart and veins.

2. **TRUE** _____ Arteries carry blood away from the heart.

3. **TRUE** _____ The circulatory system is made up of blood, blood vessels, and the heart.

4. **FALSE** **vena cava** The pulmonary vein is the largest vein.

5. **FALSE** **blood vessels** Blood pressure is the force of blood pushing against the walls of the heart.

6. **TRUE** _____ Atria are the top chambers of the heart.

7. **FALSE** **semilunar** The tricuspid valves are located between the ventricles and their arteries.

8. **FALSE** **high** Hypertension is caused by low blood pressure.

9. **FALSE** **capillary** A vena cava is the smallest kind of blood vessel.

10. **TRUE** _____ Coronary vessels carry blood to the heart.

11. **FALSE** **Pulmonary veins** Capillaries carry blood from the lungs to the left side of the heart.

12. **FALSE** **tricuspid** The semilunar valve is located between the right atrium and right ventricle.

13. **TRUE** _____ A heart attack is the death of a heart muscle.

14. **FALSE** **pulmonary artery** The aorta carries blood from the heart to the lungs.

15. **TRUE** _____ Veins carry blood back to the heart.

16. **TRUE** _____ The bicuspid valve is located between the left atrium and the left ventricle.

17. **TRUE** _____ Cholesterol can narrow arteries.

18. **FALSE** **aorta** The pulmonary artery is the largest artery.

19. **TRUE** _____ Ventricles are the bottom chambers of the heart.

66

225

Name _____ Date _____ Class _____

THE ROLE OF BLOOD

In your textbook, read about the functions of blood in Section 12:1.

Complete this outline of blood functions.

Blood jobs or functions

1. Blood picks up
   a. carbon dioxide waste from cells
   b. other chemical wastes from cells
   c. excess body heat

2. Blood delivers
   a. nutrients to all cells
   b. oxygen to all cells
   c. chemical messengers to certain cells
   d. water, minerals, and vitamins

PARTS OF HUMAN BLOOD

In your textbook, read about the living and nonliving parts of blood in Section 12:2.

1. Examine the diagram at the right of blood that has been sitting for an hour. Write the letter of the blood part being described in each of the words or phrases below. Write the correct letter next to each word or phrase.

a. plasma __A__
b. liquid part __B__
c. blood cell part __A__
d. nonliving part __A__
e. living part __B__
f. mostly water __A__
g. includes cells that carry oxygen __B__
h. includes parts that aid in blood clotting __B__
i. includes proteins, nutrients, salts, and wastes __A__
j. red __B__
k. yellow __A__
l. includes cells that destroy harmful microbes __B__

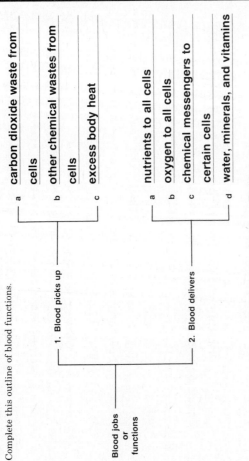

226

Name _____ Date _____ Class _____

PARTS OF HUMAN BLOOD

In your textbook, read about blood cells and platelets in Section 12:2.

2. Complete the table below by writing the phrases that follow in the correct column in the table. The first one is done for you.

Red blood cells	White blood cells	Platelets
5 million in a small drop of blood	8000 in small drop of blood	250 000 in a small drop of blood
contain hemoglobin	destroy microbes	not whole cells
transport oxygen	can move between capillaries and among body cells	aid in blood clotting
if number is low, person feels tired	increase during infections	life span of 5 days
life span of 120 days	remove dead cells	results in hemophilia if not working
cell with no nucleus	made in spleen	
look like doughnuts without holes	move like amoebas	
	life span of 10 days	
	increase abnormally during leukemia	
	cell with a nucleus	

8000 in a small drop of blood
250 000 in a small drop of blood
5 million in a small drop of blood
not whole cells
destroy microbes
aid in blood clotting
can move between capillaries and among body cells
increase during infections
contain hemoglobin
remove dead cells

transport oxygen
made in spleen
if number is low, person feels tired
life span of 5 days
life span of 10 days
life span of 120 days
increase abnormally during leukemia
cell with a nucleus
cell with no nucleus
results in hemophilia if not working
look like doughnuts without holes

67

68

Name _____ Date _____ Class _____

IMMUNITY

In your textbook, read about immunity in Section 12:4.

1. Define immune system. **proteins, cells, and tissues that identify and defend the body against foreign chemicals and organisms**

2. a. Define antigen. **a foreign substance that causes disease and also antibodies to form**

   b. Are antigens helpful? Explain. **No, they invade the body and cause diseases.**

3. a. Define antibody. **a chemical that helps destroy bacteria or viruses**

   b. Are antibodies helpful? Explain. **Yes, they keep us healthy by getting rid of antigens that enter our bodies.**

4. Figures A, B, C, and D are labeled for you. You are to:

   a. draw the antigen onto the correct cell that normally has antigens on it.

   b. draw the antibody onto the correct cell that normally has antibodies on it.

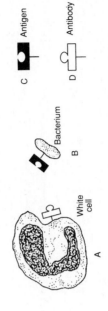

White cell — A

Bacterium — B

Antigen — C

Antibody — D

5. How is the meeting of the white blood cell and the bacterium shown in question 4 like the meeting of a lock and a key? **The shape of the white blood cell's antibody will fit together with the shape of the bacterium's antigen.**

6. List two ways that this meeting can result in the death of the bacterium. **By combining with the white blood cell, the membrane of the bacterium may break open. With antibodies stuck to it, the bacterium can then be destroyed by other white blood cells.**

Name _____ Date _____ Class _____

BLOOD TYPES

In your textbook, read about different types of blood in Section 12:3.

Examine the following chart carefully. Then, look at the four tubes of blood shown below. Fill in the spaces with the correct information from the chart and the following labels: red cells, plasma protein shape, red cell protein shape, plasma, red cell. Part of the first one is done for you.

Blood type	Red blood cell protein	Plasma protein	Cell protein plasma protein fit or no fit
O	none		no fit
A			no fit
B			no fit
AB		none	no fit

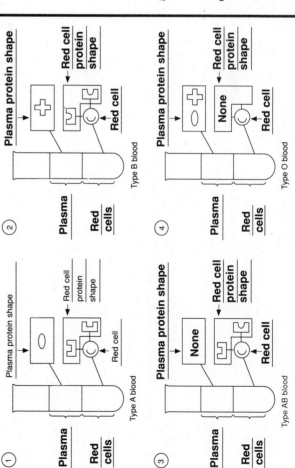

① Plasma protein shape — Plasma — Red cell protein shape — Red cells — Red cell — Type A blood

② Plasma protein shape — Plasma — Red cell protein shape — Red cells — Red cell — Type B blood

③ Plasma protein shape **None** — Plasma — Red cell protein shape — Red cells — Red cell — Type AB blood

④ Plasma protein shape — Plasma — Red cell protein shape **None** — Red cells — Red cell — Type O blood

227

Name _____ Date _____ Class _____

CHAPTER 12

IMMUNITY

7. What does the immune system do for months or years after the invasion of a certain antigen? __It will make many new white blood cells, each with the shape of the antibody just used to get rid of the antigen.__

8. If the same type of bacteria enter the body several years later, what will happen? __White blood cells with the necessary antibodies quickly destroy the bacteria.__

9. a. What do the initials *DPT* stand for? __Diphtheria, Tetanus, Pertussis__

   b. What is in a DPT shot? __proteins from these three bacterial diseases__

   c. What happens when you receive this shot? __It's as if you are getting antigens of these three diseases. Your immune system "remembers" the antigens and begins to make antibodies.__

   d. What happens later on if the actual bacteria causing these diseases were to enter your body? __Your immune system would be ready and waiting with the antibodies needed to destroy the antigens.__

10. What is immunity? __the ability of a person who has had a disease once to be protected from getting the same disease again__

11. What do the initials *AIDS* stand for? __Acquired Immune Deficiency Syndrome__

12. Is AIDS caused by a bacterium or a virus? __virus__

13. What type of cells does it attack? __white blood cells__

14. How does AIDS harm the body? __It destroys white blood cells and allows other diseases to invade the body and cause death.__

15. List four ways that AIDS can be spread from one person to another. __during intimate sexual contact, when body fluids containing the virus may be passed along through broken body tissues; by sharing needles during drug use; during pregnancy, the woman may pass the disease to her unborn child; during a blood transfusion of untested blood__

VOCABULARY

Review the new words used in Chapter 12 of your textbook. Then, use the terms below to fill in the blanks in the sentences that follow.

immunity	bone marrow	plasma	hemoglobin
antigens	immune system	anemia	platelets
hemophilia	red blood cells	leukemia	antibodies
AIDS	white blood cells		

1. __Plasma__ is the yellow, nonliving part of blood.

2. __Red blood cells__ are the cells in the blood that carry oxygen to the tissues.

3. __Hemoglobin__ is a protein in red blood cells that joins with oxygen.

4. When a person has __anemia__ there are too few red blood cells or too little hemoglobin or both.

5. The cells in the blood that remove microbes and dead cells are __white blood cells__

6. When a person has __leukemia__, the number of white blood cells increases abnormally.

7. __Platelets__ are bloodlike parts important in blood clotting.

8. The blood of a person with __hemophilia__ will not clot.

9. The __immune system__ helps keep a person free of disease.

10. __Antibodies__ are chemicals that destroy bacteria or viruses.

11. __Antigens__ are foreign substances that invade the body and cause disease.

12. __Immunity__ is the ability of a person who once had a disease to be protected from getting it again.

13. __AIDS__ is a disease of the immune system.

14. Red blood cells are made in __bone marrow__, the soft center part of the bone.

228

THE ROLE OF RESPIRATION

In your textbook, read about respiration in Section 13:1.

1. What is the function of the respiratory system? **to help with the exchange of gases; to bring in oxygen and to remove carbon dioxide**

2. Explain why a large surface area is needed in a respiratory system. **This large area provides a surface for gases to diffuse into or out of the blood or body cells.**

3. Match the main methods of getting oxygen with the animals below. Write the letter of the method below each animal.

   A = skin   B = skin and lungs   C = lungs   D = gills   E = small tubes

  B   **A**   **D**   **E**   **C**

HUMAN RESPIRATORY SYSTEM

In your textbook, read about respiratory system organs in Section 13:2.

1. Label the parts on the diagram below using these words: bronchus, nose, nasal chamber, lung, trachea, epiglottis, alveoli.

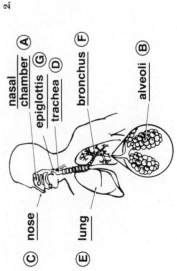

nasal chamber (A)
epiglottis (G)
trachea (D)
bronchus (F)
alveoli (B)
nose (C)
lung (E)

2. Place the letter of the description below in the correct circle next to the labeled part of the diagram.

   A = place where air is warmed or cooled

   B = clusters of air sacs where gas exchange occurs

   C = place where air first enters respiratory system

   D = the windpipe

   E = one of two major organs of respiration

   F = carries air from trachea into lung

   G = flap that prevents food from entering trachea

HUMAN RESPIRATORY SYSTEM

In your textbook, read about gas exchange in Section 13:2.

3. Examine the first diagram at the right. Then, answer the questions.

   a. What is part A? **alveolus**

       part B? **capillary**

   b. What gas moves in the direction shown by arrow C? **oxygen**   arrow D? **carbon dioxide**

4. Examine the second diagram at the right. Then, answer the questions.

   a. What is part A? **blood cell**

       part B? **body cell**

   b. What gas moves in the direction shown by arrow C? **carbon dioxide**   arrow D? **oxygen**

5. Below are two diagrams of the chest cavity during breathing. Circle the words that correctly complete the statements below each diagram.

Rib cage moves (out) / in.
Rib cage moves (up) / down.
Diaphragm is relaxed / (working)
Air is (pulled in) / pushed out.
Diaphragm pushes up / (moves down).
Lungs get squeezed / (expand).
Person is breathing (in) / out.

Rib cage moves out / (in).
Rib cage moves up / (down).
Diaphragm is (relaxed) / working.
Air is pulled in / (pushed out).
Diaphragm (pushes up) / moves down.
Lungs (get squeezed) / expand.
Person is breathing in / (out).

STUDY GUIDE

Name _____ Date _____ Class _____

PROBLEMS OF THE RESPIRATORY SYSTEM

In your textbook, read about respiratory problems in Section 13:3.

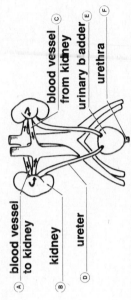

A   B   C   D

1. Drawing A shows the normal pathway of 2 oxygen molecules (black dots) going from the alveoli into a lung capillary. Finish the drawing by showing the path that the other 4 oxygen molecules will take in a normal person.

2. Drawing B shows alveoli filled with oxygen and carbon monoxide (squares). Finish the drawing by showing the path that the gas molecules will take when in the lungs of a person with carbon monoxide poisoning.

3. Explain why a person with the problem in diagram B could die. __Carbon monoxide gas is picked up more easily than oxygen by red blood cells. If too much is inhaled, too little oxygen will be delivered to the person's cells.__

4. Drawing C shows alveoli filled with pus, liquid, and mucus.
   a. What disease may cause this to occur? __pneumonia__
   b. Can oxygen (black dots) reach the capillaries surrounding these alveoli? __no__ Explain. __The alveoli are blocked with pus, liquid, and mucus. This prevents oxygen from getting into the blood.__
   c. Is this disease communicable or noncommunicable? __communicable__ Explain. __Pneumonia is caused by bacteria or viruses and can be passed from one person to another.__

5. Drawing D shows the alveoli of a person with emphysema.
   a. How do these alveoli compare with those of a normal person? __The alveoli of a normal person have more surface area. The alveoli of a person with emphysema are broken down.__
   b. How is emphysema harmful? __A person with emphysema is out of breath because there are not enough alveoli to get oxygen into the blood.__

STUDY GUIDE

Name _____ Date _____ Class _____

THE ROLE OF EXCRETION

In your textbook, read about waste removal in Section 13:4.

1. Explain what would happen if wastes were not removed from the body. __The body's tissues would fill with poisonous waste products that would destroy them. Fever, poisoning, or even death could result.__

2. In the space provided, place a checkmark next to those statements that are true. For each statement that is false, change the underlined word to one that will make the statement true, and write it in the space.
   a. __excretion__ Getting rid of wastes is called <u>digestion</u>.
   b. ✓ <u>liquid</u> Urea is a waste that results from the breakdown of body protein.
   c. ✓ Solid wastes are removed by the excretory system.
   d. ✓ Wastes are either made by body cells or are the remains of undigested food.

3. Label the parts on the diagram using these labels: ureter, urethra, kidney, urinary bladder, blood vessel from kidney, blood vessel to kidney.

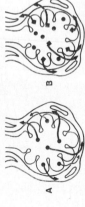

(A) blood vessel to kidney

(B) kidney

(C) blood vessel from kidney

(D) ureter

(E) urinary bladder

(F) urethra

4. Beside each phrase, write the letter from the diagram above that shows the correct location.
   a. where urea is filtered from the blood __B__
   b. where wastes are stored for a short time __E__
   c. transports wastes from kidney to bladder __D__
   d. brings wastes to kidneys __A__
   e. where urine leaves body __F__
   f. carries filtered blood away from kidney __C__

VOCABULARY

Review the new words used in Chapter 13 of your textbook. Then, complete this puzzle.

1. Put the following words into two groups by adding them to this table under the proper heading: urethra, diaphragm, bronchi, ureter, trachea, nephron, alveoli, epiglottis, urinary bladder, respiratory system, excretory system.

Parts of the **respiratory system**	Parts of the **excretory system**
lungs	kidney
rib cage	sweat glands
diaphragm	**urethra**
bronchi	**ureter**
trachea	**nephron**
alveoli	**urinary bladder**
epiglottis	

2. Put the following words into two groups by writing them in this table under the proper heading: urea, diaphragm, urine, emphysema, excess salt, pneumonia.

Respiration	Excretion
emphysema	**urea**
pneumonia	**urine**
diaphragm	**excess salt**

THE ROLE OF EXCRETION

5. Complete the chart below by writing the following phrases under the correct organ pictured.

body filter
has sweat glands
helps cool body
removes CO_2
removes water in breath

contains alveoli
removes urea
protective cover
controls water and salt loss

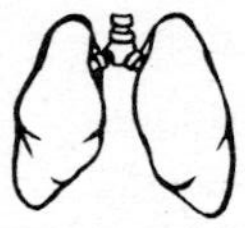	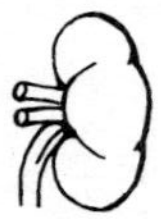	
	removes CO_2	**body filter**	**has sweat glands**
	contains alveoli	**removes urea**	**helps cool body**
	removes water in breath	**controls water and salt loss**	**protective cover**

6. In the space provided, place a checkmark next to the statements that are true. For each statement that is false, change the underlined word to one that will make the statement true and write it in the space.

a. **nephrons** Each kidney has about one million tiny filter units called <u>ureters</u>.

b. ✓ <u>Blood</u> with blood cells, salts, sugar, urea, and water enters each filter unit.

c. ✓ All materials except urea and excess water and salts diffuse back into the blood after filtering.

d. ✓ Filtered waste carried out of the kidney to the bladder is known as urine.

e. **salt** Each of the body's two to five million sweat glands gives off water and <u>sugar</u>.

f. **can't** The skin <u>can</u> control water loss.

231

THE ROLE OF THE SKELETON

In your textbook, read about functions of the skeleton in Section 14:1.

1. Below are five pictures. Under each, write what the item does or is used for. Then, write what job of the skeletal system is similar.

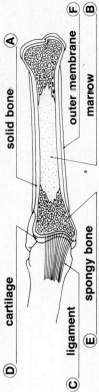

Hinge

How used? **help objects move**
Skeleton job: **helps body move**

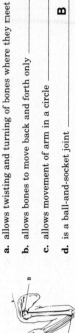

Catcher's mask

How used? **protection protects**
Skeleton job: **organs**

Trunk

How used? **storage stores**
Skeleton job: **calcium**

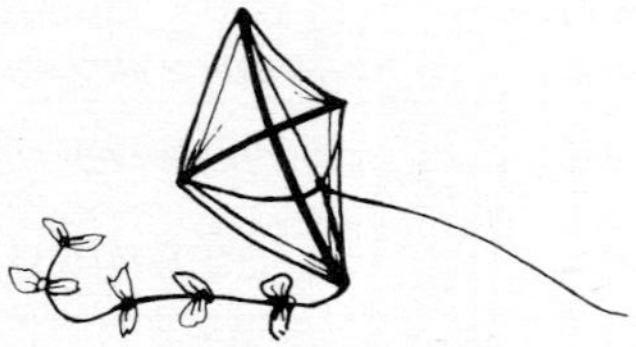

Kite (wooden part)

How used? **framework**
Skeleton job: **support for body**

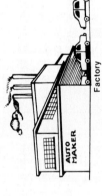

Factory

Does what? **makes things**
Skeleton job: **makes blood cells**

In your textbook, read about bone growth in Section 14:1.

2. A child has 5 wrist bones. An adult has 8 wrist bones.

a. How can these differences be used as evidence that bone tissue is alive? **The increase in the number of bones shows that bone is alive and can make more bone.**

b. How has bone length in your legs changed since you were an infant? **My leg bones have increased in length.**

c. How can this change be used as evidence that bone tissue is alive? **Something which is living can grow in size.**

THE ROLE OF THE SKELETON

In your textbook, read about bone structure in Section 14:1.

3. Label the following parts on the diagram below: cartilage, ligament, solid bone, spongy bone, marrow, outer membrane.
Put the letters of the jobs or traits below in the correct circles on the blanks in the diagram.

A = compact, and stores calcium   D = cushion between bones
B = blood cells are made here   E = lightweight but adds strength
C = fibers that hold bones together F = contains many nerves and blood vessels

solid bone Ⓐ
outer membrane Ⓕ
marrow Ⓑ
Ⓓ cartilage
Ⓒ ligament
Ⓔ spongy bone

In your textbook, read about joints in Section 14:1.

4. Examine the diagram below. Then, answer the questions by putting the letter of the correct joint on the blanks beside each phrase.

a. allows twisting and turning of bones where they meet   B
b. allows bones to move back and forth only   A
c. allows movement of arm in a circle   B
d. is a ball-and-socket joint   B
e. is a hinge joint   A

5. a. Below each of the following diagrams, label the type of joint shown. Use these labels: ball-and-socket, hinge, fixed.
b. Then, in the space provided, tell what type of movement each joint allows.

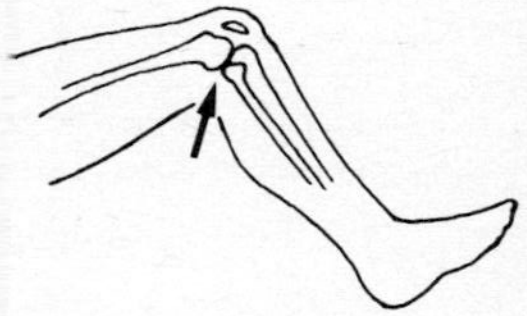

Type	fixed	ball-and-socket	hinge
Movement	no movement	turn bones in circle	back and forth

232

Name _____

THE ROLE OF MUSCLES

In your textbook, read about human muscle types in Section 14:2.

1. Identify these three drawings as smooth, skeletal, or cardiac muscle. Label them correctly. They are about 1500 times natural size.

skeletal muscle   cardiac muscle   smooth muscle

2. Complete the table by checking the correct column for each trait listed.

Trait or location	Skeletal muscle	Cardiac muscle	Smooth muscle
Makes up your small and large intestines			✓
Makes up your heart		✓	
Makes up your body muscles	✓		
Has stripelike appearance	✓	✓	
Is voluntary	✓		
Can be controlled	✓		
Moves your bones	✓		
Has no stripes			✓
Muscles form a tight weave			✓
Involuntary		✓	✓
Is not connected to bone		✓	✓
Can't be controlled		✓	✓
Can contract	✓	✓	✓
Can shorten	✓	✓	✓
Most often eaten as meat	✓		

Name _____

THE ROLE OF MUSCLES

In your textbook, read about how muscles work in Section 14:2.

3. Examine the drawing below and answer the questions.

Muscle C

Muscle A

Tendon B

Tendon D

a. As muscle A contracts, which tendon is pulled? __B__

b. Name the bone to which muscle A is attached. __femur__

c. Will the heel move up or down as muscle A contracts? __up__

d. Name the bone to which tendon B is connected. __heel__

e. As muscle C contracts, which tendon is pulled? __D__

f. Name the bone to which muscle C is attached. __tibia__

g. Will the foot move up or down as muscle C contracts? __up__

h. Name the bone to which tendon D is connected. __tarsals__

4. Examine the two diagrams below and answer the questions.

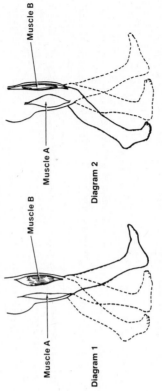

Muscle A   Muscle B   Muscle B   Muscle A

Diagram 1   Diagram 2

1   2

a. In which diagram is muscle A contracted? _____

b. In which diagram is muscle B contracted? _____

c. How can you tell which muscle is contracted? **The contracted muscle is shorter and thicker.**

d. When one muscle of a pair is contracted, the other is __relaxed__.

5. In each diagram, draw a solid line over the dotted line that shows the correct position of the leg.

233

BONE AND MUSCLE PROBLEMS

In your textbook, read about bone and muscle problems in Section 14:3.

1. What is arthritis? **Arthritis is a disease of bone joints.**

2. One type of arthritis results in breakdown of the cartilage at the joints. How would this affect a person's life? **This breakdown causes pain and swelling at the diseased joint. In time, a person may not be able to bend or move the affected part of the body.**

3. What can be done to help people whose joints are severely affected by arthritis? **Diseased joints can be replaced with plastic or metal ones.**

4. What can happen to bones if a person doesn't get enough calcium in their diet? **The bones can become brittle and break easily.**

5. What are ligaments? **Ligaments are tough fibers that connect bones to each other.**

6. What happens to ligaments that are sprained? **They are torn and blood vessels are damaged.**

7. a. What is a muscle cramp? **A muscle cramp occurs when a muscle contracts strongly and can't relax.**

   b. When does it occur? **If you exercise some muscles too long, oxygen supply to those muscles may run low.**

8. a. What is muscular dystrophy? **It's a disease that blocks nerve messages to muscle tissue.**

   b. What effect does it have on muscles? **It causes muscles to waste away.**

VOCABULARY

Review the new words used in Chapter 14 of your textbook. Then, complete the puzzle. Use the words or phrases to fill in the blanks in the sentences. Do not use any term more than once.

skeletal system	solid bone	ligaments
spongy bone	hinge joints	ball-and-socket joint
skeletal muscles	sprain	muscular dystrophy
cardiac muscle	tendons	smooth muscle
arthritis	involuntary muscle	

1. **Cardiac muscle** is found only in the heart.

2. Muscle you have no control over is **involuntary muscle**.

3. Bones are held together by **ligaments**. A **sprain** results when they are torn.

4. **Spongy bone** is usually found toward the ends of bones. The outer part of bones is usually **solid bone**.

5. The **skeletal system** is a framework for the body.

6. All the muscles in your body make up the **muscular system**.

7. Muscles are connected to bones by **tendons**.

8. Muscles you can control are **voluntary muscles**.

9. Many body organs, such as arteries, are made up of **smooth muscle**.

10. **Arthritis** is a disease of the joints.

11. **Muscular dystrophy** is a disease that causes the wasting away of muscle tissue.

12. Muscles that move the bones of the skeleton are **skeletal muscles**.

13. Your knees and elbows are **hinge joints**.

14. Bones can turn in a circle at a **ball-and-socket joint**.

15. Joints that don't move are called **fixed joints**.

Name _____ Date _____ Class _____

THE ROLE OF THE NERVOUS SYSTEM

In your textbook, read about how animals keep in touch with their surroundings in Section 15:1.

1. What is a response? **A response is the action of an organism because of a change in its environment.**

2. Complete the following chart by placing a check mark in the correct columns.

Animal	Nervous system	Nerve net	Nerve cord	Brainlike part	Brain	Eyespots	Eyes
Hydra	✓	✓					
Flatworm	✓		✓	✓		✓	
Spider	✓		✓		✓		✓

HUMAN NERVOUS SYSTEM

In your textbook, read about the complex nervous system of humans in Section 15:2.

1. Complete these facts about nerve cells.

a. Number in your body _**billions**_
b. Special name _**neurons**_
c. Length of some _**one meter**_
d. Main job _**carry messages through body**_
e. Many bunched together _**nerve**_

2. Match the parts of this diagram with the phrases below. Fill in the blanks with the correct letter.

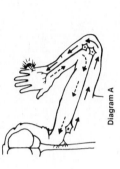

B a. Nucleus   **A** d. Part that receives messages
C b. Axon   **C** e. Part that sends messages
A c. Dendrite   **E** f. Neuron

Name _____ Date _____ Class _____

HUMAN NERVOUS SYSTEM

3. The diagrams below show the path that a message takes from the hand to the spinal cord and back again. One is incorrect. It has two major errors.

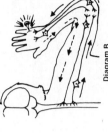

Diagram A   Diagram B

a. Which diagram is incorrect? **A**
b. Describe the two major errors? **Only one pathway of neurons is shown. There are no synapses between neurons.**

4. If the statement is true, place a check mark in the space provided. If it is false, change the underlined word to one that will make the statement true and write it down.

✓ a. When a message reaches the tip of an *axon*, a chemical is released.
synapse b. The *nucleus* is a small space between the axon of one neuron and the dendrite of another neuron nearby.
✓ c. A message moves along a neuron from the *dendrite* to the *axon*.

5. Examine this diagram. It shows a simple sketch of the human nervous system. Put the correct letter in the blank to identify the part being described.

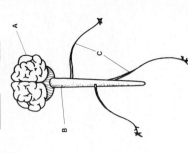

a. Part that sends and receives messages to and from all body parts _**A**_
b. Protected by your vertebrae _**B**_
c. Protected by your skull _**A**_
d. Carries messages from skin to spinal cord _**C**_
e. Spinal cord _**B**_
f. Body nerves _**C**_

Left page (236)

STUDY GUIDE

CHAPTER 15

Name _____ Date _____ Class _____

HUMAN NERVOUS SYSTEM

6. Complete this chart of the human brain.

a. Brain part b. Voluntary or involuntary	Job
a. cerebrum	controls thought, reason, senses, personality; memory; movement of muscles
b. voluntary	
a. cerebellum	helps maintain balance; makes movements smooth and graceful
b. involuntary	
a. medulla	controls heartbeat, breathing, blood pressure
b. involuntary	

*Student answers may vary.

7. a. Label the drawing of a reflex below using the letters of the statements listed here.

A. Message moves from spinal cord to arm muscle.
B. Message moves from finger to spinal cord.
C. Message reaches and enters spinal cord.
D. Muscle contracting pulls hand away.
E. Finger picks up message of sticking pin.

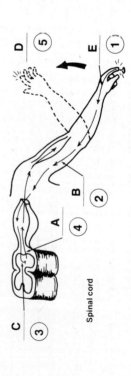

Spinal cord

C ④... b. Put the numbers 1 to 5 in the circles near the blanks to put the steps of the reflex in the correct order.

Right page (88)

STUDY GUIDE

CHAPTER 15

Name _____ Date _____ Class _____

THE ROLE OF THE ENDOCRINE SYSTEM

In your textbook, read about the endocrine system in Section 15:3.

1. On the blanks below, write the name and job of the glands being shown.

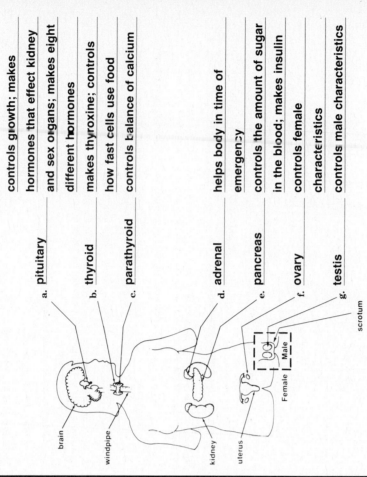

a. pituitary — controls growth; makes hormones that effect kidney and sex organs; makes eight different hormones

b. thyroid — makes thyroxine; controls how fast cells use food

c. parathyroid — controls balance of calcium

d. adrenal — helps body in time of emergency

e. pancreas — controls the amount of sugar in the blood; makes insulin

f. ovary — controls female characteristics

g. testis — controls male characteristics

brain, windpipe, kidney, uterus, Female, Male, scrotum

Name _____ Date _____ Class _____

THE ROLE OF THE ENDOCRINE SYSTEM

2. What does thyroxine do? **It controls how fast your cells release energy from food.**

3. What happens if a person makes too little thyroxine? **The person may gain weight and feel tired.**

4. What happens if a person makes too much thyroxine? **The person may lose weight and feel nervous.**

NERVOUS AND ENDOCRINE SYSTEM PROBLEMS

In your textbook, read about strokes and diabetes in Section 15:4.

1. How does a stroke affect the body? **This depends on where the blood vessel is and how much blood is lost. Usually the person loses the use of a part of the brain because brain cells die without food and oxygen. The person also loses control over the body part once controlled by that part of the brain.**

2. What does insulin do? **Insulin allows sugar in the blood to enter body cells.**

3. a. What disease results if insulin is not present or cannot be used by the cells? **If insulin is not present or cannot be used, diabetes mellitus results.**

   b. People with this disease may begin to lose weight and have a high amount of sugar in their blood. Explain how these two problems may be the result of this disease. **Sugar cannot enter the cells. Therefore, it stays in the blood. Because sugar is food and cannot get inside cells, a person begins to lose weight.**

   c. How may some people with this disease be helped? **They receive injections of insulin.**

Name _____ Date _____ Class _____

VOCABULARY

Review the new words in Chapter 15 of your textbook. Then, circle the letter of the phrase or phrases that best define or explain each word below. Each word may have more than one correct answer.

1. Axon
   - a. Releases a chemical into synapse
   - (b.) Part of a neuron
   - c. Carries message to next neuron

2. Brain
   - (a.) Made up of two regions
   - (b.) Parts can be voluntary or involuntary
   - c. Receives messages from spinal cord

3. Diabetes mellitus
   - a. Caused by too much thyroxine
   - (b.) Involves pancreas and insulin levels
   - (c.) Too much glucose in blood

4. Endocrine system
   - (a.) Made up of small glands
   - (b.) Sends messages in form of hormones
   - c. Composed of neurons

5. Hormone
   - (a.) Made by pituitary
   - b. Has a dendrite end
   - (c.) Carried by the blood

6. Insulin
   - a. Made by the parathyroid gland
   - (b.) Lets cells take in glucose
   - (c.) Can be obtained from other animals for injection in humans

7. Medulla
   - (a.) A region of the brain
   - (b.) Jobs it controls are involuntary
   - (c.) Controls blood pressure

8. Neuron
   - (a.) Many form a nerve
   - (b.) Carries messages
   - c. Usually very short and thick

9. Pituitary gland
   - (a.) Called master gland
   - b. Found on windpipe
   - (c.) Controls growth

10. Reflex
    - (a.) Allows quick reaction
    - b. May or may not involve the brain
    - (c.) Usually protective

11. Synapse
    - (a.) Space between neurons
    - b. Closes when chemical reaches it
    - (c.) Between axon of one neuron and dendrite of another

12. Thyroid gland
    - (a.) Located in front of windpipe
    - (b.) Makes thyroxine
    - (c.) Controls oxygen use by cells

OBSERVING THE ENVIRONMENT

In your textbook, read about the sense organs of four different animals in Section 16:1.

1. Use the diagrams below to answer the questions that follow. (Hint: Answers may be used once, more than once, or not at all.) Which animal:

Planarian   Cricket   Snake   Earthworm

a. uses its tongue to detect smell? **snake**

b. detects touch and chemicals with its antennae? **cricket**

c. has eyes similar to human eyes? **snake**

d. uses knobs on its front end to detect food? **planarian**

e. has grooves on the roof of its mouth for detecting odor molecules? **snake**

f. detects sound on its legs? **cricket**

2. Use the following list of sense organs to fill in the blanks below: nerve cells, eyespots, compound eyes, eyes.

a. Detects light and dark for a cricket **compound eyes**

b. Detects light and dark for a snake **eyes**

c. Detects light and dark for an earthworm **nerve cells**

d. Detects light and dark for a planarian **eyespots**

HUMAN SENSE ORGANS

In your textbook, read about the eye (Section 16:2).

1. Label the eye parts shown in the diagram and complete the chart.

Eye part	Function
Eyelid	protects and moistens outside of eye
Sclera	protects eye
Iris	controls amount of light entering eye
Pupil	light enters eye through this opening

HUMAN SENSE ORGANS

2. On the blanks below, write the name of the eye parts being shown.

G Optic nerve

H Vitreous humor

I Lens

J Retina

A **Eyelid**
B **Cornea**
C **Pupil**
D **Iris**
E **Lens muscle**
F **Sclera**

3. Match the eye parts shown in the diagram with the phrases listed below. Write the letters of the eye parts in the correct blanks.

a. Changes the shape of the lens **E**

b. Protects and moistens outside of eye **A**

c. Changes its shape for viewing at different distances **I**

d. Adjusts the amount of light entering eye **D**

e. Clear, outer covering at front of eye **B**

f. Made of rods and cones **J**

g. Opening in the center of the iris **C**

h. Gives the eye its color **D**

i. Carries messages from retina to brain **G**

j. Liquid that keeps the eye round in shape **H**

k. White outer covering of eye **F**

Name _____ Date _____ Class _____

HUMAN SENSE ORGANS

In your textbook, read about the tongue and the nose in Section 16:2.

4. Complete the chart below by writing the following phrases in the correct columns: detects molecules of gas, has taste buds, four different tastes are detected, seven different odors are detected, olfactory nerve carries message to brain, detects molecules dissolved in water

Tongue	Nose
has taste buds	detects molecules of gas
four different tastes are detected	seven different odors are detected
detects molecules dissolved in water	olfactory nerve carries message to brain

5. On the diagram below, label where the four different tastes are detected.

Bitter

Sour

Salty

Sweet

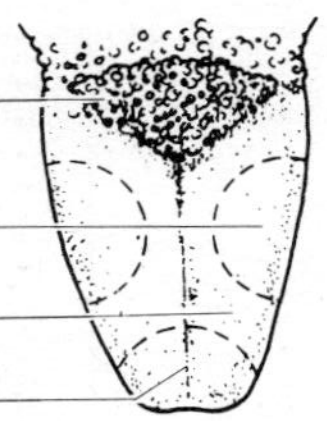

6. About how many taste buds does a person have? **10 000**

7. Label the parts of the nose shown below.

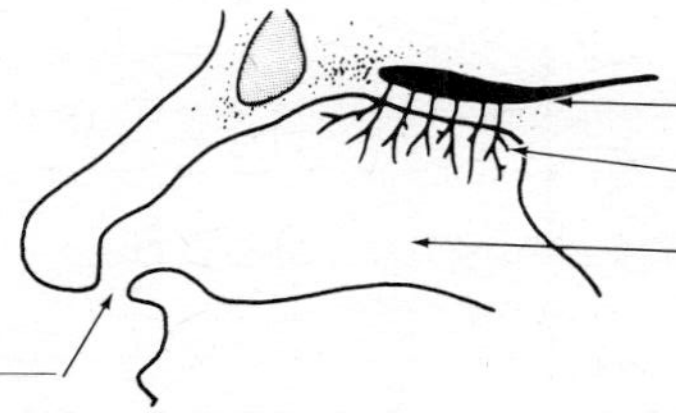

A **Nostril**

B **Olfactory nerve**

C **Nerve cells**

D **Nasal chamber**

Name _____ Date _____ Class _____

HUMAN SENSE ORGANS

In your textbook, read about the ear and the skin in Section 16:2.

8. Label the diagram of the ear. In each circle, place the letter that best matches the part shown.

a. Auditory nerve
b. Ear flap
c. Ear bones
d. Eardrum
e. Ear canal
f. Nerve cells
g. Cochlea
h. Semicircular canals

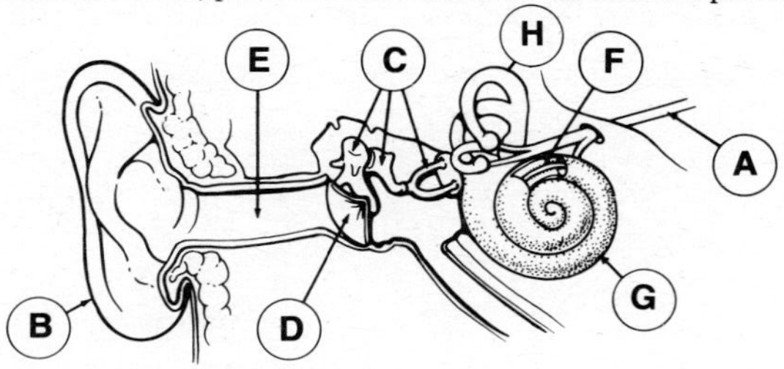

9. Match the ear part in Column I with its job or description in Column II. Write the letter of the job or description to the left of Column I.

d eardrum   a. carries messages from ear flap to eardrum

f cochlea   b. carries messages from cochlea to brain

g nerve cells   c. pick up eardrum vibrations and pass them to membrane in middle ear

a ear canal   d. membrane that vibrates at end of ear canal

c ear bones   e. inner ear parts that help keep balance

e semicircular canals   f. liquid-filled, coiled chamber that contains nerve cells

b auditory nerve   g. pick up motion of liquid in cochlea

10. Each kind of skin neuron below detects something different. On the blank after each statement, write the letter of the skin neuron that would detect that kind of condition.

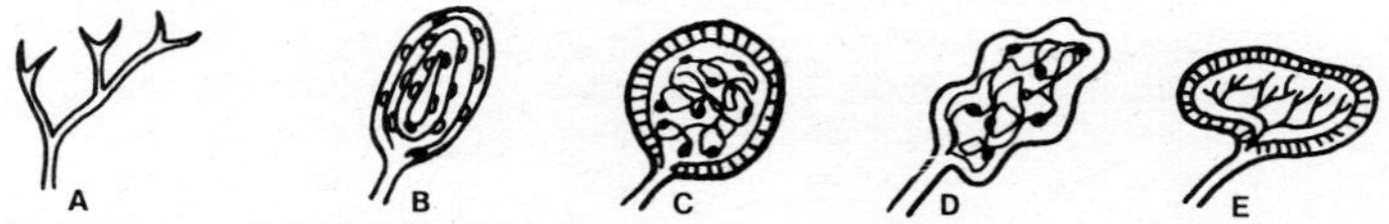

A — Detects pain
B — Detects pressure
C — Detects cold
D — Detects touch
E — Detects heat

a. Water is too chilly for swimming. **C**

b. Cut on finger hurts. **A**

c. Shoes are too tight. **B (or A)**

d. You brush up against someone. **D**

e. You get kicked in the shins. **A**

f. The stove is on. **E**

Name _____ Date _____ Class _____

PROBLEMS WITH SENSE ORGANS

In your textbook, read about problems with sense organs in Section 16:3.

1. Examine the diagrams below. Determine what vision problem is shown. In the space provided, name and describe the problem.

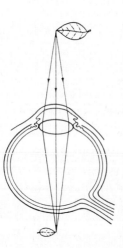

Farsighted means being able to see clearly far away but not close up.
The path of light meets in back of the retina instead of on it.

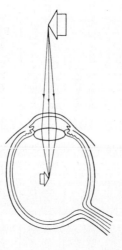

Nearsighted means being able to see clearly close up but not far away.
The path of light meets in front of the retina, instead of on it.

2. How are these problems corrected? They are corrected with special lenses that cause the path of light to meet on the retina.

3. What are two causes of deafness or hearing loss and how is each one treated?
a. The nerve cells in the cochlea do not work. An electronic ear can help.
b. The ear bones cannot move. The stirrup is removed and replaced with a small piece of plastic that vibrates properly.

95

Name _____ Date _____ Class _____

VOCABULARY

Review the new words used in Chapter 16 of your textbook. Then, use the terms below to fill in the blanks in the sentences that follow.

auditory nerve	cochlea	eardrum	rods
olfactory nerve	cones	epidermis	sclera
lens muscles	cornea	nearsighted	pupils
vitreous humor	irises	farsighted	retina
optic nerve	lenses	taste buds	dermis
semicircular canals			

1. The **sclera** is a tough, white covering that protects the eye.
2. Your **taste buds** allow you to taste sweet, salty, bitter, and sour.
3. The **olfactory nerve** carries messages from neurons in the nose to the brain.
4. When you focus on distant objects, your **lens muscles** change the shape of the **lenses** in your eyes.
5. When sound waves enter your ear, they cause the **eardrum** to vibrate.
6. The **vitreous humor** keeps your eyes round in shape.
7. The skin is made of two layers: the **epidermis** and the **dermis**.
8. The **retina** is made of two kinds of neurons: **rods** that detect motion and **cones** which detect color.
9. The **cornea** is a clear covering over the pupil.
10. The **semicircular canals** in your inner ear help you keep your balance.
11. Your **irises** determine the color of your eyes.
12. A **farsighted** person might need to wear glasses to read a book.
    A **nearsighted** person might need to wear glasses to drive a car.
13. The nerve cells in the **cochlea** send messages to the **auditory nerve**, which carries messages of sound to the brain.
14. When you enter a dark room, your **pupils** become larger.
15. The **optic nerve** carries messages from the retina to the brain.

96

240

Name _____ Date _____ Class _____

BEHAVIOR

In Section 17:1 of your textbook, read about behavior.

1. a. Define the word *stimulus*. **A stimulus is something that causes a reaction in an organism.**

   b. In the diagram, which part (A or B) shows a stimulus? **B**

   c. What is the stimulus being shown? **hot pan**

   d. How is the stimulus in the diagram being detected? **There are heat sensitive neurons in the skin that detect the heat.**

2. a. Define the word *response*. **A response is the action of an animal as a result of a change.**

   b. Which part of the diagram (A or B) shows the response? **A**

   c. What is the response shown? **pulling hand away**

   d. Are muscles being used in the response? **yes**

3. Use the choices given below to fill in the table that follows.

Definitions	Traits	Examples
something you are born with	can be changed	sneezing
something you are not born with	cannot be changed	roller skating
you must be taught to do it	aided with a reward	reading
you do not have to be taught		blinking

	Innate behavior	Learned behavior
Definitions	something you are born with	something you are not born with
	you do not have to be taught	you must be taught to do it
Traits	cannot be changed	can be changed
		aided with a reward
Examples	sneezing	roller skating
	blinking	reading

Name _____ Date _____ Class _____

BEHAVIOR

4. Determine if each of the following human behaviors is innate or learned. Write the word *innate* or *learned* on the blank beside each.

   a. speaking a foreign language **learned**

   b. coughing **innate**

   c. feeling pain **innate**

   d. sweating **innate**

   e. tying shoes **learned**

   f. biting fingernails **learned**

   g. having a fever **innate**

   h. shivering **innate**

   i. riding a bicycle **learned**

5. Determine if each of the following behaviors is innate or learned behavior for a dog. Write the word *innate* or *learned* on the blank beside each.

   a. fetching a newspaper **learned**

   b. nursing as a puppy **innate**

   c. scratching **innate**

   d. panting **innate**

   e. wagging tail **innate**

   f. "speaking" for supper **learned**

6. Place a checkmark next to the human behaviors that would get better with practice.

   a. speaking a foreign language ✓

   b. feeling pain

   c. tying shoelaces ✓

   d. sweating

   e. eating with a fork ✓

   f. riding a bicycle ✓

   g. dreaming

   h. having a fever

7. Place a check next to the dog behaviors below that would get better with practice.

   a. sleeping

   b. rolling over for a biscuit ✓

   c. fetching a newspaper ✓

   d. panting

   e. sitting up ✓

8. Using your answers from questions 6 and 7, explain if it is possible to:

   a. improve innate behaviors **No, these behaviors are automatic and cannot be changed.**

   b. improve learned behaviors **Yes, learned behaviors can be improved by repetition or practice.**

STUDY GUIDE

CHAPTER 17

Name _____ Date _____ Class _____

SPECIAL BEHAVIORS

In Section 17:2 of your textbook, read about special behaviors that help reproduction.

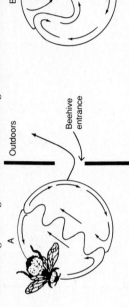

A (male)   B (male)   C (female)

1. **a.** Is frog A making a sound? **yes**

b. Is frog B making a sound? **no**

c. Is frog C able to make croaking sounds? **no**

d. Which frog (A or B) will be able to "mate" with frog C? **A**

e. Explain. **Its croaking is a reproductive behavior that attracts females.**

2. What is a pheromone? **a chemical that changes the behavior of animals of the same species**

3. A scientist experiments with silk moths. You predict the results and provide a reason why.

a. Antennae of male moths are removed. The moths are released. Females are 100 meters away.

Results **Males will ignore females.**

Why? **They cannot detect the pheromone.**

b. Eyes of female moths are covered. They are then placed in a cage that allows air to enter and leave. Males are released 100 meters away.

Results **Males will fly toward females and attempt to mate.**

Why? **Females give off a pheromone that is not dependent on sight.**

c. Antennae of female moths are removed. They are then placed in a cage that allows air to enter and leave. Males are released 100 meters away.

Results **Males will fly toward females and attempt to mate.**

Why? **The male can detect the female pheromone with its antennae.**

d. Female moths are placed in an airtight cage. Males are released 100 meters away.

Results? **Males will ignore females.**

Why? **They cannot detect the pheromone.**

STUDY GUIDE

CHAPTER 17

Name _____ Date _____ Class _____

SPECIAL BEHAVIORS

In Section 17:2 of your textbook, read about special behaviors that help get food and protection.

1. The following two diagrams show bees "talking" to other members while inside their hives.

A   Outdoors   Beehive entrance   B   Outdoors   Beehive entrance

a. Use arrows to indicate the direction that other bees will have to follow to find food.

b. Which hive members will have to fly a shorter distance? (A or B)? **B**

Why? **The number of "wags" along the middle line indicate distance—fewer "wags" means a closer food source.**

c. Explain how this behavior is helpful to the bee hive. **Other bees can be told of the exact location of food.**

2. This picture is a bird's-eye view of a musk oxen herd about to be attacked by four wolves.

Musk oxen   Wolves   Wolves

a. Describe where you would expect to find the young oxen. **the center**

b. How does this behavior help the young? **They are protected from the wolves.**

c. Describe where you would expect to find the older oxen. **forming the circle**

d. How does this behavior help the older oxen? **They are in a good position to fight.**

e. Why is this pattern of protection a useful behavior for the oxen? **It protects them against wolf attacks. Wolves have a harder time fighting a group.**

Name _____ Date _____ Class _____

SPECIAL BEHAVIORS

In Section 17.2 of your textbook, read about migration and parental care.

1. Define migration. **A behavior in which animals move from place to place in response to the season of the year.**

2. Give two examples of animals that migrate. **Atlantic golden plover, fur seals**

3. Give two reasons why animals migrate. **Animals move to new areas as their food supply drops and to find safe places to reproduce and raise young.**

4. Using your answer to question 3, explain why the:

   a. plover migrates. **It migrates to find food.**

   b. fur seal migrates. **They find warmer and safer places to reproduce and care for their young.**

5. Using Figure 17-11 in your text, describe the path of migration for:

   a. plover **from northern Canada to South America**

   b. fur seal **from Alaska to Mexico**

6. What seems to be the main way in which adult Adelie penguins can find their way back to their nests? **using the sun as a guide**

7. a. Does migration seem to be innate or learned? **innate**

   b. What experimental proof can be given using Adelie penguins as an example? **Baby penguins could find their way home, never having been taught by parents.**

8. What is meant by parental care? **behavior in which adults give food, protection, and warmth to eggs or young**

9. Is parental care as important to most fish as it is to most mammals? Explain. **No, parental care is more important to animals that produce fewer young. Parental care gives the small number of offspring of mammals a better chance to survive. Most fish produce hundreds or thousands of eggs at one time.**

Name _____ Date _____ Class _____

VOCABULARY

Review the new words used in Chapter 17 of your textbook.

Write the words next to their definitions below. Then, find and circle the words in the puzzle. The words are written forwards or backwards in either a horizontal, vertical, or diagonal direction.

```
t f s r o p t l c o u r t i n g b e h a v i o r p
c m b r c k r o e z y x a b n c f m p s t u s a n
e s b o l m k s u l u m i t s f k n p g h r l e
s k l i a u r t s v z x h k m n t p k l b e d f r
n c d v r t t b e f u a k n c d e i t i n s t u o
i n n a t e b e h a v i o r l c d o n t c k m k m
l r s h m f l e f r k s n b a k l e a c s k u v o
a w l e a r n e d b e h a v i o r l s t b a c n
i d w b x l x a p m o n t t s t c i t r k j h i c
c a l f g e f l m o t z h r a r m b d f h l z s
o z o t a k l r b n o i t a r g i m d k c w m o e
s e r a k g j k l e t b d e c d m r s o t z a x t
```

1. a chemical that changes the behavior of animals of the same species — **pheromone**

2. behavior that must be taught — **learned behavior**

3. movement of animals in response to the season of the year — **migration**

4. the way an animal acts — **behavior**

5. adults giving food, protection, and warmth to eggs or young — **parental care**

6. behavior that does not require learning — **innate behavior**

7. something that causes an animal to react — **stimulus**

8. complex pattern of behavior an animal is born with — **instinct**

9. used by males and females to attract one another — **courting behavior**

10. lives in a group in which each individual does a certain job — **social insect**

AN INTRODUCTION TO DRUGS

In Section 18:1 of your textbook, read about drugs and drug labels.

1. Complete this outline by writing in the correct definition below each word.

Drug

A chemical that changes the way a living thing functions when it is taken into the body.

Legal

A drug used legally to treat a disease or its symptoms

Two types

Prescription

A doctor must direct you to take it.

Over-the-counter

You may purchase it legally without a prescription.

Controlled

A drug controlled by law, used illegally by many people to change their behavior.

2. Examine the drug label below. Notice that parts of the label are marked with letters. Choose the lettered part of the label that best matches each of the items below and write the correct letter on the blank.

(A) Provides temporary relief from the symptoms of allergies, hay fever, and the common cold.

(B) Directions: *Adults:* 1 to 2 tablets every 4 to 6 hours not to exceed 12 tablets in 24 hours. *Children 6 to under 12 years:* 1 tablet every 4 to 6 hours, not to exceed 6 tablets in 24 hours. *For children under 6:* ask your doctor.

(C) Do not take this drug if you have asthma, glaucoma, emphysema, or shortness of breath unless directed by your doctor. May cause excitability, especially in children.

(D) May cause drowsiness. Alcohol may increase this effect. Avoid alcohol while taking this drug. Use caution while driving a motor vehicle or operating machinery. If you are pregnant or nursing a baby, ask your doctor before using this drug.

(E) Keep this and all medicines out of the reach of children.

(F) In case of accidental overdose, contact your doctor or a Poison Control Center immediately.

(G) Each tablet contains 25 mg rhinamine.

a. dosage **B**
b. cautions **E**
c. main use of drug **A**
d. possible side effects **D**
e. warnings **C**
f. drug contained in tablets **G**
g. what to do in case of overdose **F**

244

AN INTRODUCTION TO DRUGS

In Section 18:1 of your textbook, read about drug dose and overdose.

3. Examine the drug label below and answer the questions that follow.

DIRECTIONS: Adults— 2 tablets every 4 hours as needed. Do not take more than 8 tablets in 24 hours.
Children (6-12) — ½ adult dosage
WARNING: THIS DRUG MAY CAUSE DROWSINESS

CAUTION: Do not give to children under 6 years. Do not use for more than 5 days. If problem continues, see a physician.

a. Define drug dosage. **Drug dosage is how much and how often to take a drug.**

b. What is the adult dose of this drug? **2 tablets every four hours as needed**

c. What is the proper dose of this drug for a child under the age of six? **None—this drug is *not* to be given to a child under the age of six.**

d. What warning is given on this label? **This drug may cause drowsiness.**

4. The drawings below can be compared to drugs entering and leaving the body in proper drug dose and drug overdose.

B

A

a. What is meant by a drug overdose? **The result of too much of a drug in the body**

b. Which drawing (A or B) is more like a drug overdose? **B**

c. Why? **In an overdose, the body cannot get rid of a drug fast enough. The sink is unable to get rid of the water entering it.**

d. Which drawing (A or B) is more like a correct dose? **A**

e. Why? **The sink is able to get rid of the water entering it.**

103

104

Name _____ Date _____ Class _____

USES OF OVER-THE-COUNTER DRUGS

In Section 18:3 of your textbook, read about antihistamines, cough suppressants, and antacids.

1. Explain how an antihistamine works. **It reduces swelling of tissues in the nose by stopping leaking of blood plasma from capillaries.**

2. Explain how a cough occurs. **Nerves in the trachea send a message to the part of the brain that controls coughing. The brain sends the message to your diaphragm, which then moves up, and to your epiglottis, which closes. Pressure builds up in the chest, the epiglottis opens, and a burst of air under high pressure is pushed from your lungs.**

3. What does a cough suppressant do to help stop coughing? **It slows down or suppresses the part of the brain that controls coughing.**

4. Use the diagrams below to answer the questions. Some answers will require more than one letter.

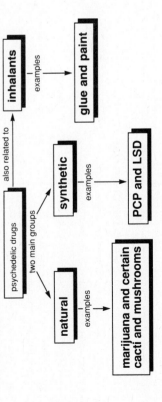

▨ STOMACH ACID
▧ WATER AND SALT

a. Sodium bicarbonate is being added to the stomach. ___B___

b. Person has heartburn. ___A, B___

c. Heartburn is gone. ___C___

d. Antacid is being taken. ___B___

e. Carbon dioxide gas is given off. ___C___

f. Water and salt are in stomach. ___C___

g. Acid is present in stomach. ___A, B___

h. Acid was chemically changed. ___C___

Name _____ Date _____ Class _____

HOW DRUGS AFFECT BEHAVIOR

In Section 18:2 of your textbook, read about stimulants, depressants, and psychedelic drugs.

1. Complete the following table about stimulants.

Definition	drugs that speed up body activities controlled by nervous system
Examples, controlled	amphetamines, cocaine
Examples, not controlled	caffeine and nicotine
Two ways nervous system may be affected	axon gives off more of the chemical messenger than normal, or chemical messenger not destroyed once it reaches the dendrite of the next neuron
Effects on body	increase heart rate; increase blood pressure; decrease appetite; increase alertness

2. Complete the following table about depressants.

Definition	drugs that slow messages in the nervous system
Examples, controlled	codeine, morphine, barbiturates
Two ways nervous system may be affected	block axon from giving off chemical messenger or block chemical messengers across synapse
Effects on body	calm behavior, reduce pain, help people sleep

3. Complete the following idea map about psychedelic drugs. Use these words or phrases: natural, PCP and LSD, inhalant, synthetic, glue and paint, marijuana and certain cacti and mushrooms.

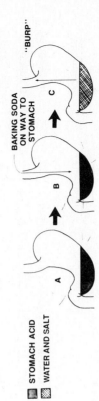

STUDY GUIDE

Name _____ Date _____ Class _____

CARELESS DRUG USE

In Section 18:4 of your textbook, read about careless drug use. Place a checkmark in front of those sentences that are true.

_____ 1. It is safe to use the drugs that a physician has told someone else to use.

_____ 2. The dose of a drug prescribed by a physician for someone else is always the same as the dose that you would need.

✓ 3. A drug allergy means that you are sensitive to a particular drug.

_____ 4. Allergic drug reactions can never cause death.

✓ 5. Drug abuse is the incorrect or improper use of a drug.

_____ 6. Drug abuse can never lead to drug dependence.

✓ 7. Codeine, alcohol, and heroin are examples of drugs that may cause dependence.

8. Complete the following table by placing checkmarks in the correct columns.

	Cocaine	Caffeine	Nicotine	Alcohol
May cause breathing or heart to stop suddenly	✓			
Causes feeling of alertness and difficulty in falling asleep		✓		
Stimulant	✓*	✓	✓	
Depressant				✓
Leads to dependence	✓	✓	✓	✓
When BAC is 0.4-0.5, unconsciousness or coma can occur				✓
Causes cancer and linked to heart disease			✓	
One form, crack, can cause death with first use	✓			
Can lead to withdrawal symptoms if stopped after dependent use	✓	✓	✓	✓

*Large doses can result in severe depressant effects.

STUDY GUIDE

Name _____ Date _____ Class _____

VOCABULARY

Review the new words in Chapter 18 of your textbook. Then, write the term that each of the phrases below describes on the blank that follows the phrase.

1. a drug that slows messages in the nervous system _____ depressant

2. too much of a drug _____ overdose

3. will form carbon dioxide in the stomach _____ antacid

4. a drug in cigarettes _____ nicotine

5. a chemical that changes the way a living thing functions when it is taken into the body _____ drug

6. a drug that speeds up body activities controlled by the nervous system _____ stimulant

7. the incorrect or improper use of a drug _____ drug abuse

8. a change that is not expected caused by a drug _____ side effect

9. drug that relieves a stuffy nose _____ antihistamine

10. a drug you can buy legally without a prescription _____ over-the-counter drug

11. a change that takes place in the body due to disease _____ symptom

12. needing a certain drug in order to carry out normal daily activities _____ dependence

13. a drug in cola, tea, and coffee _____ caffeine

14. a drug that a doctor must tell you to take _____ prescription drug

15. drug made from the leaves of the coca bush _____ cocaine

16. drugs that are controlled by law _____ controlled drug

17. how much and how often to take a drug _____ dosage

18. drug that changes the signals from the sense organs _____ psychedelic drug

19. drug breathed in through the lungs _____ inhalant

20. drug found in alcoholic drinks _____ ethyl alcohol

Name _____ Date _____ Class _____

THE STRUCTURE OF LEAVES

In your textbook, read about leaf traits in Section 19:1.

1. Label the following parts of this diagram: stalk, midrib, blade, smaller vein.

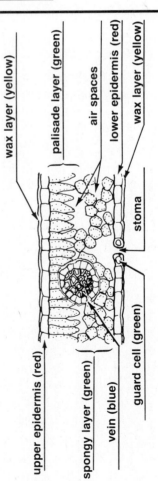

midrib

blade

stalk

smaller vein

In your textbook, read about the cells in a leaf in Section 19:1.

2. Label the following parts of this diagram of a leaf section: air spaces, upper epidermis, lower epidermis, wax layer, guard cell, wax layer, vein, stoma, spongy layer, palisade layer.

wax layer (yellow)

palisade layer (green)

air spaces

lower epidermis (red)

wax layer (yellow)

stoma

spongy layer (green)

vein (blue)

guard cell (green)

upper epidermis (red)

3. Using these colors, shade in the following parts on the diagram above:
Green—leaf cells that make food   Blue—leaf cells that carry water and food
Red—leaf cells that protect   Yellow—waterproof layer

Name _____ Date _____ Class _____

THE STRUCTURE OF LEAVES

4. The chart below describes several different kinds of leaves and gives an example of each. Read each description and example. Examine the diagrams carefully. Then, write the letter of the leaf type on the blank next to the diagram that it best matches.

Shape	Other traits	Example
Fan		Ginkgo (a)
Heart	Edges have teeth.	Cottonwood (b)
Heart	Edges are smooth. Tip is very pointed.	Catalpa (c)
Heart	Edges are smooth. Tip is not very pointed.	Redbud (d)
Oval	Edges are smooth.	Magnolia (e)
Oval	Edges have a few large teeth.	Holly (f)
Oval	Edges have many small teeth.	Elm (g)
Needle	Needles are in twos.	Virginia pine (h)
Needle	Needles are in threes.	Pitch pine (i)
Needle	Needles are in fives.	White pine (j)
5-part	All leaflets attach at same point.	Buckeye (k)
5-part	Three leaflets attach at top, two near bottom.	Shagbark hickory (l)
More than 5-parts	Edges have teeth. Leaflets are oppositely attached.	Sumac (m)
More than 5-parts	Edges are smooth. Leaflets are oppositely attached.	White ash (n)
Oval	Edges are toothed. Tip is very pointed.	Hackberry (o)
Wavy lobed	Lobes are pointed.	Pin oak (p)
Wavy lobed	Lobes are rounded.	White oak (q)

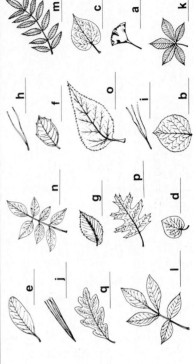

m

c

a

k

h

f

o

i

b

e

j

q

n

g

p

d

l

247

THE STRUCTURE OF LEAVES

In your textbook, read about water loss in plants in Section 19:1.

5. The path of water movement through a plant is shown below. Complete the diagram by writing each of these sentences in the place that best shows what is stated.
   Water moves into the leaves where some is used in photosynthesis.
   Water enters roots through the root hairs.
   Water escapes from stomata into the air during transpiration.
   Tubelike cells (xylem) carry water through the stem to the leaves.

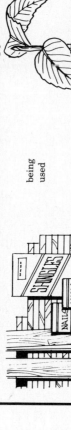

③ **Water moves into the leaves where some is used in photosynthesis.**

④ **Water escapes from stomata into the air during transpiration.**

Stomata

① **Water enters roots through the root hairs.**

② **Tubelike cells (xylem) carry water through the stem to the leaves.**

Root hairs

6. Circle the conditions under which a plant will lose much water through its stomata.

   (a.) Hot, dry days   b. Cool, damp days   c. In humid greenhouse

7. Circle the conditions under which a plant will lose little water through its stomata.

   a. Hot, dry days   (b.) Cool, damp days   (c.) In humid greenhouse

8. a. The diagram below shows the outline of a plant in two conditions. Assume the plant receives no water through its roots and its stomata are open. Complete the diagram by drawing over the dashed lines that best show what the plant would look like.

   POSITION A   POSITION B

   b. Which of the following words best describes what has happened to the plant from position A to position B? (Circle one.)

   transpiration, (wilting,) respiration, photosynthesis

LEAVES MAKE FOOD

In your textbook, read about photosynthesis in Section 19:2.

The two columns of pictures below relate a carpenter's building a house to a leaf's making food. For each step in both processes, fill in the blanks with the name of what is being produced or used.

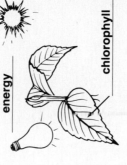
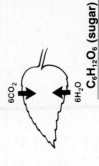

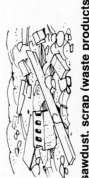

lumber, nails, shingles   *being used*

water and carbon dioxide   *being used*

energy—human, electric   *being used*

energy / **chlorophyll**   *being used*

house   *being produced*

$6CO_2$ $6H_2O$ $C_6H_{12}O_6$ (sugar) / **oxygen**   *being produced*

sawdust, scrap (waste products)   *being produced*

STUDY GUIDE

Name _____ Date _____ Class _____

VOCABULARY

Review the new words used in Chapter 19 of your textbook. Then complete this puzzle.

1. On the diagram below, label the following leaf structures: blade, midrib. Then write a sentence describing each structure.

blade

midrib

a. The blade is the <u>thin, flat part of a leaf</u>

b. The midrib is the <u>main vein of a leaf</u>

2. Tell which of the following processes is helpful for the plant and which is harmful.

a. wilting _____ <u>harmful</u>

b. transpiration _____ <u>helpful</u>

3. Write these words in the proper places in this table: palisade layer, stoma, spongy layer, epidermis, guard cell.

Parts on outside of leaf	Parts inside leaf
epidermis	palisade layer
stoma	spongy layer
guard cell	

STUDY GUIDE

Name _____ Date _____ Class _____

LEAVES FOR FOOD

In your textbook, read about leaf color changes in Section 19:3.

1. These two diagrams show sections of a leaf. The left leaf has been in the light for 10 days. The right leaf has been in the dark for 10 days. Color the cells of the leaves either green or yellow depending on what they would look like to us. Color only those cells within the brackets. **Students should not color cells of vascular bundles.**

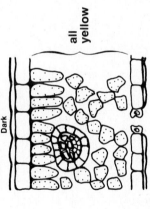

Light

all green

Dark

all yellow

2. Label the two diagrams with the leaf parts you can see. Use colored pencils to shade in what color a red oak leaf will be during each season shown.

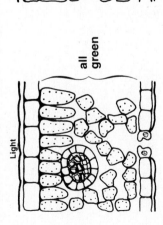

stem

stalk

blade

Summer

smaller vein

green

midrib

blade

midrib

stalk

Autumn

stem

smaller vein

red

Name _____ Date _____ Class _____

STEM STRUCTURE

In your textbook, read about herbaceous and woody stems in Section 20:1.

1. Use the letters of the correct words or parts from the following chart to complete the table below.

	A	B	C
Outer covering	Soft	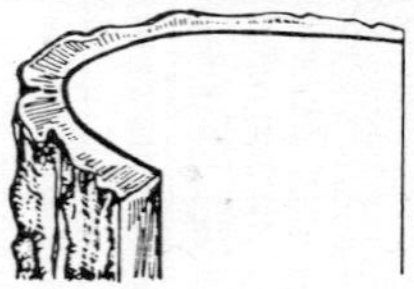	Epidermis
Outer color	Brown	Yellow	Green
Xylem and phloem			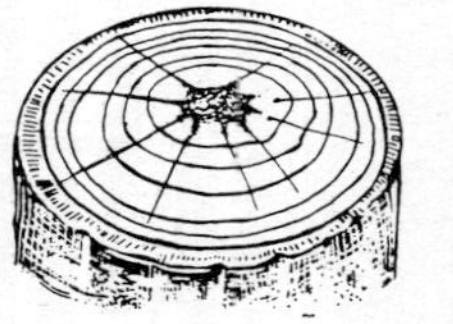
Example of stem type			

	Woody stem	Herbaceous stem
Outer covering	B	A, C
Outer color	A	C
Xylem and phloem	C	A, B
Example of stem type	A	B, C

Name _____ Date _____ Class _____

STEM STRUCTURE

In your textbook, read about stem growth in Section 20:1.

2. Examine the diagram of a core sample taken from a tree. Then, answer the following questions.

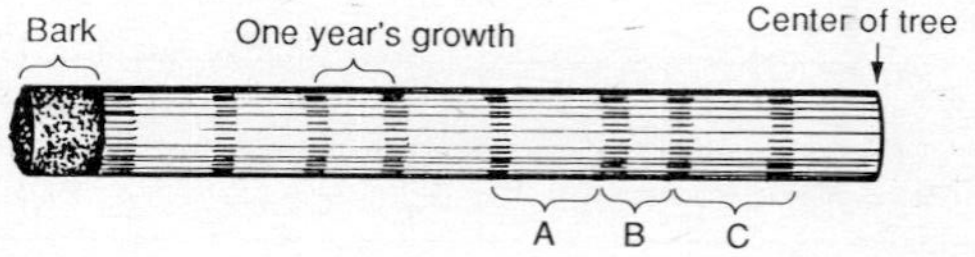

a. What is counted to determine the age of a tree? __rings of xylem__

b. In what part of the year do the dark bands form? __summer__

c. Why are they dark? __The xylem cells are smaller (because growth is slower).__

d. In what part of the year do the light bands form? __spring__

e. Why are they light? __The xylem cells are larger (because growth is faster).__

f. How old was this tree when the core sample was taken? __8 years old__

g. Which band (A, B, or C) shows the poorest year of growth? __B__

h. Which band (A, B, or C) shows the year with the most rainfall? __A__

3. Examine the diagram below of a core sample taken in 1991.

Students may need help identifying growth rings.

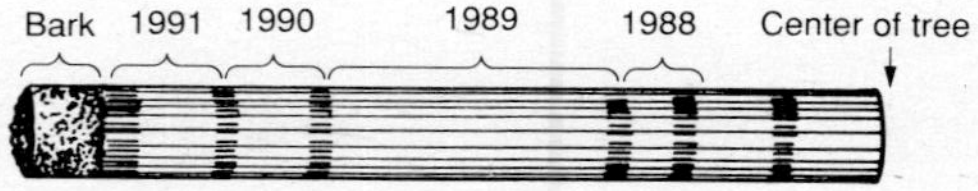

__6 years old__

a. How old was this tree in 1991? __6 years old__

b. What year was rainfall the least where this tree was growing? __1988__

c. What year did the tree grow the least? __1988__

d. What year was rainfall the most where this tree was growing? __1989__

e. What year did the tree grow the most? __1989__

THE JOBS OF STEMS

In your textbook, read about transport and storage in Section 20:2.

1. How do leaves get the water and minerals they need? **Water and minerals are taken in by the roots and transported up through the stem through long, tubelike cells called xylem.**

2. How does new water enter the roots? **by osmosis**

3. How is the movement of water through a plant like a thread being pulled through a straw? **The molecules of water stick together in a threadlike stream through the plant.**

4. In what form is sugar stored in plants? **as starch**

5. a. What kind of cells allow the transport of water upward in a plant? **xylem cells**

   b. What kind of cells allow the transport of food downward in a plant? **phloem cells**

6. Examine the diagrams below. Which one (A or B) best shows the path water takes through a stem? **A**

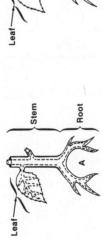

7. Explain what is wrong with the diagram that you did not choose as the answer to the last question. **The xylem does not connect from roots through the stem to the leaves in diagram B.**

ROOT STRUCTURE

In your textbook, read about root cells and growth in Section 20:3.

1. Label the drawing below using these labels: root hair, cortex, xylem, phloem. epidermis, endodermis.

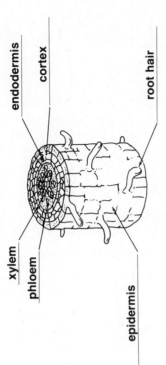

endodermis
cortex
xylem
phloem
epidermis
root hair

2. Label the diagram below using these labels: primary root, secondary root, root hairs.

(A) secondary root
(B) root hairs
(C) primary root

3. From the diagram above, put the correct letters on the blanks below.
   a. largest root of plant __C__
   b. absorb water and minerals __B__
   c. first root to form in plants __C__
   d. would measure greatest distance if put in line __B__
   e. forms from primary root __A__

ROOT STRUCTURE

In your textbook, read about taproots and fibrous roots in Section 20:4.

4. Examine the drawings below. Then, put A or B on the blank after each phrase or word.

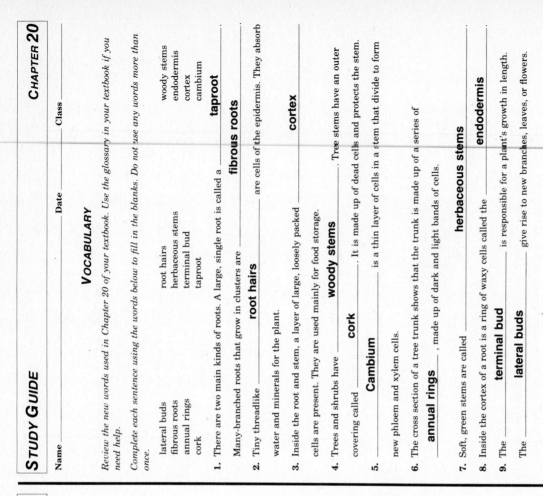

a. taproot   **B**
b. fibrous roots   **A**
c. often spreads out   **A**
d. often grows very deep   **B**

THE JOBS OF ROOTS

In your textbook, read about absorption, anchorage, and storage in Section 20:4.

Examine the pictures below. Beside each picture write a sentence describing what the object pictured does. Then, write a sentence describing a similar job of roots. The first one is done for you.

Sponge   1. A sponge absorbs water. Roots absorb water and minerals from the soil.

Suitcase   2. **A suitcase helps to store and move items. Roots store food and move water and minerals to the stem.**

Hair net   3. **A hair net holds hair together. Roots hold soil particles together.**

Paper clip   4. **A paper clip holds things together. Roots hold soil particles together.**

Anchor   5. **An anchor holds a boat in place. Roots hold a plant in place.**

Paper towels   6. **Paper towels absorb water. Roots absorb water and minerals from the soil.**

Stapler   7. **A stapler holds papers together. Roots hold soil particles together.**

Silo   8. **A silo stores food. A root stores food.**

Tent stake   9. **A tent stake anchors a tent. Roots anchor a plant.**

VOCABULARY

Review the new words used in Chapter 20 of your textbook. Use the glossary in your textbook if you need help.

Complete each sentence using the words below to fill in the blanks. Do not use any words more than once.

lateral buds	root hairs	woody stems
fibrous roots	herbaceous stems	endodermis
annual rings	terminal bud	cortex
cork	taproot	cambium

1. There are two main kinds of roots. A large, single root is called a **taproot**.

2. Many-branched roots that grow in clusters are **fibrous roots**.

3. Tiny threadlike **root hairs** are cells of the epidermis. They absorb water and minerals for the plant.

4. Inside the root and stem, a layer of large, loosely packed cells are present. They are used mainly for food storage. **cortex**

5. Trees and shrubs have **woody stems**. Tree stems have an outer covering called **cork**. It is made up of dead cells and protects the stem.

6. **Cambium** is a thin layer of cells in a stem that divide to form new phloem and xylem cells.

7. The cross section of a tree trunk shows that the trunk is made up of a series of **annual rings**, made up of dark and light bands of cells.

8. Soft, green stems are called **herbaceous stems**.

9. Inside the cortex of a root is a ring of waxy cells called the **endodermis**.

The **terminal bud** is responsible for a plant's growth in length.

The **lateral buds** give rise to new branches, leaves, or flowers.

PLANT RESPONSES

In your textbook, read about growth and flowering in Section 21:1.

Look at the pictures of the plants below. Then, answer the questions that follow.

	May 15	June 15	July 15	August 15
Plant A				
Plant B				
Plant C				

1. Which plant is called a short-day plant? _____ **plant A**

   Explain your answer. **The plant forms flowers in the fall of the year when the days are getting shorter, thereby providing less sunlight each new day.**

2. Which plant is called a long-day plant? _____ **plant C**

   Explain your answer. **The plant forms flowers in the spring of the year when the days are getting longer, thereby providing more sunlight each new day.**

3. Which plant is called a day-neutral plant? _____ **plant B**

   Explain your answer. **The plant forms flowers at most times of the year; it does not depend on day length to produce flowers.**

PLANT RESPONSES

In your textbook, read about tropisms in plants in Section 21:1. Then, read the description below and answer the questions that follow.

Some plants in a greenhouse were tipped over and not set upright for several weeks. When the greenhouse manager found them, and stood them up, they looked like those in the diagram.

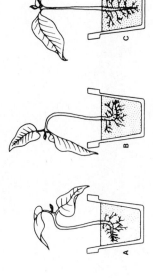

4. Which plant(s) were not tipped over? _____ **C** _____ Explain your answer. **The plant roots are growing down into the soil and the stem is growing upward toward the light. This is the way plants normally grow.**

5. Which plant(s) were tipped over? _____ **A and B** _____ Explain your answer. **When a plant is turned on its side, the plant roots begin to grow downward and the stem begins to grow upward.**

6. What is the name of the tropism that describes how the roots are responding? _____ **gravitropism**

7. What is the name of the tropism that describes how the stem is responding? _____ **phototropism**

8. Define each tropism. Gravitropism is the response of plants to gravity. **Phototropism is the response of plants to light.**

9. Which part of the plant responds to gravity? _____ **roots** _____ How can you tell? **Roots grow toward Earth, where the pull of gravity is strongest.**

10. Which part of the plant responds to light? _____ **stem** _____ How can you tell? **Stems grow toward light.**

Name _____ Date _____ Class _____

GROWTH REQUIREMENTS

In your textbook, read about growth requirements of plants in Section 21:2. Then, read the following description of a set of experiments on plant growth.

Experiments were done to find what effects the amount of water, light, minerals, and soil had on some plants. In each experiment, the amounts of light, water, minerals, soil, and temperature were kept the same except where shown in the figure on the next page. The plants were grown for nearly two months. Answer the questions after you have studied the diagrams.

1. In experiment 1, which plant grew best? __**plant C**__ How often was this plant
watered? __**every three days**__

2. What would happen to the plant in answer 1 if it were planted in an area where it rained four
days each week? __**The plant would not grow as well as it did in the experiment.**__

3. Does the kind of plant used in experiment 1 grow well with a great amount of water? __**no**__
Explain your answer. __**Comparing plants A, B, and C shows that too much**__
__**water slows growth.**__

4. What growth requirement is being tested in experiment 2? __**light**__

5. In experiment 2, which plant grew best? __**plant A**__ How much sun did the plant
receive? __**full sun**__

6. Suppose you bought several of these plants to put in your flower beds. Where would you *not*
plant them? __**in shady areas**__ Why? __**This kind of plant does not**__
__**grow well in the shade.**__

7. What growth requirement is being tested in experiment 3? __**type of soil needed**__

8. In experiment 3, which plant grew best? __**plant B**__ What type of soil was this plant
grown in? __**potting soil**__

9. Could the type of plant in experiment 3 be grown in the desert? __**no**__ Why or
why not? __**The desert is mostly sandy soil. This plant does not grow well in**__
__**sandy soil.**__

Name _____ Date _____ Class _____

GROWTH REQUIREMENTS

	Plant A	Plant B	Plant C	
	watered 3 times a day	watered 1 time a day	watered every 3 days	Experiment 1
	full sun	partial sun	shade	Experiment 2
	clay and sand	potting soil	sand	Experiment 3

Name _____ Date _____ Class _____

PLANT DISEASES AND PESTS

In your textbook, read about factors that can slow down or stop plant growth in Section 21:3.

1. List two ways that bacteria can enter a plant. **through stomata and through small cuts**

2. Once inside, how do bacteria harm plants? **They destroy plants when they invade the cytoplasm and spread throughout the plant.**

3. What can happen to the leaves of plants infected by viruses? **They might develop yellow spots or tumors, depending on the type of virus.**

4. How are diseases that are caused by fungi carried to plants? **Some spores are carried by insects, others by wind and rain.**

5. How do insects infect plants with diseases? **Insects take in disease microbes when they eat the tissues of infected plants. They visit uninfected plants, and transfer these microbes from their mouthparts to the tissues of the uninfected plants.**

6. How else can insects be harmful to plants? **They can damage or even kill plants by eating too many leaves. A plant with damaged or missing leaves can't make enough food by photosynthesis to keep the plant alive.**

7. Complete the table below by placing checkmarks in the correct columns.

Condition in plants	Cause		
	Bacteria	Viruses	Fungi
Corn smut			✓
Mosaic disease		✓	
Dutch elm disease			✓
Blister spots on fruit and leaves	✓		
Wheat rust			✓

Name _____ Date _____ Class _____

VOCABULARY

Review the new words in Chapter 21 of your textbook. Then, complete this puzzle.

Across

6. response of a plant to light
7. substance made of minerals that makes soil productive for plant growth
8. plant that needs two years to complete growth and produce seeds
9. plant that flowers when the length of day rises above 12 to 14 hours
10. plant that completes its life cycle in one year
11. response of a plant to contact

Down

1. plant that doesn't depend on the number of hours of light to flower
2. response of a plant to gravity
3. plant that lives longer than two years
4. growth response of a plant to a stimulus
5. plant that flowers when the day falls below 12 to 14 hours

Name _____ Date _____ Class _____

MITOSIS

In your textbook, read about the steps of mitosis in Section 22:1.

1. The following steps of mitosis are out of order. Place the numbers *1-5* in the blanks to show the correct order.

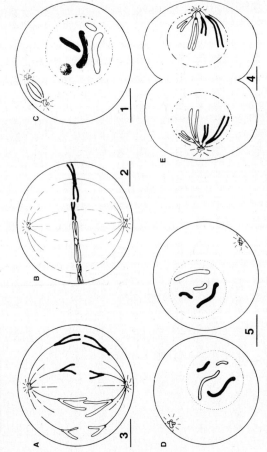

2. In the blanks below, write the letter of the diagram above that is being described.

a. Two new identical cells are formed. _____ D

b. Cytoplasm begins to separate. _____ E

c. Sister chromatids are first pulled apart. _____ A

d. Chromosomes are completely separated and at opposite ends of the cell. _____ B

e. Sister chromatids can be seen for the first time. _____ B

f. This is what cells look like before going through mitosis. _____ C

g. Nuclear membrane begins to break down. _____ C

h. Sister chromatids move to the cell's center and line up on fibers. _____ B

i. A nuclear membrane begins to form around chromosomes. _____ D

256

Name _____ Date _____ Class _____

MEIOSIS

In your textbook, read about meiosis in Section 22:2.

1. Examine the table below. Fill in the missing information based on the numbers that are given.

Organism	Body cell chromosome number	Chromosome number sex cell
Human	46	23
Cat	38	19
Onion	16	8
Rye	14	7
Guinea pig	64	32
Chicken	78	39

2. Graph the data in the table above on the graph below. Follow the example on the graph.

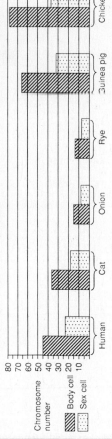

3. Using the information above, complete the following table. The first one is done for you.

Organism	Sperm chromosome number	Egg chromosome number	Fertilized egg chromosome number	Chromosome number in each body cell of offspring
Human	23	23	46	46
Cat	19	19	38	38
Onion	8	8	16	16
Rye	7	7	14	14
Guinea pig	32	32	64	64
Chicken	39	39	78	78

127

128

MEIOSIS

In your textbook, read about mitosis and meiosis in Section 22:2.

4. The chart below shows the steps of mitosis and meiosis in the correct order. Complete the chart by answering the questions beside the diagrams.

Mitosis   **Meiosis**

a. Where are the chromosomes?	**in nucleus**
b. How many are present in each cell?	**four**
c. What happened to the chromosomes in each cell?	**They doubled forming sister chromatids.**
d. Where are the sister chromatids?	**cell center**
e. What is happening to the sister chromatids?	**They move apart. Pairs move apart in meiosis but sister chromatids remain together.**
f. How many cells are formed in mitosis?	**two**
g. Are the chromosomes single or double?	**single**
h. Are the chromosomes single or double now in meiosis?	**double**
i. What happens in meiosis now?	**Sister chromatids move to opposite ends of the cell.**
j. How many cells are formed in meiosis?	**four**

MEIOSIS

In your textbook, read about the steps of meiosis in Section 22:2.

5. Match each of the following steps of meiosis with the statements below. Letters may be used more than once. Write the correct letter on each blank. Note: The statements describing the steps of meiosis are not in the correct order.

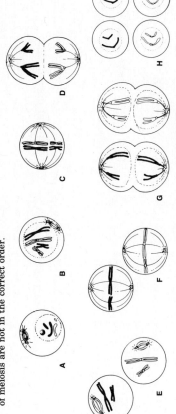

A   B   F   C   G   D   H

a. Matching chromosomes come together to form pairs. **C (or B)**

b. Each chromosome has two strands of sister chromatids. Pairs of sister chromatids are lined up near cell's center; original and copy still together. **C**

c. One cell division completed and two new cells formed. **E**

d. Each chromosome becomes doubled, forming sister chromatids. **B**

e. Original and copy chromosome move to opposite ends of cell. **G**

f. Centrioles move again to opposite ends of cells. **E**

g. Pairs of sister chromatids move to center of cell. **C**

h. Four new cells have formed from original. **H**

i. Nuclear membrane begins to fade away. **B**

j. Sister chromatid pairs move to opposite ends of cell. **D**

k. Four single chromosomes are present in cell. **A**

l. Each cell is now a sex cell. **H**

m. Nuclear membrane is reappearing. **G**

MEIOSIS

In your textbook, read about sperm, eggs, and fertilization in Section 22:2.

6. Look at the drawing below. Label the parts as egg, sperm, or chromosomes.

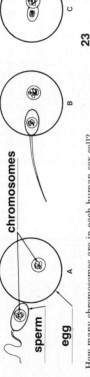

chromosomes

sperm

egg

A   B   C

a. How many chromosomes are in each human sex cell? __**23**__

b. How many pairs of chromosomes are in each sex cell? __**none**__

c. What process has occurred between diagram B and C? __**fertilization**__

d. How many chromosomes are in the human egg cell in diagram C? __**46**__

CHANGES IN THE RATE OF MITOSIS

In your textbook, read about aging and cancer in Section 22:3.

1. What happens to fingernail growth as a person ages? Explain your answer. __**Fingernail growth slows down because mitosis in cells of the fingernails slows down.**__

2. Why is the heart weaker and less able to pump blood as a person ages? __**As a person grows, muscle cells get bigger, but no new cells are made. As a person ages, the muscle cells wear out, and no new ones replace them.**__

3. How are cancer cells different from normal cells? __**They undergo rapid mitosis, and they no longer have their usual shape and nucleus.**__

4. List three causes of cancer. __**chemicals, radiation, and viruses**__

VOCABULARY

Review the new words used in Chapter 22 of your textbook. Then complete this exercise.

1. Match one of these choices to each of the following statements. Write the proper choice on each blank: mitosis, meiosis.

a. Four new cells are formed from each original. __**meiosis**__

b. This process makes sperm cells. __**meiosis**__

c. Two new cells are formed from each original. __**mitosis**__

d. New skin cells are made this way. __**mitosis**__

e. This type of cell reproduction helps you grow. __**mitosis**__

f. This type of cell reproduction makes egg cells. __**meiosis**__

g. This makes cells with half the original cell chromosome number. __**meiosis**__

h. This makes cells with the same chromosome number as the original. __**mitosis**__

2. Match one of the choices to each of the following phrases. Write the proper choice on each blank: testes, ovaries, cancer, polar body, puberty, sex cells, body cells, sister chromatids

a. stage when person produces sex cells __**puberty**__

b. organs that produce eggs __**ovaries**__

c. small cell formed and then dies during meiosis in female __**polar body**__

d. organs that produce sperm __**testes**__

e. egg and sperm __**sex cells**__

f. cells that make up the skin, blood, bones, and stomach __**body cells**__

g. the two strands of a doubled chromosome __**sister chromatids**__

h. a disease in which body cells reproduce faster than normal __**cancer**__

ASEXUAL REPRODUCTION IN PLANTS

In your textbook, read about reproduction by roots, leaves, and stems in Section 23:1.

1. Complete the table below.

Plants	Plant part being used	Egg or sperm cells needed? (yes or no)	Number of parents needed	Mitosis or meiosis occurring
African violet	leaf	no	1	mitosis
Tuber (white potato)	stem	no	1	mitosis
Tuber (Sweet Potato)	root	no	1	mitosis
Onion bulb	stem and leaves	no	1	mitosis
Delicious apple Macintosh apple	stem	no	2	mitosis
Strawberry	stem	no	1	mitosis

2. Were sex cells or fertilization involved in any of the situations shown above? __no__

259

SEXUAL REPRODUCTION IN PLANTS

In your textbook, read about flowers and sexual reproduction in Section 23:2.

1. Label these four parts: pistil, petal, stamen, sepal.

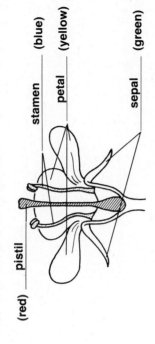

(red) ____ pistil

stamen (blue)

petal (yellow)

sepal (green)

2. Use the following colors to shade in the above drawing.
   a. yellow, for parts that attract insects
   b. green, for parts that protect flower in bud stage
   c. red, for parts that are female
   d. blue, for parts that are male

3. Label the parts shown here. Use these choices: sticky tip, pollen grains, pistil, ovary, stamen, ovule, saclike part, stalk.

saclike part

stamen

pollen grains

pistil

sticky tip

stalk

ovary

ovule

4. Name the part being described. Use these choices: saclike part, ovary, ovule, pollen grains, sticky tip, pistil, stamen.

   a. contains ovules ____ovary____
   b. male flower part ____stamen____
   c. contains pollen ____saclike part____
   d. will form sperm ____pollen grains____

   e. female flower part ____pistil____
   f. traps pollen grains ____sticky tip____
   g. hold female reproductive cells ____ovules____

133

134

SEXUAL REPRODUCTION IN PLANTS

In your textbook, read about pollination and fertilization in plants in Section 23:2.

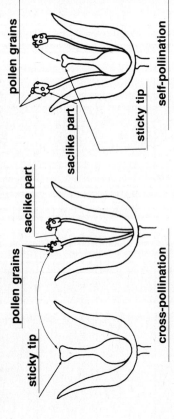

pollen grains

saclike part

sticky tip

pollen grains

saclike part

sticky tip

cross-pollination

self-pollination

5. Examine the pictures shown above.
   a. Label the saclike part, pollen grains, and sticky tip in both diagrams.
   b. Use arrows to draw the pathway that pollen grains take in order for pollination to occur.
   c. On the line below each diagram, label the process self-pollination or cross-pollination.

6. The diagrams below show pollination and fertilization of a flower. However, the diagrams are out of order. Put the letter of each step below the diagram that it best matches.

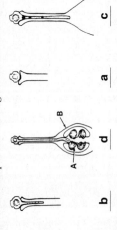

b   d   a   c

   a. A pollen grain lands on the sticky tip of the pistil.
   b. A tube from the pollen grain grows down into the stalk.
   c. Two sperm nuclei and a tube nucleus travel down the tube.
   d. One sperm fertilizes the egg in the ovule. One sperm fertilizes a nucleus to form a food supply.

7. Examine the diagram above that has labels A and B on it.
   a. Which part (A or B) becomes the seed? __A__
   b. Which part (A or B) becomes the fruit? __B__
   c. Which part (A or B) contains the embryo? __A__

PLANT DEVELOPMENT

In your textbook, read about the formation of seeds and fruits in Section 23:3.

1. The diagrams below show 60 days in the life of a bean flower. Pollination takes place on Day 10. Examine the pictures and then answer the questions.

Ovary
Egg

Day 1   Day 10   Day 15   Day 45   Day 60

Seed
Fruit

   a. How many ovaries are present in the bean flower? __one__
   b. How many ovules are present in the bean flower? __four__
   c. What are the little dots shown on Day 10? __pollen grains__
   d. What happens to the petals, pollen sacs, and stalk after Day 10? __They wither and fall off.__
   e. Explain what happens to the ovary from Day 10 to Day 60. __It enlarges and forms the fruit.__
   f. Explain what happens to the ovules from Day 10 to Day 60. __They form the seeds.__

2. The diagram shows a sliced peach.
   a. Which part (A or B) was the ovary from the flower? __B__
   b. Which part was the ovule? __A__
   c. Which part is the fruit? __B__
   d. Which part is the seed? __A__

3. Are tomatoes, green peppers, and cucumbers fruits? Explain your answer. __Yes, all grew from ovaries and all have seeds inside.__

4. List four ways that seeds may be carried before they land in the place where they eventually grow. __They may pass through an animal's digestive system and drop far away, be carried by wind or water, cling to fur of animals.__

PLANT DEVELOPMENT

In your textbook, read about plant development from seeds in Section 23:3.

5. What is germination? **first growth of a young plant from a seed**

6. Examine these diagrams of a developing plant. Then, fill in the blanks with the following labels: main root appears, leaves spread out and trap sunlight, secondary roots, first leaves and stem appear aboveground, seed halves drop off plant.

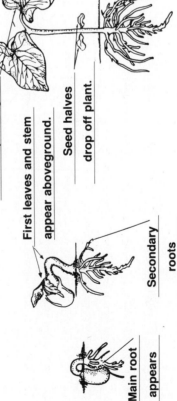

Leaves spread out and

trap sunlight.

First leaves and stem

appear aboveground.

Seed halves

drop off plant.

Main root   **Secondary**

appears   **roots**

7. How does asexual reproduction help a plant? **Only one parent is needed in this form of reproduction. Plants grow in the same place in a short time, and are exact clones of the parent so that helpful traits will be passed along.**

8. How does sexual reproduction help a plant? **Seeds can germinate after hundreds of years of being buried in the ground. This form of reproduction involves two parents so that a wide variety of traits can appear in the offspring, a fact that can improve survival chances if environmental conditions change.**

VOCABULARY

Review the new words used in Chapter 23 of your textbook. Then, complete this puzzle.

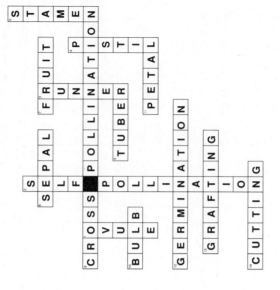

Across

6. green, leaflike, protective part of flower
7. enlarged ovary containing seeds
8. pollen from stamen of one flower carried to pistil of another flower
9. underground root or stem swollen with stored food
10. short, underground stem surrounded by fleshy leaves
11. brightly colored, scented part of flower
12. first growth of young plant from a seed

Down

13. joining the stem of one plant to the stem of another
14. small section of plant stem that is removed and planted
1. tiny, round part containing egg cell
2. pollen from stamen of flower carried to pistil of same flower
3. stem that grows along the ground or in air
4. female flower part
5. male flower part

15. What is the process by which pollen goes from stamens to pistils? _____ **pollination**

STUDY GUIDE

Name _____ Date _____ Class _____

ASEXUAL REPRODUCTION

In your textbook, read about asexual reproduction in Section 24:1.

1. Identify the type of asexual reproduction shown in each picture.

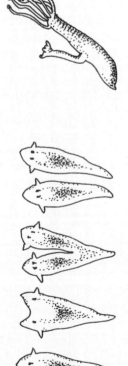

a. ____regeneration____   b. ____budding____

2. On each blank write T if the statement is true or F if the statement is false.

____F____ a. During asexual reproduction animals reproduce by meiosis.

____F____ b. A hydra forms buds in its ovaries.

____F____ c. An offspring produced by sexual reproduction is identical to its parent.

____T____ d. Complex animals reproduce by sexual reproduction.

____T____ e. Regeneration occurs when an organism separates into pieces and each piece forms a new organism.

____F____ f. Organisms produce eggs and sperm when they reproduce asexually.

____T____ g. A planarian regenerates by mitosis.

____T____ h. A hydra is a simple animal.

____F____ i. Asexual reproduction requires two parents.

____T____ j. When a planarian regenerates, it can form two heads.

____F____ k. All the offspring of a hydra are different from each other when formed by budding.

3. Answer the question below.

What is a clone? ____A clone is an offspring that is an exact copy of its parent.____

STUDY GUIDE

Name _____ Date _____ Class _____

SEXUAL REPRODUCTION

In your textbook, read about external and internal fertilization in Section 24:2.

1. Define external and internal fertilization.

a. external fertilization: ____External fertilization is the joining of egg and sperm outside the body.____

b. internal fertilization: ____Internal fertilization is the joining of egg and sperm inside the body.____

2. Where do most animals that have external fertilization live? ____Most animals with external fertilization live in water.____

3. What would happen to sperm and eggs if land animals had external fertilization? ____They would dry out.____

4. List two advantages of internal fertilization. ____Internal fertilization increases the chance that an egg will become fertilized. It allows reproduction to take place out of water.____

In your textbook, read about breeding seasons in Section 24:2.

5. What is a breeding season? ____A breeding season is a certain time of the year when animals reproduce.____

6. How does the breeding season of frogs help them? ____The breeding season takes place when a lot of water is available and the temperature is warm enough for the young to survive.____

7. How does the breeding season of large mammals such as deer help them? ____Since their young take longer to develop, the breeding season helps make sure that the young are born in the warm part of the year when they have a better chance to survive.____

8. What is an estrous cycle? ____An estrous cycle is a time when a female is ready to mate.____

REPRODUCTION IN HUMANS

In your textbook, read about the human reproductive systems in Section 24:3.

1. Label the diagram below using these words: oviduct, ovary, uterus, egg, vagina.

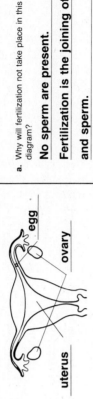

(Ⓒ) ovary   (Ⓐ) uterus   (Ⓓ) vagina   (Ⓔ) oviduct   (Ⓑ) egg

2. In each circle on the diagram, write the letter of the job listed below that the body part does.
A. Muscular organ where fertilized egg develops.
B. Cell formed in the ovary.
C. A place where the egg is formed.
D. Receives sperm during mating.
E. Tubelike parts that connect ovary to uterus.

3. Fill in the blanks below with the correct numbers.
a. Ovaries in a human female **2**   c. Eggs usually produced by human at one time **1**
b. Testes in a human male **2**

4. Label the diagram below using these words: testes, penis, vas deferens, urethra, scrotum, glands.

5. In each circle on the diagram, write the letter of the job listed below that the body part does.

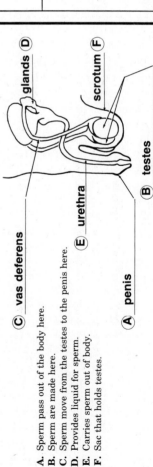

glands (Ⓓ)   scrotum (Ⓕ)   (Ⓒ) vas deferens   (Ⓔ) urethra   (Ⓐ) penis   (Ⓑ) testes

A. Sperm pass out of the body here.
B. Sperm are made here.
C. Sperm move from the testes to the penis here.
D. Provides liquid for sperm.
E. Carries sperm out of body.
F. Sac that holds testes.

REPRODUCTION IN HUMANS

In your textbook, read about stages of reproduction in Section 24:3.

6. Examine the diagrams below and label the parts. Then, answer the questions.

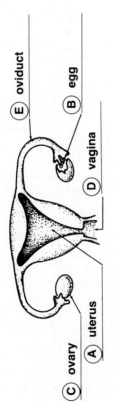

uterus   egg   ovary

a. Why will fertilization not take place in this diagram?
No sperm are present. Fertilization is the joining of egg and sperm.

sperm   vagina

b. Why will fertilization not take place in this diagram?
No egg is present.

embryo

c. Why will fertilization not take place in this diagram? (HINT: Note that an embryo is already present.)
Usually no eggs are released if fertilization and attachment within the uterus have occurred.

oviduct

d. Why will fertilization not take place in this diagram?
There are no ovaries to produce eggs, and no eggs or sperm.

Name _____ Date _____ Class _____

VOCABULARY

Review the new words used in Chapter 24 of your textbook. Then, fill in the blank next to each definition with the word or phrase it defines.

penis	1. male reproductive organ that deposits sperm inside a female
scrotum	2. sac that holds testes
uterus	3. organ in which a fertilized egg will develop
vagina	4. tube leading from outside the female's body to the uterus
oviducts	5. tubelike organs that connect the ovaries to the uterus
regeneration	6. reproduction in which parent separates into two or more pieces, each of which forms a new organism
menstruation	7. loss of the uterine lining
estrous cycle	8. cycle in which the female will mate only at certain times
external fertilization	9. joining of egg and sperm outside the body
menstrual cycle	10. monthly cycle that takes place in female reproductive organs
internal fertilization	11. joining of egg and sperm inside the female's body
estrogen	12. a female hormone
sexually transmitted diseases	13. diseases transmitted through sexual contact
reproductive system	14. system used to produce offspring

Name _____ Date _____ Class _____

REPRODUCTION IN HUMANS

In your textbook, read about the menstrual cycle in Section 24:3.

7. The following chart shows the changes in a female's reproductive system in 28 days. These changes take place when an egg is not fertilized.

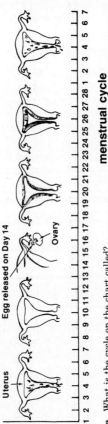

Uterus   Egg released on Day 14   Ovary

1 2 3 4 5 6 7 8 9 10 11 12 13 14 15 16 17 18 19 20 21 22 23 24 25 26 27 28 1 2 3 4 5 6 7

a. What is the cycle on the chart called? **menstrual cycle**

b. What are the changes that take place on days 1 to 4 (loss of the lining of the uterus) called? **menstruation**

c. When is the egg released from the ovary? **day 14**

d. Describe the changes that take place in the uterus from day 5 through day 28. **The uterine lining thickens.**

e. What happens to an egg that is not fertilized? **It does not attach to the uterus.**

8. Match the following diagrams with their places on the chart by writing each letter on the chart below the proper diagram. A is done for you.

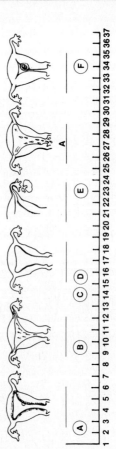

(A) (B) (C) (D) (E) (F)

1 2 3 4 5 6 7 8 9 10 11 12 13 14 15 16 17 18 19 20 21 22 23 24 25 26 27 28 29 30 31 32 33 34 35 36 37

a. How many of the days in this chart match those in the chart in question 7? **about 14 days**

b. How long (in months) will step F last? **about 9 months**

Name ______ Date ______ Class ______

DEVELOPMENT INSIDE THE FEMALE

In your textbook, read about early stages of development in Section 25:1.

1. Arrange the following events in their proper order by placing the numbers 1-7 in the spaces provided.

a. 5 The embryo forms a solid ball of cells.

b. 1 An egg is fertilized.

c. 4 About three days later, the embryo is sixteen cells in size.

d. 7 The embryo attaches itself to the lining of the uterus.

e. 2 The fertilized egg undergoes mitosis to form two cells.

f. 6 The embryo, now a hollow ball of cells, moves out of the oviduct into the uterus.

g. 3 Mitosis continues and two cells form four cells, four cells form eight cells.

In your textbook, read about the needs of the embryo in Section 25:1.

2. Complete the diagram below by coloring the correct end of each arrow to show the proper direction the material takes.

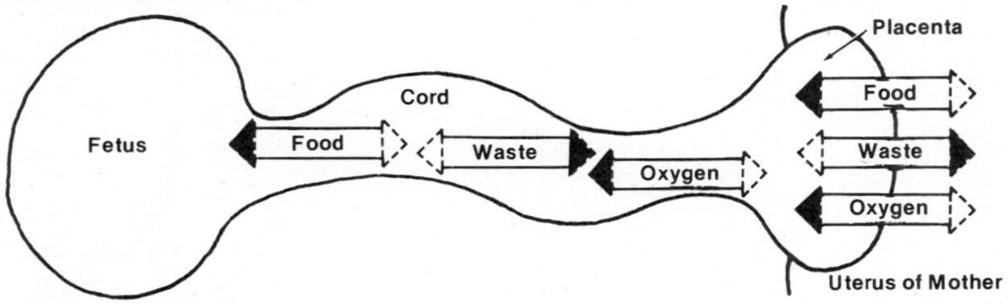

3. Place the numbers from the diagram on the right next to the correct statements below.

a. 2 The *umbilical cord* connects the young to the placenta.

b. 3 The young is protected by a *liquid-filled sac.*

c. 1 Wastes are carried away by the *placenta.*

d. 4 The *fetus* grows in the uterus.

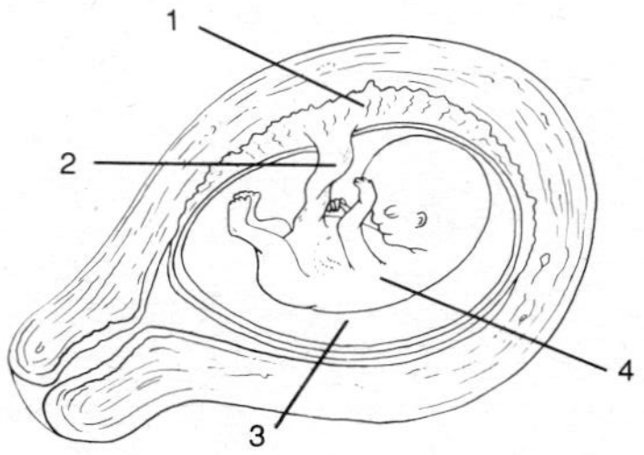

Name ______ Date ______ Class ______

DEVELOPMENT INSIDE THE FEMALE

4. Why are proper nutrition and good health important during pregnancy? **A pregnant female is living for two—eating, breathing, and getting rid of wastes for herself and the developing embryo.**

5. How does the amniotic sac help the developing embryo? **This tissue is filled with liquid that cushions and protects the embryo from injury.**

In your textbook, read about human development in Section 25:1.

6. Complete the following table by placing a checkmark in the column that tells when the traits listed form.

Trait	Month			
	1	2	3	4 to birth
Muscles and bones form.		✓		
Liver and ears appear.	✓			
Kicking, bending, and turning occurs.				✓
Embryo is 1.0 gram.		✓		
Arms and legs form.		✓		
Stomach starts to form.	✓			
Fetus is 3000 grams.				✓
Sex of child can be seen.			✓	
Eyes begin to develop.	✓			
Fingers and toes appear.		✓		
Brain and heart start to form.	✓			
Fetus is 100 grams.				✓
Eyes have eyelids.		✓		
Embryo is 0.02 grams.	✓			
Heart is beating.	✓			

DEVELOPMENT OUTSIDE THE FEMALE

In your textbook, read about eggs and the needs of the young before hatching in Section 25:2.

1. Write the names of the parts of the developing chicken in the correct blank.

A. **embryo**
B. **yolk**
C. **shell**
D. **sac with waste**
E. **albumen**

2. Match the terms with their definitions by writing the correct letter from Column II on the blanks after the words in Column I.

I		II
yolk **h**		a. place where liquid wastes are stored
blood vessels just below shell **e**		b. the protein in egg white
eggshell **g**		c. the young chicken
sac within egg **a**		d. leave the egg through the shell
albumen **b**		e. pick up oxygen that passes to embryo
embryo **c**		f. diffuses into shell from air outside
gas wastes **d**		g. protects embryo from water loss and injury
oxygen **f**		h. the yellow part of egg containing protein and stored fat

3. How is development in frogs, birds, and reptiles similar to that in humans? **The fertilized eggs of all of these animals undergo cleavage.**

4. How is development in frogs, birds, and reptiles different from that in humans? **Only human fertilized eggs develop inside the female's body. The other animals listed lay eggs outside the female.**

5. How are the eggs of birds and reptiles suited to the environment in which they develop? **Since these eggs develop on land, the eggshells of these animals protect the young from drying out.**

DEVELOPMENT INSIDE THE FEMALE

In your textbook, read about human births in Section 25:1.

7. Study the diagrams of a human before and during birth. Then, complete the table below by writing *yes* or *no* in the blanks.

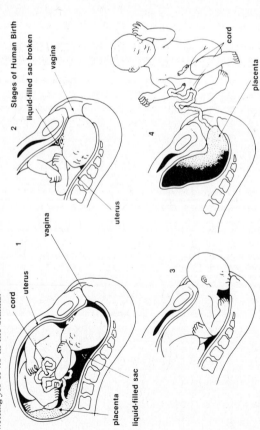

Diagram	1	2	3	4
Time	Three days before birth	Three hours before birth	During birth	A few minutes after birth
Is baby in vagina?	no	no	yes	no
Is bottom of uterus closed?	yes	no	no	no
Is baby inside liquid sac?	yes	yes	no	no
Is liquid sac broken?	no	yes	yes	yes
Is baby attached to umbilical cord?	yes	yes	yes	yes
Is umbilical cord attached to placenta?	yes	yes	yes	yes
Is placenta attached to uterus?	yes	yes	yes	no

Name _____ Date _____ Class _____

METAMORPHOSIS

In your textbook, read about frog metamorphosis in Section 25:3.

1. Complete the table below showing frog development. Measure the drawings and record your measurements in the second column. (In the tadpole and frog stages, measure from the head to the tip of the tail.) Then, list at least one major trait of each stage. **Answers will vary.**

Gills

A B C D E F

Stage	Size (mm)	Traits of stage
A	6	Eggs have a jellylike covering.
B	13	Tadpole larva looks like small fish.
C	34	Larva has gills and long tail.
D	36	Legs form; gills are replaced by lungs.
E	26	Tadpole is replaced by adult frog.

2. Label the stages of metamorphosis shown below.

a.

egg   larva   nymph   adult

b.

egg   larva   pupa   adult

149

Name _____ Date _____ Class _____

VOCABULARY

Review the new words in Chapter 25 of your textbook. Then, complete this puzzle.

Below are five tables. List the following words in every table in which they are correct. Some words are used more than once.

amniotic sac breaks   incomplete   metamorphosis   placenta
complete   metamorphosis navel   pupa
metamorphosis   labor   nymph   umbilical cord
fetus   larva
cleavage

A change that takes place in all living things
cleavage

Changes or stages that take place in insects
nymph
larva
incomplete metamorphosis
pupa
complete metamorphosis

Changes or stages that take place in frogs
larva
metamorphosis

Parts or stages in humans
placenta
umbilical cord
fetus
navel

Changes that occur during a human birth
amniotic sac breaks
labor

150

Name _____ Date _____ Class _____

GENETICS, HOW AND WHY

In Section 26:1 of your textbook, read about genes and how they are passed to offspring.

1. Examine the drawings of horsefly chromosomes below. Complete the table by filling in the information about the chromosomes.

	Body cell	Sex cell
Number of chromosomes present	12	6
Can the chromosomes be put in pairs? (yes or no)	yes	no

2. a. Genes are often shown as lines on a chromosome. Examine the diagrams below of a pair of body cell chromosomes and a sex cell chromosome of a horsefly. Complete the diagrams by drawing the genes on the unmarked chromosomes and labeling them by trait.

Body cell chromosomes — Wing length gene, Body color gene, Leg number gene, Eye size gene

Sex cell chromosome — Wing length gene, Body color gene, Leg number gene, Eye size gene

b. How many genes for wing length are present in this body cell? __2__

c. How many genes for wing length are present in this sex cell? __1__

3. In dogs, black fur is dominant to brown fur. Write the color each dog will be if the dog is:

pure dominant __black__   pure recessive __brown__   heterozygous __black__

Name _____ Date _____ Class _____

EXPECTED AND OBSERVED RESULTS

In Section 26:2 of your textbook, read about possible combinations of eggs and sperm.

1. Here are six dogs. In the small box below each dog, write the genes present in the body cells of that dog. Use the letters *B* for black and *b* for brown.

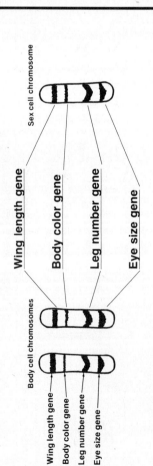

Pure dominant Female 1 — BB → B B

Heterozygous Female 2 — Bb → B b

Pure recessive Female 3 — bb → b b

Pure dominant Male 4 — BB → B B

Heterozygous Male 5 — Bb → B b

Pure recessive Male 6 — bb → b b

In the large boxes in the diagrams, draw 2 sex cells below each dog. Draw sperm like this. Draw eggs like this.
Complete the drawings by marking the genes *B* or *b* on the sex cells you have drawn.

2. The following table shows possible results of mating the dogs. Complete the table.

Mother	Father	Possible gene in eggs	Possible gene in sperm	Gene combinations in fertilized eggs	Likely fur color of 4 puppies
Dog 1	Dog 4	B	B	all BB	all black
Dog 1	Dog 5	B	B b	BB BB Bb Bb	all black
Dog 2	Dog 4	B b	B	BB BB Bb Bb	all black
Dog 2	Dog 5	B b	B b	BB Bb Bb bb	3 black 1 brown
Dog 3	Dog 5	b	B b	Bb Bb bb bb	2 black 2 brown
Dog 3	Dog 6	b	b	all bb	all brown

Name _____ Date _____ Class _____

EXPECTED AND OBSERVED RESULTS

In Section 26:2 of your textbook, read about solving genetics problems using the Punnett square.

3. Examine the diagrams below. Each is a step in the Punnett square method. Put the steps in order by writing the numbers 1 to 4 below them on the correct blanks.

__2__   __3__   __1__   __4__

4. What do the letters outside the Punnett square stand for? __genes in eggs and sperm__

What do the letters inside each box stand for? __genes in offspring__

5. Examine the following Punnett squares and circle those that are correct.

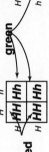

6. Complete the following to determine the expected offspring.

	T	t
T	TT	Tt
T	TT	Tt

	R	r
R	RR	Rr
r	Rr	rr

	e	e
E	Ee	Ee
e	ee	ee

Name _____ Date _____ Class _____

EXPECTED AND OBSERVED RESULTS

7. In corn plants, normal height *H* is dominant to short height *h*. Complete these four Punnett squares showing different crosses. Then, shade red all the pure dominant offspring. Shade green all the heterozygous offspring. Leave all the pure recessive offspring unshaded.

8. In flies, long wings *L* are dominant to short wings *l*. Complete these four Punnett squares showing different crosses. Then, shade red all the offspring that will have long wings. Leave all the shortwinged offspring unshaded.

9. In guinea pigs, short hair *S* is dominant to long hair *s*. Complete the following Punnett squares according to the directions given. Then, fill in the blanks beside each Punnett square with the correct numbers.

a. One guinea pig is *Ss* and one is *ss*.

	S	s
s	Ss	ss
s	Ss	ss

Offspring expected (number)

__2__ Short hair

__2__ Long hair

b. Both guinea pigs are heterozygous for short hair.

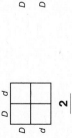

	S	s
S	SS	Ss
s	Ss	ss

Offspring expected (number)

__3__ Short hair

__1__ Long hair

Name _____ Date _____ Class _____

EXPECTED AND OBSERVED RESULTS

In Section 26:2 of your textbook, read about the work done by Gregor Mendel in genetics.

10. Mendel made the following crosses with pea plants. Complete the Punnett squares and answer the questions about each cross.

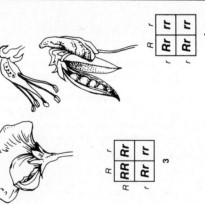

	R	R
r	**Rr**	**Rr**
r	**Rr**	**Rr**

1

	R	R
R	**RR**	**RR**
r	**Rr**	**Rr**

2

	R	r
R	**RR**	**Rr**
r	**Rr**	**rr**

3

	R	r
r	**Rr**	**rr**
r	**Rr**	**rr**

4

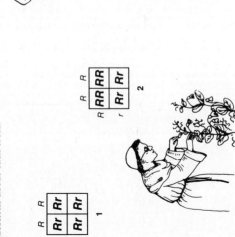

a. He crossed a red flowered *R* plant with a white flowered *r* plant. His results were 126 red flowered plants and 122 white flowered plants. Which of the Punnett squares above best shows the parents and offspring that could give these results? _____4_____

b. He crossed a red flowered plant with a white flowered plant. His results were 307 red flowered plants and 0 white flowered plants. Which of the Punnett squares above best shows the parents and offspring that could give these results? _____1_____

c. He crossed a red flowered plant with a red flowered plant. His results were 306 red flowered plants and 110 white flowered plants. Which of the Punnett squares above best shows the parents and offspring that could give these results? _____3_____

d. He crossed a red flowered plant with a red flowered plant. His results were 300 red flowered plants and 0 white flowered plants. Which of the Punnett squares above best shows the parents and offspring that could give these results? _____2_____

Name _____ Date _____ Class _____

VOCABULARY

Review the new words used in Chapter 26 of your textbook. Then, answer these questions.

1. Below each of the following words are choices. Circle the choices that are examples of each of those words.

   a. Dominant gene

   D   e   k   (L)   (N)   o   (R)   (S)

   b. Recessive gene

   M   (n)   (d)   F   G   (i)   (k)   P

   c. Pure dominant

   (AA)   Gg   (KK)   ll   pp   Rr   (TT)

   d. Pure recessive

   (ee)   Ff   HH   Oo   (qq)   Uu   (ww)

   e. Offspring combinations in which dominant gene *must* show

   (AA)   (Dd)   (EE)   ff   (Jj)   (RR)   Ss

   f. Offspring combinations in which recessive gene *must* show

   (aa)   Gg   Ff   KK   Oo   PP   (ss)   (tt)

2. Fill in the blanks below using these choices: dominant, genes, genetics, heterozygous, pure, recessive, chromosomes, Punnett square.

   a. Chromosomes have parts that determine traits. These parts are __**genes**__.

   b. A person having two genes that are alike is said to be __**pure**__.

   c. A gene that prevents others from showing is said to be __**dominant**__.

   d. A gene that may not show up even though it is there is said to be __**recessive**__.

   e. Long rod-shaped bodies inside a cell's nucleus are called __**chromosomes**__.

   f. One who studies how traits are passed on is studying __**genetics**__.

   g. A person with one dominant and one recessive gene for a trait is __**heterozygous**__.

   h. A way to show which genes can combine when an egg and sperm join is a __**Punnett**__ __**square**__.

Name _____ Date _____ Class _____

THE ROLE OF CHROMOSOMES

In your textbook, read about sex—a genetic trait in Section 27:1.

1. Examine the chromosomes shown below from two people. Then, answer the questions that follow.

a. Is person A male or female? **male**   How do you know? **Person A has one X and one Y chromosome.**

b. Is person B male or female? **female**   How do you know? **Person B has two X chromosomes.**

c. Circle the sex chromosomes of each of the above people.

2. Complete the Punnett square. Then, answer the questions below.

	X	X
X	XX	XX
Y	XY	XY

a. Out of four children, how many are expected to be female? **2**

b. Out of four children, how many are expected to be male? **2**

c. Which sex chromosome do both males and females have? **X**

d. Which sex chromosome do only males have? **Y**

e. Shade the female offspring in the above Punnett square. Leave the male offspring unshaded.

Name _____ Date _____ Class _____

HUMAN TRAITS

In your textbook, read about incomplete dominance in Section 27:2.

1. Red blood cell shape shows incomplete dominance in humans. R is the gene for round cell shape and R' is the gene for sickle cell shape.

a. Put checkmarks in the following table to show the shape of cells for persons with the genes listed.

b. Which gene, R or R', is dominant? **neither**   Which is recessive? **neither**

2. a. Describe the condition that a person with $R'R'$ genes has. **The person has all sickled blood cells. Sickled red blood cells do not carry oxygen as well as normal red blood cells. Thus, people with all sickled red blood cells have serious health problems and their lives may be shortened.**

b. What is the name of this disease? **sickle-cell anemia**

3. Human blood types show incomplete dominance as well as dominance. Fill in the table at the right showing possible genes a person with each blood type might have.

Blood type	Possible genes
A	*AA* or *AO*
B	*BB* or *BO*
O	*OO*
AB	*AB*

4. Which blood type genes are dominant to other blood type genes? **A and B are dominant to O.**

5. Which blood type genes show incomplete dominance to each other? **A and B**

STUDY GUIDE

Name _____ Date _____ Class _____

HUMAN TRAITS

In your textbook, read about color blindness in Section 27:2.

1. Color blindness is a trait carried on the sex chromosomes. Let C be normal color vision and c be red-green color blindness. Use the diagrams to answer the questions.

   a. What is the sex of each of these people? Write either male or female on the blank below each.

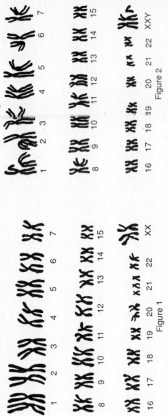

   A **female**   B **female**   C **male**   D **male**   E **female**

   b. Which are red-green color blind? __**D and E**__

   c. Which have normal color vision? __**A, B, and C**__

   d. Which has normal color vision even with the gene for color blindness? __**B**__

2. a. Complete the following Punnett squares. The first one has been done for you.

   b. Using these colors, shade the following parts of the Punnett squares.

      Blue—normal females   Red—color blind females
      Yellow—normal males   Green—color blind males

STUDY GUIDE

Name _____ Date _____ Class _____

GENETIC DISORDERS

In your textbook, read about errors in chromosome number in Section 27:3.

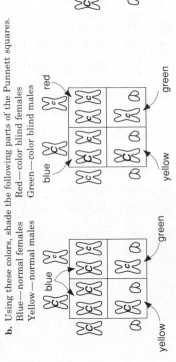

Figure 1

Figure 2

1. Suppose a child was found to have the chromosome pattern shown in Figure 1 above.

   a. Is the child a male or female? __**female**__

   b. Explain your answer. __**She has two X chromosomes.**__

   c. Down syndrome is caused by one extra autosome in each cell. What pair of chromosomes has an extra chromosome? __**21st**__

   d. How did this child get an extra chromosome? __**During meiosis, one of the parent's autosomes did not pull apart from its sister chromatid.**__

2. Suppose a child was found to have the chromosome pattern shown in Figure 2 above.

   a. Is the child a male or female? __**male**__

   b. Explain your answer. __**There is a Y chromosome present and males have a Y chromosome.**__

   c. Which chromosome is the extra chromosome, an X or Y? __**X**__

   d. How did the child get an extra chromosome? __**The two X chromosomes in the mother failed to separate during meiosis. Instead of one X chromosome going to each egg cell, two X chromosomes went to the same egg cell. The X and Y chromosomes in the father failed to separate, ending up in the same sperm cell.**__

GENETIC DISORDERS

In your textbook, read about hemophilia in Section 27:3.

1. In the boxes below of each of these people, draw the sex chromosomes. Then, on the chromosomes write the genes they have for hemophilia. The dominant gene is *H*. The recessive gene is *h*.

Normal, pure dominant female	Female with hemophilia	Normal male	Male with hemophilia	Normal, heterozygous female

2. Complete the following Punnett squares. Then, match the correct Punnett square with each one of the following expected results. Write the letter of the Punnett square on the line next to the expected result it matches.

Expected results

2 normal females 1 normal male 1 male with hemophilia	B
1 normal female 1 normal male 1 female with hemophilia 1 male with hemophilia	A
2 normal females 2 males with hemophilia	C

3. Circle the Punnett squares that show individuals with hemophilia.

4. Describe the condition of hemophilia. **Hemophilia is a genetic disorder in which the person's blood will not clot.**

	H	h
H	HH	HH
h	Hh	hh

VOCABULARY

Review the new words in Chapter 27 of your textbook. Then, complete this puzzle.

Crossword answers:
- SICKLE-CELL ANEMIA
- GENETIC COUNSELING
- INCOMPLETE DOMINANCE
- AUTOSOME
- PEDIGREE
- X CHROMOSOMES
- SEX

Down

1. Genetic disorder called word blindness
2. Disorder in which some colors are not seen as they should be
3. Way of looking at chromosomes of a fetus
4. Sex chromosomes of a male

Across

5. Use of genetics to predict and explain traits in children
6. Condition in which neither gene is dominant
7. Chromosome that does not determine sex
8. Disorder in which red blood cells are not round
9. Sex chromosomes of the female
10. Chromosomes that determine if child is male or female
11. Diagram that can show how a trait is passed along in a family

Name _____ Date _____ Class _____

THE DNA MOLECULE

In your textbook, read about the structure of DNA in Section 28:1.

1. What do the letters *DNA* stand for? **Deoxyribonucleic acid**

2. Where is DNA found? **DNA is found in the nuclei of cells of all living things.**

3. Label the following parts of a DNA model: nitrogen bases, sugar, acid, upright side, ladder rung.

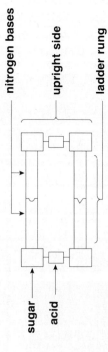

nitrogen bases

upright side

ladder rung

sugar

acid

4. Use the parts shown below to draw a section of DNA in the box provided. You design the order in which the bases appear, but remember that they only join in certain ways.

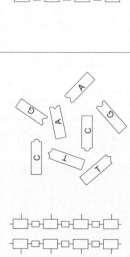

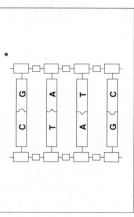

*

*The order of the bases will vary. However, C and G must join; A and T must join

In your textbook, read about DNA and chromosomes in Section 28:1.

5. Define a gene in three ways. **A gene is a short piece of DNA. A gene is a certain number of bases on the DNA molecule. A gene is a small section of a chromosome that determines traits.**

Name _____ Date _____ Class _____

THE DNA MOLECULE

In your textbook, read about proof that DNA controls traits in Section 28:1.

6. Study Figure 28-4 and page 590 of your textbook. Then, explain why you would expect a mouse to:

a. live if given an injection of living harmless bacteria. **No disease will result if the bacteria are harmless.**

b. die if given an injection of living harmful bacteria. **A disease that kills the mouse could result from injection of harmful bacteria.**

c. live if given an injection of dead harmful bacteria. **Dead bacteria, though once harmful, cannot harm the mouse.**

d. die when given a mixture of living harmless bacteria and dead harmful bacteria. **Harmless bacteria can be changed into harmful bacteria when they pick up DNA from the dead harmful bacteria.**

In your textbook, read about making proteins in Section 28:1.

7. What do the letters *RNA* stand for? **ribonucleic acid**

8. Why is RNA called a messenger? **It carries the DNA message from the nucleus to the ribosomes.**

9. Examine the diagram of a cell and some of its parts. Then, write the letter of the labeled part that shows:

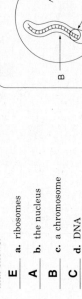

E a. ribosomes

A b. the nucleus

B c. a chromosome

C d. DNA

D e. RNA

F f. cytoplasm

E g. the worktable for making proteins

D h. DNA's helper molecule

THE DNA MOLECULE

In your textbook, read about how DNA copies itself in Section 28:1.

10. The model of DNA on the left is ready to be copied. The copies on the right labeled 1-3 show the resulting molecules as drawn by several students.

DNA to be copied

```
1              AT           2     AT           3     AA
AT             TA                 TA                 TT
TA             CG                 CG                 CC
CG      and    CG                 AG                 GC
CG             GC                 GC                 GG
GC             GC                 GC                 TT
TA             TA                 TA                 GG
GC             GC           and   GC           and
               GC
```

a. Explain why number 1 is incorrect. **The order of nitrogen bases must be exactly the same as the original. One copy is correct and one is not.**

b. Explain why number 2 is correct. **Both models are identical to each other and to the original.**

c. Explain why number 3 is incorrect. **The base pairs in this model are incorrectly joined. Also, two copies must be made, not just one.**

11. How does the genetic message compare in the original cell and the two new cells that form after the cell reproduces? **It should be the same.**

HOW THE GENETIC MESSAGE CHANGES

In your textbook, read about mutations in Section 28:2.

1. Complete the diagram on the left. Then, circle the areas in the diagram on the right that show a mutation.

DNA correctly copied

DNA incorrectly copied

```
AT     AT      AT               AT      AT
TA     TA      TA               TA      TA
CG     CG      CG               CG      CG
CG     CG      CG               CG      CG
GC     GC      GC               GC      GC
TA     TA      TA               TA      TA
GC     GC      GC         and   GC      CA
AT     AT      AT               AT      GC
                                        AT
       and
```

2. List three causes of mutations. **An error may take place when DNA is being copied. The cell may be exposed to certain chemicals. The cell may be exposed to radiation.**

HOW THE GENETIC MESSAGE CHANGES

In your textbook, read about cloning in Section 28:2.

3. A mother has four children. Children A and B were born at the end of her first pregnancy. Children C and D were born at the end of her second pregnancy. Which of her children:

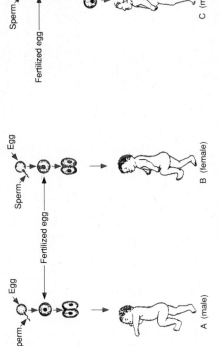

A (male)   B (female)   C (male) D (male)

a. are identical twins? __C and D__

b. were formed from two different eggs and sperm? __A and B__

c. are clones? __C and D__

d. have identical DNA? __C and D__

e. are fraternal twins? __A and B__

f. have different genes? __A and B__

g. were formed from one egg and one sperm? __C and D__

4. Use Figure 28-12 on page 599 of your textbook to answer the following questions.

a. In the cloning process shown, what cell part does the dark frog contribute? __its nucleus__

b. What does the light frog contribute? __egg cell__

c. Which frog is contributing its DNA? __dark frog__ Explain your answer. **Its DNA is in the nucleus.**

d. Why does the cloned frog resemble the dark parent instead of the light parent? **The DNA from the dark frog is responsible for all traits in the newly cloned frog.**

HOW THE GENETIC MESSAGE CHANGES

In your textbook, read about breeding of plants and animals and splicing genes between organisms in Section 28:2.

5. This diagram shows two bulls. Below each is a description of that bull's traits.

Bull A
Sleek, clean, solid-colored fur
Long tail, long legs
Milk production of his offspring is low.

Bull B
Rough, spotted fur
Short tail, short legs
Milk production of his offspring is high.

a. Which bull would you choose to breed with a cow to produce a herd of cows that would supply a lot of milk? __B__ Why? **The milk production of bull B's offspring is high.**

b. Which bull would you choose for breeding to produce "beautiful" offspring? __A__ Why? **Bull A has a sleek, clean, solid-colored fur.**

c. Which bull would you choose for breeding to produce offspring that would not jump over fences? __B__ Why? **Bull B has shorter legs.**

d. Explain the value of plant and animal breeding. **The value of breeding is producing offspring with desired traits. It's been used to breed plants that won't get certain diseases and cattle that have less fat or greater milk production.**

6. What is recombinant DNA? **Recombinant DNA is the DNA that is formed when DNA from one organism is put into the DNA of another organism.**

7. Why does gene splicing work? **It works because the genetic code for all living things is the same.**

8. List four ways that gene splicing is of value to humans now or may be of value in the future. **Gene splicing can help make human insulin, growth hormone, and plants that are not harmed by chemical sprays. Someday, it may help to cure certain genetic diseases.**

VOCABULARY

Review the words used in Chapter 28 of your textbook. Then, complete this exercise.

Each word listed here has at least three statements after it. Place a checkmark in front of all the statements that are either correct or are examples of the word.

1. DNA
   - ✓ makes up chromosomes
   - ___ are proteins in cells
   - ✓ deoxyribonucleic acid
   - ✓ controls the traits of living things

2. Breeding
   - ___ the act of bringing oxygen into the lungs
   - ✓ can be done with plants and animals
   - ✓ can result in better crops

3. Genetic message
   - ✓ order of bases in DNA
   - ___ used for computers
   - ✓ is copied

4. Fraternal twins
   - ✓ form from different egg and different sperm
   - ✓ are not clones
   - ✓ have different genes

5. Radiation
   - ✓ can cause mutations
   - ✓ is a form of energy
   - ✓ released by the sun

6. Identical twins
   - ✓ form from one egg and one sperm
   - ✓ have exactly the same genes
   - ___ a brother and a sister
   - ✓ have the same DNA

7. Mutation
   - ✓ any change in the DNA message
   - ✓ error in base pairing
   - ___ a computer card error

8. Nitrogen bases
   - ✓ A, C, G, T
   - ✓ join only in certain ways
   - ___ present in the cell nucleus

9. RNA
   - ✓ ribonucleic acid
   - ✓ carries DNA message from nucleus to ribosome
   - ✓ directs the forming of protein
   - ___ rung of the DNA ladder

10. Recombinant DNA
    - ✓ formed by splicing of DNA
    - ___ occurs in wires
    - ✓ has produced human insulin
    - ✓ adding human DNA to bacteria

CHANGES IN LIVING THINGS

In your textbook, read about adaptations and natural selection in Section 29:1.

1. Circle the adaptations below that aid survival in water.

2. Circle the adaptations below that aid survival on land or in the air.

3. Suppose a bird eats moths that land on tree trunks. Circle the moths on each of these tree trunks that would probably be eaten by the bird. Then, answer the following questions by filling in the blanks with the words *dark* or *light*.

Which moths in picture:

a. A blend well with the color of the tree trunk? __dark__

b. B blend well with the color of the tree trunk? __light__

c. A will be eaten first by the birds? __light__

d. B will be eaten first by the birds? __dark__

e. A have the best chance to survive and reproduce? __dark__

f. B have the best chance to survive and reproduce? __light__

CHANGES IN LIVING THINGS

In your textbook, read about mutations in Section 29:1.

4. These two polar bears are alike except for their fur color. Answer the following questions about the polar bears.

a. Which has a trait that could be harmful to survival? _____

Explain your answer. __The dark bear would be easily seen in its snowy surroundings. It would be less able to catch animals as food as a result.__

b. Suppose all polar bears had fur like A, and suddenly a bear with fur like B is born. Could the change be the result of a mutation? __yes__

c. Would the mutation have produced an adaptation? (Is the change helpful to the bear?) __yes__ Explain your answer. __The white bear would blend better in its surroundings and could thus, catch animals as food more easily.__

5. Below are several mutations. After each, write how the trait could be harmful. Then, write how each trait could be helpful. __Answers may vary.__

	How trait could be harmful	How trait could be helpful
Albino squirrel	easily seen by enemies	can blend in with light or white surroundings
Hornless cattle	has less protection from enemies	can get untangled from fencing or brush easier
Short-legged dog	cannot run away from danger as fast	can get in smaller places for protection
Long eyelashes in humans	can interfere with vision	can keep water or dust particles out of eyes

STUDY GUIDE

Name _____ Date _____ Class _____

CHANGES IN LIVING THINGS

In your textbook, read about species formation in Section 29.1.

6. a. How can the word *species* be defined as it relates to the classification of living things? **A species is the smallest group of living things.**

   b. How can the word *species* be defined as it relates to breeding? **A species is a group of living things that can breed with others of the same species and form fertile offspring.**

7. Use Figure 29-5 on page 611 of your textbook to help you do this exercise. The following statements involve events that can result in the formation of a new species. Number them from 1-6 in the proper order. Number one is done for you.

   3   a. animals are separated into two groups and must now live apart

   4   b. environments on either side of the river change with time

   1   c. animals of the same species living on either side of a stream can move from one side to the other

   2   d. the stream changes into a river

   5   e. animals, due to natural selection, undergo change

   6   f. after thousands of years, two different species of animals form

8. In the example in Figure 29-5, what three events led to the formation of new species? **A barrier formed that separated members of the species. Members of the species found themselves living in different environments. The groups began to show different traits as a result of natural selection.**

9. How do the finches of the Galapagos Islands differ? **Each has a differently shaped beak.**

10. Describe how a single finch ancestor probably evolved into many different species. **The ancestor probably flew to the islands from the mainland of South America. New species began to evolve when the finches spread out over the islands and became adapted to their new environments. Without contact with one another, the groups became less alike.**

STUDY GUIDE

Name _____ Date _____ Class _____

EXPLANATIONS FOR EVOLUTION

In your textbook, read about Darwin's work in Section 29.2.

1. The four diagrams below each show a main point in Darwin's theory of evolution. Below each, write the sentence from this list that is best shown.

   Living things overproduce.
   There is variation among the offspring.
   There is a struggle to survive.
   Natural selection is always taking place.

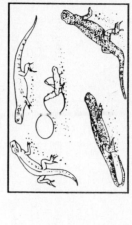

Living things overproduce.

There is a struggle to survive.

Natural selection is always taking place.

There is variation among the offspring.

2. What phrase describes the hawk choosing the light lizard? **natural selection**

3. What is evolution? **Evolution is a change in the hereditary features of a group of organsims over time.**

Name _____ Date _____ Class _____

EXPLANATIONS FOR EVOLUTION

In your textbook, read about evidence of evolution in Section 29:2.

4. List five examples of fossils. **print of leaf, footprint of animal, bones of skeleton, animal trapped in ice, insect trapped in hardened sap**

5. a. You are on an expedition digging down through Earth's crust. You uncover the materials shown below. Put an X through those objects that are *not* fossils.

   b. What made you decide that the objects you put an X through in part *a* were *not* fossils? **Fossils are the remains of living things from past ages.**

6. Examine the diagram of a side view of sedimentary rocks in the Earth's crust. Which layer:

   a. is the oldest? __**C**__
   b. was formed last? __**A**__
   c. has life forms most like those of today? __**A**__
   d. was formed first? __**C**__
   e. is the youngest? __**A**__
   f. has life forms least like those of today? __**C**__

7. How does Figure 29-3 on page 620 of your textbook provide evidence of evolution. **Each of the embryos is a chordate with common ancestry. The embryos share some of the same traits from their common ancestry that result in their similar appearance.**

8. How is the genetic code similar in early and modern forms of life? **All have nitrogen bases, A, T, C, and G.**

9. a. What is a vestigial structure? **a body part that no longer has a function**
   b. How do vestigial structures provide evidence of evolution? **Many of these parts have functions in other related animals and provide evidence of a common ancestor.**

173

Name _____ Date _____ Class _____

VOCABULARY

Review the new words in Chapter 29 of your textbook. Then, write a sentence defining each word.

1. species — **a group of living things that can breed with others of the same species and form fertile offspring**

2. old-world monkeys — **monkeys that can't grasp with their tails and that have nostrils that open downward**

3. natural selection — **process in which something in the surroundings determines if a living thing survives to have offspring**

4. vestigial structure — **a body part that no longer has a function**

5. sedimentary rocks — **rocks that form from layers of mud, sand, and other fine particles**

6. primate — **mammal with eyes that face forward, a well-developed cerebrum, and grasping thumbs**

7. evolution — **change in the hereditary features of a group of organisms over time**

8. new-world monkeys — **monkeys that have a grasping tail and nostrils that open upward**

9. extinct — **a life-form that no longer exists**

10. competition — **a struggle among living things to get their needs for life**

11. fossils — **remains of once-living things from ages past**

12. fertile — **able to reproduce by forming egg or sperm cells**

13. variation — **trait that makes an individual different from others in its species**

174

POPULATIONS

In your textbook, read about population size in Section 30:1.

1. Make a population count of the crabs in the diagram below. Place a checkmark on the shell of each crab to avoid counting any twice. Keep track of how long it takes you to do it. **Show students how to place checkmarks on the crabs.**

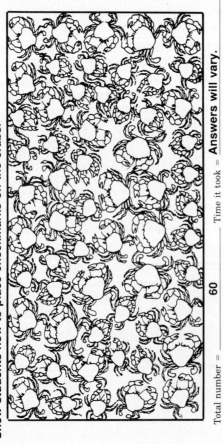

Total number = ____60____   Time it took = ____Answers will vary.____

2. A faster way to count a population is to sample it. Count the number of crabs in the small square on the right below.

Total number = ____8____

Time it took = ____Answers will vary but will be shorter than the above time.____

This square is ⅛ the size of the large square above. Therefore, you need to multiply the number you counted by 8 to get the total population size.

____8____ × 8 = ____64____

3. a. Were the results from counting about the same regardless of which method was used to count?
Yes, the results were almost the same.

b. What is the advantage of counting a population by sampling it? **It is much faster and almost as accurate.**

POPULATIONS

In your textbook, read about population changes in Section 30:1.

4. Many things change the numbers of individuals in a population. One important factor is food supply. For example, foxes eat mice. The table below shows how their numbers change.

Year	Number of mice	Number of foxes
1983	1050	200
1984	800	425
1985	426	581
1986	730	300
1987	980	153
1988	620	399
1989	380	548
1990	680	403
1991	1010	255

a. Plot the number of mice on the graph below and connect all the points with a black line.

b. Plot the number of foxes on this graph. Connect all the points with a red line.

c. In the boxes at the right of the graph, indicate which animal is the predator and which is the prey by writing *predator* and *prey* in the correct box.

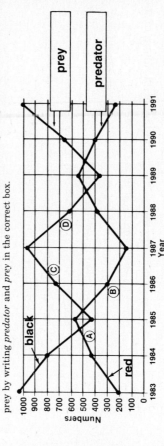

5. After each of the phrases below, write the letter from the graph (A, B, C, or D) that best matches.

a. Fox population increasing ____A____   c. Mouse population increasing ____C____

b. Fox population decreasing ____B____   d. Mouse population decreasing ____D____

Name _____ Date _____ Class _____

ENERGY IN A COMMUNITY

In your textbook, read about energy and food chains in Section 30:3.

1. Write the letter of the diagram above that best matches each of these words or phrases.

needs sun's energy to make food __C__

consumers __A__ and __B__   primary consumers __A__

secondary consumer __B__   gets the least energy available __B__

2. a. Count the number of living things in each of the pictures above and record the numbers in the blanks. rabbits __4__   foxes __1__   carrots __7__

b. Complete the diagram below by following these steps.
  1) On the blanks at the left, write the names of the living things in correct order.
  2) On the right side, write each of these terms on the correct blank: producer, secondary consumer, primary consumer.

fox _____   secondary consumer

rabbits _____   primary consumer

carrots _____   producer

3. Explain why the picture has fewer living things at the top of the pyramid. **Less and less of the original food energy remains as you move from the bottom to the top of the pyramid. Therefore, fewer animals can live at the top.**

4. a. Explain why the top of an energy pyramid does not have an arrow showing energy going back down to the bottom. **Energy is not recycled in a food chain.**

b. Where does the energy go? **It is lost as heat or used in the body processes of the living things in the food chain.**

Name _____ Date _____ Class _____

COMMUNITIES

In your textbook, read about the parts of a community in Section 30:2.

1. This picture of a community shows many different kinds of living things. Using these colors, shade the following parts.

Green—producers   Yellow—secondary consumers
Red—primary consumers   Blue—decomposers

2. What is the habitat of the deer? _____ the field

3. What is the niche of the deer? _____ primary consumer

4. List two decomposers in this community. bacteria, fungi (mushrooms and molds)

5. What producers are present in this community? grass, trees, plants

6. List two secondary consumers and tell what they eat. bird—worm; large member of cat family—cattle or deer

RELATIONSHIPS IN A COMMUNITY

In your textbook, read about relationships in a community in Section 30·4.

1. This picture shows an example of parasitism. This boy has a condition called elephantiasis (el uh fun TI uh sus). The condition is caused by a small roundworm in his body. The worm reproduced and the many worms blocked small blood vessels in his body. Fluids then became trapped in his leg. The swelling resulted from the fluid buildup.

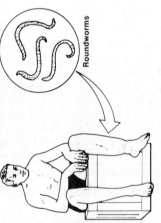

Roundworms

Define parasitism. __relationship between two organisms in which one is helped and the other is harmed but not usually killed__

2. The picture below shows an example of mutualism. This living thing, called a lichen (LI kun), is made of an alga and a fungus. The alga cells make food for themselves and the fungus. The fungus holds water and minerals that they both use. They live better together than either could live alone.

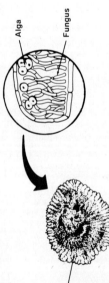

Alga

Fungus

Lichen

a. Define mutualism. __relationship in which two organisms live together and depend on each other__

b. Circle the correct answers.
   The alga in a lichen supplies (food), water.
   The fungus in a lichen supplies food, (water).

VOCABULARY

Review the new words used in Chapter 30 of your textbook. Then complete this puzzle. Use the words listed below to fill in the blanks in the sentences that follow.

commensalism   population   immigration
energy pyramid   habitat   emigration
niche   community   limiting factor
primary consumers food chain   secondary consumers
prey   food web   predator
predation   parasitism

A group of organisms of the same species make up a __population__.

The size of this group of organisms can change because new organisms enter and leave. This is called __immigration__ and __emigration__.

A condition that keeps the size of a population from increasing is a __limiting factor__. The

Living things of different kinds live together in a __community__. The job of the

place where a plant or animal lives is its __habitat__.

organism is its __niche__. Animals that eat only plants are __primary consumers__. Animals that eat other animals are __secondary consumers__.

Energy and materials are passed from one living thing to another in a community through a __food chain__. A __food web__ shows how food chains are connected in a community. An __energy pyramid__ is a diagram that shows energy loss in the food chain.

Living things depend on each other in several ways. In __commensalism__, one organism is helped and the other is not affected. In __parasitism__, one organism is helped and the other is harmed but not usually killed. In __predation__, one animal hunts and kills another animal. The __prey__ is the animal that is eaten. The __predator__ is the animal that hunts and kills the other animal.

Name _____ Date _____ Class _____

ECOSYSTEMS

In your textbook, read about cycles in an ecosystem in Section 31:1.

1. The incomplete diagram below shows the water cycle. Complete the diagram by following these steps.

   a. Use blue to shade the arrow that shows evaporation of water into air from ground or streams.

   b. Use green to shade the arrow that shows evaporation of water into air from plants.

   c. Leave unshaded the arrow that shows water falling from the clouds.

green

blue

unshaded

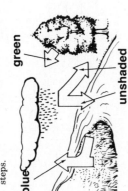

2. Complete the diagram below of the oxygen and carbon dioxide cycle by following these steps. Write the symbols for the gases in all the spaces marked A. Use O_2 as the symbol for oxygen and CO_2 as the symbol for carbon dioxide. Then, identify the process that takes place in all the spaces marked B. Use P as the symbol for photosynthesis and R as the symbol for respiration.

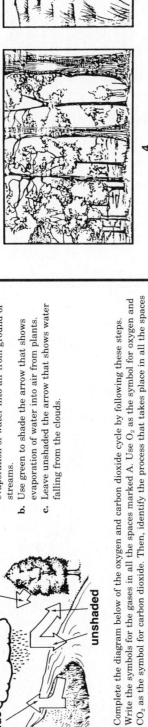

Producers give off O_2 during P _____ B, and use it during R _____ B

Consumers use O_2 A _____ during R _____ B

Producers use CO_2 A _____ during P _____ B, and give off CO_2 during R _____ B

Consumers give off CO_2 A _____ during R _____ B

Name _____ Date _____ Class _____

SUCCESSION

In your textbook, read about succession in a land community in Section 31:2.

1. These diagrams of succession are not in the correct order. Show the correct order by writing the numbers 1 to 4 on the blanks below the diagrams.

_____ 2

_____ 3

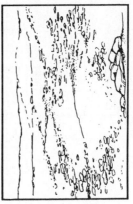

_____ 4

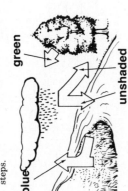

_____ 1

2. Match each diagram to the phrases below. Write the correct number of the diagram on each blank.

   a. Climax community ___4___

   b. Weeds begin to appear ___2___

   c. Soil good for larger plants ___3 or 4___

   d. Few primary consumers ___1 or 2___

   e. Most animals present ___4___

   f. Rabbits, mice, and fox might be here ___3 or 4___

STUDY GUIDE

Name _____ Date _____ Class _____

SUCCESSION

In your textbook, read about succession in a water community in Section 31:2.

3. Examine the diagrams below and the one on the next page. Measure the width and depth of the pond from the center of the X's in each diagram and record your measurements on the table on page 184. Then, answer the questions that follow.

Stage A   1883

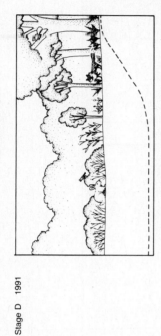

Stage B   1899

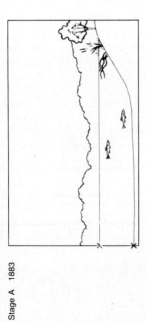

Stage C   1945

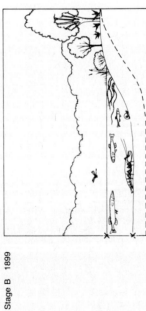

STUDY GUIDE

Name _____ Date _____ Class _____

SUCCESSION

Stage D   1991

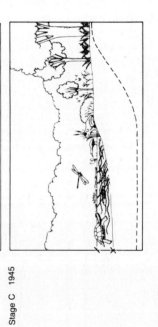

Measurements may vary slightly.

Stage	Year	Pond depth (mm)	Pond width (mm)
A	1883	15	86
B	1899	11	70
C	1945	7	50
D	1991	0	0

4. Describe the changes that take place in pond depth and width as the pond ages. **The pond depth and width decrease as the pond ages.**

5. How have the numbers and types of animals changed from stage A to stage B? **The numbers and types of animals have increased.**

6. a. What has happened to the pond by stage C? **It has become more shallow because dead plants and algae are piled up on the bottom.**

   b. How has this event affected the types of animals that are living in the pond? **There are more animals that can live out of the water part of the time.**

7. What has replaced the pond in stage D? **a forest community**

8. What word describes these changes in the pond? **succession**

HOW LIVING THINGS ARE DISTRIBUTED

In your textbook, read about biomes in Section 31:3.

1. The picture below shows the major world biomes. Using colored pencils, shade in the biomes described.

   a. Use blue for the biome that has an almost constant temperature. **tropical rain forest**

   b. Use brown for the biome that has temperatures from −28° to 15°C. **tundra**

   c. Use green for the biome that has evergreen trees, moose, weasels, and mink. **taiga**

   d. Use purple for the biome that has grasses. **grasslands**

   e. Use yellow for the biome that has less than 25 cm of rainfall each year and whose common plants are cacti and small bushes. **desert**

   f. Use red for the biome that has trees such as hickory, maple, beech, and oak. **temperate forest**

Refer to corresponding map on page 664 of text for key to biomes.

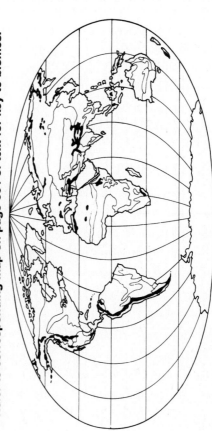

2. In which biome do you live? **Answers will vary.**

3. Which biome makes up most of the United States? **temperate forest**

4. a. Which two biomes have the least amount of rainfall? **desert and tundra**

   b. Why do no trees grow in these two biomes? **Trees require more water for growth than is present in these biomes.**

VOCABULARY

Review the new science words used in Chapter 31 of your textbook. Then, complete this puzzle.

Across

6. changes that take place in a community as it ages
7. water in the air that falls to Earth
8. study of how organisms interact with each other and the environment
9. last stage in succession

Down

1. community interacting with the environment
2. an area with a distinct climate and organisms
3. reusing of nitrogen in an ecosystem
4. path that water takes through an ecosystem
5. average temperature and precipitation in an area

RESOURCES AND HUMAN ACTIVITIES

In your textbook, read about natural resources in Section 32:1.

1. Each year during the five years from 1986 through 1990, millions of square kilometers of rain forests were cut down and cleared in Africa and Asia to make room for farmland. Use the information in the table below to help you answer the questions that follow.

| Year | Number of square kilometers of forest removed | |
	Africa	Asia
1990	24 000	16 000
1989	24 000	16 000
1988	24 000	16 000
1987	24 000	16 000
1986	24 000	16 000

2. a. How many square kilometers of forests were destroyed in Africa during the last five years? __120 000__

   b. How many square kilometers of forests were destroyed in Asia during the last five years? __80 000__

3. What happens to the soil when all of the plants are removed from the forests? __The soil is not protected and erosion occurs. The soil is worn away by wind and water.__

4. What happens to this soil when it is washed into a stream? __It settles to the bottom and covers the habitats of plants and animals.__

5. How does clearing the forests affect the level of gases in the air? __There will be a decrease of oxygen and an increase of carbon dioxide.__

6. How does the removal of the forest environments affect the extinction of organisms? __It speeds up the process of extinction.__

PROBLEMS FROM POLLUTION

In your textbook, read about air and water pollution in Section 32:2.

1. Fill in the boxes of the pollution table below with the correct words or phrases: burning coal, oil, gasoline, and natural gas; PCBs; harmful gases; heavy metals; pesticides and weed killers; tiny particles; sulfur dioxide. Several are already done for you.

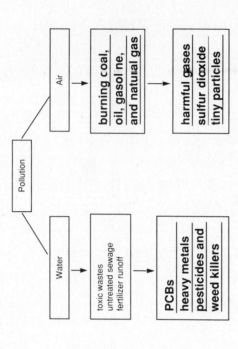

Pollution

Water: toxic wastes / untreated sewage / fertilizer runoff → PCBs / heavy metals / pesticides and weed killers

Air: burning coal, oil, gasoline, and natural gas → harmful gases / sulfur dioxide / tiny particles

2. How is smog produced? __Smog is produced when harmful gases react with the energy in sunlight to produce new, irritating chemicals.__

3. What is the greenhouse effect? __The carbon dioxide formed by burning fossil fuels forms a layer around Earth and traps heat so it can't escape into the atmosphere. The trapped heat may eventually cause Earth's temperature to rise.__

4. Why are chemicals such as PCBs and DDT so harmful to the environment? __Because they are not biodegradable and cannot be excreted by animals, they accumulate in the environment and in the bodies of animals.__

PROBLEMS FROM POLLUTION

In your textbook, read about acid rain in Section 32:2.

1. Study the map below.

U. S. Acid-Sensitive Areas

▨ High Sensitivity
▦ Moderate Sensitivity
▢ Low Sensitivity

2. Using an atlas and the map above, list the states that have a high sensitivity to acid rain. Place a checkmark by those states that have only small areas of high sensitivity to acid rain.

West		East	
Washington	Tennessee	Vermont	Minnesota
Oregon	Kentucky	North Carolina	Wisconsin
California	West Virginia	South Carolina	✓ Michigan
✓ Nevada	Pennsylvania	Florida	✓ Texas
Idaho	Maryland	Louisiana	✓ Oklahoma
Montana	New Jersey	Georgia	✓ Missouri
Wyoming	Delaware	Alabama	
Utah	New York	Arkansas	
Colorado	Massachusetts	Mississippi	
New Mexico	Connecticut	Rhode Island	
Arizona	District of Columbia	Maine	
	New Hampshire		

PROBLEMS FROM POLLUTION

3. What are two reasons that the eastern part of the United States has a greater acid rain problem than other parts?

 a. __Winds carry acid rain from the western and central parts of the United__ __States toward the east.__

 b. __Most of the industry in the United States is located in the east.__

4. What does the pH scale measure? __The pH scale measures how strong an acid or__ __base a substance is.__

5. What are some examples of acids? __vinegar, lemon juice__

6. What are some examples of bases? __ammonia, lye__

7. What pH do acids have? __Acids have pH values lower than 7.__

8. What pH do bases have? __Bases have pH values higher than 7.__

9. What is the pH of pure water? __The pH of pure water is 7.__

10. What is the pH of normal rain? __The pH of normal rain is above 5.5.__

11. What is the pH of acid rain? __The pH of acid rain is between 1 and 5.5.__

12. How is acid rain formed? __Harmful gases such as sulfur dioxide react with__ __water to form acid rain.__

13. List three results of acid rain in the United States.

 a. __It has been estimated that 15% of all Minnesota lakes are now__ __too acid for life.__

 b. __Over 200 lakes in the state of New York are "dead".__

 c. __Some lakes and ponds have a pH value below 4.5.__

14. What things other than lakes does acid rain damage? __Acid rain damages forests,__ __crops, soil, and buildings.__

15. Why must countries work together to solve the acid rain problem? __The gases that cause__ __acid rain are carried by the wind from one area to another.__

WORKING TOWARD SOLUTIONS

In your textbook, read in Section 32.3 about conserving our resources and keeping our environment clean.

1. How do National Wildlife Refuges help endangered animals? **These refuges are areas set aside to protect or shelter living things from being harmed by humans.**

2. What is the Endangered Species Act of 1973? **This law states that anyone found guilty of killing, capturing, or removing any endangered species from its environment can be fined up to $20 000 and spend one year in jail. The law also protects the habitat of any endangered species.**

3. What can be done to slow down or prevent erosion? **planting crops across the slope of the land, planting windbreaks and strips of grass between fields**

4. What can you do to help conserve water? **Answers will vary: turn off the tap when brushing your teeth, water lawns less.**

5. Since Congress passed laws to help clean up the air, what are industries required to do? **Power plants that use coal must have scrubbers in their smokestacks.**

6. Instead of using coal or oil for energy, what cleaner sources of energy can be used to make electricity? **solar or nuclear energy**

7. How have scientists been able to destroy insect pests without the use of pesticides? **by releasing the pests' own natural enemies against them, or by using specific bacteria or viruses**

8. What things can you do to conserve resources and prevent pollution? **Answers will vary: participate in recycling programs, buy products wrapped in paper or packed in cardboard or glass containers, walk or bike short distances, shop wisely, clean up litter, turn off lights and water, use biological pesticides.**

VOCABULARY

Review the new words in Chapter 32 of your textbook. Use the terms below to fill in the blanks of the sentences that follow.

acid	biodegradable	endangered	radon
base	greenhouse effect	fossil fuel	recycling
erosion	natural resource	pesticide	sediment
ozone	acid rain	pollution	smog
			threatened
			toxic

1. A **base** has a pH value greater than 7.

2. **Pollution** makes surroundings unclean.

3. Any part of the environment used by humans is a **natural resource** .

4. An **endangered species** is in danger of becoming extinct.

5. A **threatened species** is one that is close to being endangered.

6. **Sediment** is material on the bottom of a stream.

7. Any poisonous material is **toxic** .

8. A **pesticide** is a chemical used to kill rodents or insects.

9. A combination of smoke and fog is called **smog** .

10. Something is **biodegradable** if it can be broken down by microbes into harmless chemicals.

11. **Erosion** is the wearing away of soil by wind and water.

12. **Acid rain** causes living things to die in lakes and ponds.

13. Vinegar and lemon juice are **acids** that have pH values lower than 7.

14. A **fossil fuel** is the remains of organisms that lived millions of years ago.

15. The **greenhouse effect** is caused by a carbon dioxide layer around Earth that traps heat.

16. **Ozone** is a molecule made of three oxygen atoms.

17. **Radon** is found naturally in the ground and might cause cancer.

18. **Recycling** is the reusing of resources.